THE WORDSEARCH BOOK

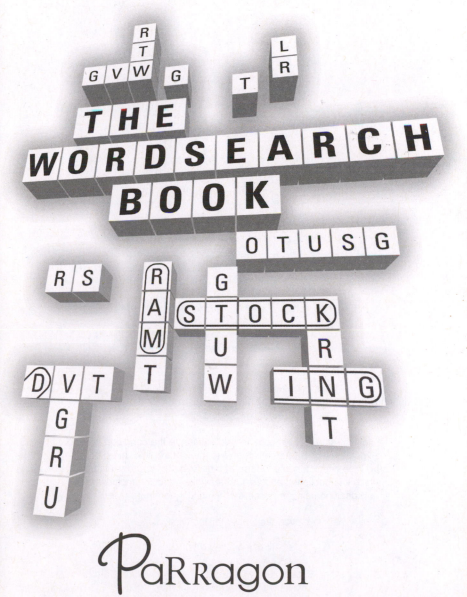

PaRragon

Bath · New York · Singapore · Hong Kong · Cologne · Delhi · Melbourne

This edition published by Parragon in 2010
Parragon
Queen Street House
4 Queen Street
Bath BA1 1HE, UK

Cover design by: Talking Design

ISBN 978-1-4054-7511-2

A copy of the British Library Cataloguing-in-Publication Data is
available from the British Library.

Printed and bound in China

MANITOBA LAKES

MANITOBA, one of Canada's three Prairie Provinces, is known as the land of 100,000 lakes. Both residents and tourists enjoy boating, fishing, and swimming in the sparkling waters.

AIKENS   PELICAN   SWAN

BASKET   PLUM   VICKERS

CARROLL   ROCK   WALLACE

CEDAR   SHOAL   WEAVER

CHARRON   SLEMON   WINNIPEG

CLEAR

DAUPHIN

ELBOW

ETAWNEY

FALCON

GARNER

GRANVILLE

HORSESHOE

HUDWIN

KAWINAW

LAURIE

LEWIS

LONELY

MANITOBA

MOAR

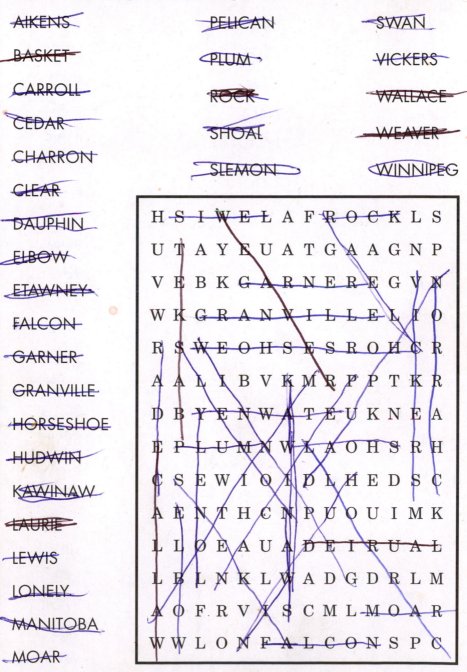

```
H S I W E L A F R O C K L S
U T A Y E U A T G A A G N P
V E B K G A R N E R E G V N
W K G R A N V I L L E L I O
R S W E O H S E S R O H C R
A A L I B V K M R P P T K R
D B Y E N W A T E U K N E A
E P L U M N W L A O H S R H
C S E W I O I D L H E D S C
A E N T H C N P U O U I M K
L L O E A U A D E I R U A L
L B L N K L W A D G D R L M
A O F R V I S C M L M O A R
W W L O N F A L C O N S P C
```

2 "HAND" OR "FOOT" FOLLOWERS

This puzzle is filled with fancy footwork and elaborate handiwork. That is, some of the entries below can be preceded by the word "foot," some by the word "hand," and others by both words to form new terms.

BALL — BRIDGE — LIGHT
BASKET — CART — LOCKER
BILL — DRILL — LOOSE
BOARD — HILL — MADE
BOOK — HOLD — MAID
BRAKE — KERCHIEF — NOTE
PATH
PICK
PRINT
PUPPET
RACE
RAIL
REST
SHAKE
SOLDIER
SPRING
STAND
STEP
STOOL
TRUCK
WEAR
WORK
WOVEN
WRITING

```
F L L A B A M R K H H N U K
O S I W W D G F K R D L G K
P G G E N F N C E H O L D C
S S H A K E S S F C M W C P
B R T R V P T E K S A B F B
L S K O O B I E T P E T S V
V L W D O H R S P R I N G A
W I I B C L W A T R T I A T
I A W E L B R L K W U R D U
M R E I D L O S C E G P A P
L K H D F O I A U T P W C C
C B M G S I R B R A C E B P
M A D E T O N M T D B P B T
I L W F P I L H D F F G T D
```

4

WOODEN EXPRESSION

During the Middle Ages, wood was used extensively for sculpture, especially in Germany and central Europe. The first American wood sculptor of significance was William Rush (1756-1833) of Philadelphia. He was trained to make ornamental ship carvings and figureheads but is best known for a life-size carving of George Washington he made in 1814, which stands in the city's Independence Hall.

ABRADERS
ART FORM
CARVE
CHERRY
CHISELS
CLAMPS
CRACKS
CRAFT
FIGURE
FILES
FINISH
GOUGES
GRAIN
HARDWOOD
MAHOGANY
MALLET
OILSTONE
RASPS
RIDGES
SANDPAPER
SCULPT

SMOOTH
SPLITS
SURFACE
TECHNIQUES

TOOLS
VISE
WALNUT
WORK

```
V C I V A Y N A G O H A M V
V C Q V V Y R R E H C E S D
F D E E E T A M T E V R A C
S L O R F I E O S E F I N A
F U M O N S O R E C L H D C
G I R C W M E N U I U L P O
T M N F S D O C Q G A L A Q
M O K I A T R R I O I A F M
G E O R S C S A N S L F E T
O E B L L H E C H T M I R U
U A I A S K L K C I K R V N
G O M V C H I S E L S R V L
E B O C R A F T T P P G O A
S P S A R I D G E S I V H W
```

SOUNDS "DEAR"

The 33 words which make up the list below all rhyme with the word "dear." We ask you to conduct a SINCERE search, from front to REAR, in the diagram we've presented HERE. Is that CLEAR?

ADHERE	CHANDELIER	HEAR
AUCTIONEER	CHEER	HEMISPHERE
BEER	CLEAR	HERE
BUCCANEER	ENGINEER	NEAR
CAREER	FEAR	PEER
CAVALIER	GEAR	PERSEVERE
		PIER
		PIONEER
		REAR
		REVERE
		SINCERE
		SMEAR
		SNEER
		SOUVENIR
		SPEAR
		SPHERE
		STEER
		TEAR
		TIER
		VOLUNTEER
		YEAR

```
T F Y B H S G F A N T C S F
O I B C L E A R G T R A E H
L D E A A D R G V A B V U D
N A E R H B V E E L S A E E
R E R E H P S M V C P L S R
E E R E H P S I M E H I E F
A E E R I N E V U O S E E R
R A E T M L R N V L P R E R
H R N R N F E N G I N E E R
V L A A E U F D O M N C R P
N E C E R V L N N S F N C R
F A C P Y A E O N A F I B P
E R U S T E E R V C H S A R
O Y B P R E E N O I T C U A
```

A FEATHERED FLOCK

Without looking at the theme of this puzzle, you may not be able to figure out its subject. As it turns out, these are names of different types of birds. The BEE EATER, for example, will grind out the stinger of its prey on a branch before it is swallowed. Understandably, it is unpopular with beekeepers! Please note that each line is a separate entry.

BABBLER

BEE EATER

BUMP

CUTTHROAT

DREAMER

GAUNT

GOONEY

HERMIT
(thrush)

JUMPER

KITE

MACARONI
(penguin)

MINER

MONK

NOPE

NUN

OLIVE

PASTOR

PICKET

POOR
SOLDIER

POP

RAIL

REDHEAD

SCARF

SEA MOUSE

SHAKER

SHOVELER

SLEEPYHEAD

SPRITE

TATTLER

TEASER

YARDKEEP

YELPER

```
F R R B L J N U U C D H D I
M J E E V I L O U G A U N T
R I D K S T A T T L E R U B
L R N B A A T R R B H U N G
J O R E D H E A D E Y O O O
M O Y O R R S T R E P S L O
M M B O O K E M U E E L R N
L H A S T P I A E A E E E E
I T B C S T U K M T L T P Y
U E B A A Y D O I E S I M P
J K L R P R U K V R R R U Y
S C E F A S O O E P O P J R
E I R Y E E H N C O N S U B
T P M U B S R E I D L O S C
```

IN THE MISSION INN

The Mission Inn in Riverside, California, is one of the most famous hotels in the United States. The inn has been host to celebrities as well as ordinary citizens since the turn of the last century. For example, Richard and Pat Nixon were married there, and Ronald and Nancy Reagan honeymooned there. Here's a list of things associated with this historic inn.

ANTIQUES
BALCONY
BELL
BUFFET
CANNON

CHANDELIER
CHAPEL
CLOCK
COLUMN
CONCIERGE

COURT
DESK
FLOWER
FOUNTAIN
GARDEN
GIFT SHOP
GUEST
GUIDE
LOBBY
MUSEUM
PAINTING
PALM
PATIO
POOL
ROTUNDA
SCULPTURE
STAGE
SUITE
TAVERN
TILE
TOUR
TOWER
WROUGHT
IRON

```
R Y C O T A V E R N T K P Y
E L B U C C M H T E C R S W
I D I B O O O F L O W E R T
L D Y L O T N M L S U O Y G
E R U T P L U C S Q U R T U
D M P O H S T F I G I I O I
N W A N E O L T H E L G T D
A L L U I E N T G E R T G E
H O M T P A I N T I N G U N
C O A A A R T R Q E K S E D
F P H R O T U N D A F H S L
P C A N N O N R U Y Q F T L
V H S F C B A L C O N Y U E
Q M I B E G A T S N F M M B
```

"HI" THERE!

Test your skills with this challenging puzzle whose HIDDEN entries all contain the letter combination "HI."

ACHIEVE

BEHIND

CASHIER

CHIEF

CHILD

CHILL

CHIME

CHIRP

CHISEL

FASHION

HIBACHI

HIBISCUS

HICKORY

HIDDEN

HIGHWAY

HIKER

HIMSELF

HINDER

HINGE

HISTORY

HITCH

INHIBIT

ORCHID

SHIELD

THICK

THIMBLE

THINK

THIRST

VEHICLE

WHILE

WHITE

WITHIN

```
K F C H I L D E M I H C V E
H D A N B U L W C H I R P L
C H D S E I H I N G E U Y M
F O U P H D C T H D V F T H
P E L W I I D H N C E H B H
A T I H N N O I C H I S E L
W H C H D H H N H M H L H O
Y R O K C I H I B A C H I A
O P B N M B B L S I A P G W
L C A S H I E R H T F O H K
P V E M S T S E I C O I W N
O L K C Y Y V K E L T R A I
F M U B O T O I L E B I Y H
T S R I H T Y H D K C I H T
```

Fly casters reel in their fish one at a time using lures made of feathers, rubber, and metal that are expertly assembled and tied. You might land the "big one" with the aid of the 36 flies below.

ABBEY

ADAMS

BEEFSTEAK

BLUE QUILL

BRADY

CAHILL

CARTER

CHANTREY

COLE

DAMSEL

DARK TIGER

DORSET

DUNHAM

HAMMAR

HONEY BEE

KATE

LADY MITE

LAST CHANCE

LOGIE

MATUKA

MCALPINE

MIKE

MITCHELL

MURDOCH

PRIEST

ROYAL

SAIL

SALMON

SAND

SKY BLUE

SPIDER

SPITFIRE

STONE

THOR

TORRISH

ZULU

```
N E O B E P R I E S T A Y N
L R E T R A C E I G O L N O
A A A B M A U H C O D R U M
Y K D M Y L D A A E K I M L
O O A Y B E H Y L N U I B A
R H R Y M I N O M M T L L S
H L K S L I C O A C Z R U E
K S T L A S T C H A N C E Z
S P I T F I R E N L D M Q Y
A I G R F Z L N U P O Y U R
N D E M R L D O D I R E I D
D E R Y R O H T P N S B L I
F R B K A E T S F E E B L A
T L E S M A D A K U T A M H
```

"ABC" WOMEN

It's ladies first with this puzzle. That's because all of the female names listed here begin with "A," "B," or "C."

ABIGAIL

AGATHA

ALEXIS

ALICE

ALICIA

ALISON

AMANDA

AMBER

ANDREA

ANGELA

ANITA

ANNETTE

ASHLEY

BARBARA

BERNICE

BEVERLY

BONNIE

BRANDY

BRENDA

BRIDGET

BRITTANY

CANDACE

CARMEN

CAROL

CATHERINE

CHARLOTTE

CHELSEA

CHERYL

CINDY

CLAUDIA

COLLEEN

COURTNEY

CRYSTAL

```
A L I C I A O E I N N O B U
S I X E L A C H E L S E A B
H A N I C L A T I N A A R R
L L C E C I T E G D I R B E
E E A N E O N C T B H X A N
Y G N I L L U R B T S A R D
Y N D R L Y L R E V E B A A
X A A E T L I O T B L N D H
S H C H V T A C C N M A N T
C Y E T T C G T A H E A A A
A C L A U D I A S R E Y M G
R M N C R L B N D Y M R A A
O Y G U B R A N D Y R E Y I
L N O S I L A E X Y U C N L
```

Here we have some STRONG words for you — but don't worry, it's nothing you can't handle. Just scan through this BEEFY word list and find all 32 words that indicate strength.

ATHLETIC

BEEFY

BIONIC

BRAWNY

BUILT

BURLY

FIRM

FORCEFUL

GUTSY

HALE

HARDY

HEARTY

HEFTY

HUSKY

INTENSE

MIGHTY

MUSCULAR

POTENT

RIGID

ROBUST

RUGGED

SOLID

SOUND

STABLE

STALWART

STAUNCH

STOUT

STRONG

TOUGH

UNBOWED

VIGOROUS

WIRY

```
V G S G T V T O H S U G Y E
Y Y U U R O B U S T O U T L
T G W T U Y S I U A M H U A
R B N G S K E M O U D F O H
A I H O Y Y U E S N E T N I
W I G V R S Y W U C I B E D
L Y P I C T U O R H S C S B
A T W U D A S O L I D N Y B
T R L Y H B F A R B P N D I
S A B F F L U N B O W E D B
R E C I T E L H T A G W U G
R H A R D Y E E R G E I R H
D T T M A O N B U R L Y V P
T M I G H T Y R Y T F E H A
```

"TASTE"FUL TERMS

In this puzzle we offer 30 ways to describe different types of food. We know this is the kind of puzzle you solvers will want to sink your teeth into!

ACIDIC

BITTER

BRINY

BURNT

CHEWY

CREAMY

CRISP

FATTY

FLAKY

FLAT

FRESH

FRUITY

GREASY

JUICY

LEMONY

MILD

MOIST

MUSHY

OILY

RICH

RIPE

SALTY

SHARP

SOUR

STALE

SUGARY

SWEET

TANGY

TART

VINEGARY

```
F A M O F S S P D L I M M R
H B I F R Y N G S H O R P K
B T B U R N T Y C I U J E J
G R Y L I O M I S H R P I I
J K U K D M R T U C I C W F
P K P T A E A O G R S U A P
G B R B F L A T A Y F R C R
H H S C E A F F R E S H E A
M N B W H C I A Y A E T P H
U Y S A E R G T C W T Y S S
U H R L I E L T Y I V E O R
N S Y G N A T Y B Y D U M P
T U K I S M E I P B R I N Y
T M V M C Y I D K B P C F
```

Aristotle once said, "Happiness is at once the best, the noblest and the pleasantest of things." Here is a list of things that we do when we are feeling good and happy.

BEAM

BOAST

CACHINNATE
(laugh loudly)

CACKLE

CAPER

CAVORT

CHEER

CHORTLE

CHUCKLE

CLAP

CROW

DANCE

DISPORT (play)

EXULT

FRISK

FROLIC

GAMBOL

GIGGLE

GRIN

GUFFAW

LAUGH

PLAY

PRANCE

REJOICE

RELAX

REVEL

ROLLICK

ROMP

SHOUT

SING

SKIP

SKYLARK
(frolic)

SMILE

WHISTLE

WHOOP

```
S V T A B C R O W R S K F L
B M A O H L A U G H H R Y V
K R A E O V P P W K O T A T
I S E J K M T A E L U O L X
T R I J O R D L I R T W P A
I R T R O V A C R L M A E B
S K I P F I N L U H I F T A
T G S O R P C X Y E O F W K
S I A G S A E E L K C U H C
D G D M C L N T E B S G I I
E G I K B N R C V G N I S L
E L L A K O C R E L A X T L
E E D K H U L G R I N I L O
I C A C H I N N A T E T E R
```

HOME-GROWN

You don't need a green thumb to have fun with this puzzle. Just grab a writing tool, plant yourself down, and start digging up as many words as you can. You'll be pleased as your list grows and you reap the benefits of a job well done.

APPLES

BEANS

BEETS

BERRIES

CORN

CUCUMBERS

DILL

GOURD

KALE

LETTUCE

LIMAS

LIMES

MELON

OKRA

ONIONS

ORANGES

PARSLEY

PARSNIPS

PEACHES

PEARS

PEAS

PEPPERS

PLUMS

POTATOES

PUMPKIN

SAGE

SHALLOTS

SPINACH

SQUASH

THYME

TOMATOES

TURNIPS

ZUCCHINI

```
I A S Q S N O I N O L E M T
M E T A T R L S P I N R U T
Z P E L I M E S E G N A R O
E P E C H O T P Q I Q P H E
S S B A T L T S P U R A D Z
M S R A C L U N P E A R S S
U E T E L H C A N I P S E G
L O M I B C E I C A N L H B
P T D Y D M K S R R P E I E
U A S R H P U S O P O Y L A
G M U A M T N C A E G A S N
R O B U M I I E U O K R A S
G T P Q P I N I H C C U Z U
B K K S H A L L O T S C O E
```

DON'T BE CHICKEN!

The wise words "If at first you don't succeed, try, try again," inspire many of us when faced with failure. Read how one man, who held jobs such as a streetcar conductor, insurance salesman, ferryboat driver, and cook, took the phrase to heart and became the proprietor of one of America's most successful restaurant chains.

Harlan held many odd jobs in his lifetime before taking a one-hundred-and-five-dollar Social Security check and starting his own business. At the age of sixty-five, "Colonel" Harlan Sanders opened the first Kentucky Fried Chicken franchise.

```
O D N W O S I H D A Y A A V
P Y V J O G S B U E O N V G
E K M T E R X S G N I K A T
N C H F M M D X E G D R P M
E U A E E S I H C N A R F A
D T R U S I X T Y F I V E O
S N L S M L S V E S N S G D
E E A K F R E R A F H N U S
C K N K I M A N D F I V E B
U C H F C L D E O T S L R O
R I E B L E H A R L A N O J
I H L O R T H A G E O F F D
T C D S T V T C J P B C E D
Y D U A G S O C I A L L B O
```

SEA TURTLES

There are seven species of sea turtle: Flat Back, GREEN, Hawksbill, Kemp's Ridley, Leatherback, Loggerhead, and Olive Ridley. These large, GENTLE creatures can be found in all the world's oceans except for the Arctic, and some species even TRAVEL between oceans.

AQUATIC

BEACH

COURSE

CRAWL

EGGS

EYES

FLIPPERS

GENTLE

GIANT

GREEN

HATCHING

HEAD

HEAVY

MARINE

MIGRATORY

NECK

NETS

OCEAN

PACE

PADDLE

PLODDING

SAND

SHELL

SHORE

SWIM

TRAVEL

```
S W P D N D B L B R K S O Y
T G E N T L E U K G A W G S
W Y G N E D A L I N M I W S
R L A E O A C W D I F E P V
W I A R N S H A G D O M A A
G V N O Y H E R C D A V K W
D W I I N H A C M O Q P B Q
M K P L F T V T A L U B H N
G S B P O N Y L C P A R E I
P E T R A V E L F H T N S P
Y S Y E B S R E P P I L F E
L K C E N B O H R R C N M B
L O R H S F H S A G K N G G
V R T F N A S M R C P D O G
```

This puzzle contains a lexicon of financial and accounting terms with a hidden quotation from the famous tycoon John D. Rockefeller. Reading the leftover diagram letters will reveal his interesting comparison of business with Darwin's theory of evolution.

BOND

BONUS

BUDGET

CASH

COIN

COST

CREDIT

DISCOUNT

DIVIDEND

DOLLAR

EARNINGS

EQUITY

EXPENSE

FINANCE

FUND

GAIN

GROSS

INCOME

INTEREST

INVESTMENT

LIQUID

LOAN

NOTE

PRICE

PROFIT

RATE

REBATE

REVENUE

SALE

VALUE

```
E T H E G E C I R P R O W T
A H O T E F A L V A L U E A
R R D L I Q U I D G T E B E
N U O T S F U I N S E E S S
I A L N T S O I E I F S F N
N T L U C N M R T E I U R E
G E A O O G E E P Y N L D P
S G R C I T R M C D A E I X
S D T S N Y A O T S N U V E
A U U I R I S V S S C N I M
L B N D D T A I V S E E D O
E A N O T E L G O F T V E C
H D N O B E R E B A T E N N
F I T T H S A C E S T R D I
```

GRAB A GIFT

If you need to pick up a bunch of items for a special occasion, you might want to visit a CARD store. These specialty shops sell cards, decorations, and gifts for all kinds of celebrations. Browse through the diagram below which has been stocked with items that can be found in a card store.

ADDRESS (book)

ALBUM

BALLOON

BOOK

CALENDAR

CANDLE

CARD

DIARY

DOLL

FIGURINE

FRAME

GIFT BAG

JEWELRY

JOURNAL

MUSIC BOX

NOTEPAD

ORNAMENT

PAPERWEIGHT

PENCIL

POTPOURRI

PUZZLE

RIBBON

STATIONERY

STICKER

STREAMER

STUFFED (animal)

TISSUE (paper)

VASE

WRAPPING (paper)

```
L M U B L A N R U O J Y N P
X S T U F F E D L K O O B A
Z Z G G R K R I B B O N F P
W O W N C E C L J L V R U E
G E G I P N M E L Y A X J R
K U T P E K W A R M S O O W
N S G P W E B E E J E B R E
A S C A L E N D A R S C N I
D I R R U O P T O P T I A G
D T Y W I C Z U G L R S M H
R N O T E P A D Z U L U E T
E C A N D L E R G Z J M N H
S T M F Y R A I D M L S T A
S J G A B T F I G B B E A S
```

Mining is an ancient process. As early as 6000 BC, people delved into the earth for flint to make weapons and tools. Today, mining ranks as a major global industry. In the U.S. alone the mining industry employs nearly 270,000 people and almost three million others are employed by mining-related industries. Dig into the diagram below and see if you can STRIKE gold by finding all 34 mining terms.

ADIT
BOOM
BRINE
CROSSCUT
DEPOSIT

DRAWPOINT
DREDGE
DRIFT
FOOTWALL
GIANT

HANGING WALL
LEACHING
LEVELS
MINERALS
ORE PASS
ORES
OVERBURDEN
PANNING
PLACER
QUARRY
RAISE
RAMP
RIFLE BOX
SHAFT
SKIPS
SLOPE
SPOIL
STOPE
STRIKE
STRIPPING
SUBLEVEL
TUNNEL
VEIN
WINZE

```
L L A W T O O F Y R R A U Q
B E K T Q V P H A D I T T V
T N A I G M A A C P F K U W
S I L C O G N N A D L N N T
S U S O H W N G M S E N N U
A P B O V I I I O T B I E C
P Z M L P U N N P O O E L S
E L C A E G G G Z P X V Y S
R I C D R V D W W E I R T O
O O G A R Q E A B Z U R W R
R P L A C E R L D R I F T C
E S I A R D D L S K I P S S
S H A F T Q V G E P O L S R
O V E R B U R D E N I R B O
```

GET YOUR PROTEIN HERE

Have no fear, bean lovers, RATTLESNAKE beans do not bite! They get their name from the shape and markings of their pods that can twist and coil like their reptilian namesake. We've hidden a BROAD variety of beans in the diagram, and finding them all should be a SNAP!

ADZUKI

APPALOOSA

BLACK

BROAD

BUTTER

CALYPSO

CANNELLINI

CRANBERRY

FAVA

FLAGEOLET

GARBANZO

GIGANDES

GREAT NORTHERN

GREEN

KIDNEY

LIMA

MUNG

NAVY

PIGEON

PINTO

RATTLESNAKE

REFRIED

SHELL

SNAP

SNOWCAP

TURTLE

WHITE

```
N C K F D E I R F E R Z N Y
W R I C I S T A K A Y A B L
S H E P A N S T O F V D K T
P H I H W L I T L Y N A E U
G R E T T U B L L R C L U R
S I N L E R N E L R O L S T
A P P A L O O S A E T O E L
U D F G E S N N G B N Z D E
M U N G P O Y A T N I N N R
M I I Y W E L K B A P A A Z
A P L C N F W E M R E B G C
C A A D Z U K I G C O R I L
C P I C T G L F D K K A G S
U K W Z L Y D N E E R G D N
```

It's not surprising that "Dallas" star Larry HAGMAN or country singer Willie NELSON are both originally from Texas, but did you know that funnyman Steve MARTIN and Broadway choreographer Tommy TUNE also hail from the Lone Star State? Altogether we've hidden 30 Texan gents in the puzzle below for you to round up.

ARMSTRONG (Lance)
BUSEY (Gary)
DONALDSON (Sam)
FOREMAN (George)
FOXX (Jamie)
HAGMAN (Larry)
HARRELSON (Woody)
HAWKE (Ethan)
HENLEY (Don)
JONES (Tommy Lee)
KRISTOFFERSON (Kris)
LOVETT (Lyle)
MARTIN (Steve)
MATHIS (Johnny)
MCCONAUGHEY (Matthew)
MEAT LOAF
NELSON (Willie)
NESMITH (Mike)
PAXTON (Bill)
QUAID (Dennis)
RATHER (Dan)
ROGERS (Kenny)
STILLS (Stephen)
STRAIT (George)
SWAYZE (Patrick)
THOMAS (Henry)
TORN (Rip)
TREVINO (Lee)
TUNE (Tommy)
WHITAKER (Forest)

```
S T M J O N E S F O X X D S
E T B C H N I F A N L K I A
K Z I M C H A S N I T R A M
W X Y L T O E M R V L I U O
A N P A L T N N E E F S Q H
H Z M T W S E A U R G T N T
J H A S X S R V U T O O S O
T E N A M G A H O G S F R D
M O H I X N T R Z L H F A L
D S T F O I H Y E L N E H D
W H I T A K E R T X Z R Y R
U I X R M S R O N E L S O N
U A T A U A R M S T R O N G
P S V B H N O S D L A N O D
```

PACIFIC ISLES

MAUI is the second largest island of the Hawaiian chain (after Hawaii Island). It takes its name from a Polynesian demigod and was created by two volcanoes, Puu Kukui and Haleakala. Cruise through the diagram and see how many Pacific isles you can find.

ALOR
ARU
AUSTRAL
BAKER
BASS
BERU
BURU
COOK
EASTER
EFATÉ
ELLICE
FIJI
GILBERT
GUAM
HUON
IWO (Jima)
KAUAI
LANAI
LAU
MAKIN
MARÉ
MARIANAS
MARSHALL
MAUI
MIDWAY
MILI

MOLOKAI
NEW GUINEA
OCEAN
OENO
PONAPE
ROTA

SAIPAN
SAMOA
TASMANIA
TRUK
VOSTOK
WOTJE

```
E  Y  G  I  L  B  E  R  T  M  T  R  F  A
E  Y  I  B  M  L  A  N  A  I  M  N  C  L
O  F  U  W  R  K  A  U  A  I  J  U  N  B
F  I  A  M  O  P  G  H  L  S  N  R  F  Y
L  J  M  T  I  A  E  I  S  C  D  E  P  S
N  I  S  A  E  E  T  C  U  R  U  B  A  J
H  O  S  S  R  N  G  N  I  K  A  M  V  H
V  U  V  M  B  I  A  K  O  L  O  M  V  E
P  W  O  A  R  U  A  E  U  A  L  O  R  O
U  N  S  N  J  G  M  N  J  R  K  E  C  T
D  S  M  I  D  W  A  Y  A  T  T  N  R  F
V  A  B  A  K  E  R  M  W  S  O  O  S  F
Y  V  O  O  C  N  E  G  A  U  T  W  O  J
U  L  T  O  D  Y  G  E  P  A  N  O  P  W
```

Anne Frank and her family were forced to hide in a warehouse attic for two years during the Nazi regime of Adolf Hitler. She could not attend school, nor was she allowed to see her friends. In spite of everything, she was still a young child of hope. When you feel down, think of Anne Frank and remember her words.

I don't
think
of all
the
misery,

but of
the beauty
that
still
remains.

My advice
is: Go
outside,
to the
fields,
enjoy
nature
and the
sunshine,
go out
and try
to recapture
happiness
in yourself
and in God.
Think of
all the
beauty
that's
still left
in and
around
you
and be
happy!

```
E N I H S N U S D N A N I S
R D O G N I D N A J G S E T
U O F A L L N T E F G S H I
T H E B E A U T Y O Z E T L
P Y L I Q R O S V U B N L L
A S F L E S R U O Y N I L L
C M E O I C A Y P R Q P A E
E H Y D K T K T C E D P E F
R E M A I N S X H S T A H T
O H N E D S I I M I L H T U
T T T J B V T H D M N H O O
U D W R O D I U T O A K T O
A N D T R Y N C O T N Q A G
H A P P Y T U A E B U T O F
```

THE FLYING MAN

The events described below took place on St. Patrick's Day in 1884. For this feat and others, the man mentioned was known as the father of basic flying.

John Montgomery is credited with being the first man to fly in a glider. Weighing one hundred thirty pounds, he climbed onto a thirty-pound glider on March seventeenth, and traveled six hundred feet across a California valley.

```
C N U X F D G X G W E B E M
E Y M P M E G L N W Y G H A
S A T O T H E F I R S T S G
I S C R E D I T E D N H D F
X S I P I O H M B E E I N L
H O G T N H O J E L D R U Y
U R N T L G T T C E W T O I
N C O O T A N D B V W Y P N
D A A N T E G M E A B P O A
R Y O M V N I L F R I O L C
E M Y E L L A V I T D U G H
D A S H C R A M T D J N H T
W E I G H I N G O N E D U B
P A I N R O F I L A C R E H
```

24 BUTTERFLY BLOSSOMS

If you were meandering around a MARIGOLD, or hovering over a HOLLYHOCK, what might you be? Why, a butterfly! The 31 plants listed below are known to attract butterflies.

ACACIA

AGAVE

ALDER

ALFALFA

ASTER

BEAN

BIRCH

BLUE FLAG

CANNA

CAPER

CEDAR

CLOVER

CRESS

CROTON

DOCK

HOLLYHOCK

IRIS

LUPINE

MALLOW

MARIGOLD

MILKWEED

MIMOSA

MUSTARD

NETTLE

ROSE

SAGE

SUNFLOWER

THISTLE

VETCH

VIOLET

WILLOW

```
S R E D L A U M S O T W V H
O G M R C R Y S C R O T O N
E N G A L F E U L B Y L A T
N M C T R R V N S A L E H E
C I C S C I A F F Y B I C L
A W K U L C G L H N S L R O
L M I M O S A O L T O E I I
D P A L I F C W L V O A B V
C H M I L K W E E D O C K U
A H C A D O V R D N S S F E
N E T T L E W O E A I I L Y
N D I L E A C S G P R P R A
A D A A U V R E T S A B U I
M M I W H L O C N K S C T L
```

HORSIN' AROUND

Although the theme song from the classic TV sitcom "Mister Ed" begins "A horse is a horse, of course, of course," horses have various colors and markings which make them look different. The word list below is filled with 29 terms that can describe horses of a different color.

BLACK

BLUE ROAN

BROWN

BUCKSKIN

CHESTNUT

COPPER

CREAM

GOLDEN

GRAY

GRULLA

LEOPARD

OVERO

PAINT

PALOMINO

PIEBALD

PINTO

RED DUN

RED ROAN

SILVER

SKEWBALD

SNIP

SOCK

SORREL

SPOTTED

STAR

STOCKING

STRIPE

TOBIANO

WHITE

```
G P A K N P M G Y V W N D S
G S D B Y L T R K S H W P O
B N I K S K C U B D I O H C
Y L I S N K D L N D T R A K
K G U K N U C L R T E B B V
M L H E C I D A E M S C R O
M V M W R O P D L A B E I P
L M O B W O T D E B D S H N
M N N A E V A S T R I P E C
H P A L O M I N O L H D B P
N V I D Y T I A V R L R G S
U S B I P A N E O O R E V O
O C O P P E R I G C R E A M
I S T A R V N G P B Y T L E
```

If you're a late-night talk show fan, here's a chance for you to be a guest host with this talk-show list. When you've circled all the entries, the leftover letters will finish this comment: "Fascinating CONVERSATION is the art of telling people..."

ACTS
ANNOUNCER
AUDIENCE
BAND
CAMERA
CELEBRITY

COMEDIAN
CONVERSATION
COUCH
CROWD
CURTAIN
DESK

EMCEE
ENTERTAINER
GAGS
GUEST
HOST
INTERVIEW
JOKES
JUGGLER
LAUGHS
MUSIC
ORCHESTRA
PERSON-
ALITIES
SINGER
SKITS
SPOTLIGHT
STAFF
STAGE
STARS
STORIES
STUDIO
WRITERS

```
S A L E I T H G I L T O P S
F T T I N T E R V I E W T E
F T A L E T S E K O J C N I
A J U G G L E R C L A E O T
T S O H E S A R E M A C I I
S S T I K S R A T S E S T L
T S H U C R O W D A A N A A
E T N T D C R H N K I E S N
C O M E D I A N S A Y N R O
N R W A T S O E T G L R E S
E I D E N U D R T T A E V R
I E R N N M U T S E U G N E
D S O C A C O U C H G N O P
U C E L E B R I T Y H I C K
A R T S E H C R O N S S O W
```

DOUBLE PLAY

You can get twice as much use out of these words if you double them up. Each of them, when preceded by "double," yields a word or phrase that may have quite a different meaning. We double DOG DARE you to find all 30!

AGENT

BACK

CHECK

CROSS

DATE

DEALING

DECKER

DOG DARE

DOOR

DRIBBLE

DUTCH

DUTY

EDGED

EXPOSURE

FAULT

FEATURE

JEOPARDY

JOINTED

KNIT

NEGATIVE

OR NOTHING

PLAY

SPACE

SPEAK

STANDARD

TAKE

TALK

TIME

TROUBLE

VISION

```
E Y H X K T F J J I V Y Y B
D O Y C S F A D E G D E D B
R D E Y T U D E C K E R R E
N H Y I I U D O A B A U I R
C K M E R A D G O D L T B J
J E V I T A G E N T I A B L
T E T E E K L A T P N E L B
I B O R N O T H I N G F E R
N E X P O S U R E O I X O B
K V C F A U L T S I L O N C
I C R A D R B V P S D E J N
Y K A E P S D L M I O T T B
V F M B A S A Y E V T R O Y
G I B E T Y E L V A B Y C S
```

28 — JAPANESE & KOREAN SURNAMES

Common surnames in Japan include **KATO, SATO, SUZUKI,** and **TAKA-HASHI.** In Korea there are only roughly 250 family names in use today. **CHUNG, JEONG, PARK,** and **YOON** are among those that make up over half of the Korean population. Note that the headings are not hidden in the diagram.

Japanese

HAYASHI
INOUE
KATO
KIMURA
KOBAYASHI
MATSUMOTO
NAKAMURA
SAITO
SASAKI
SATO
SHIMIZU
SUZUKI
TAKAHASHI
TANAKA
WATANABE
YAMADA
YAMAGUCHI
YAMAMOTO
YOSHIDA

Korean

CHANG
CHOE
CHOI
CHUNG
GANG
GWON
HONG
HWANG
JANG
JEONG
JUNG
KANG
KWON
PARK
SHIN
SONG
WHANG
YOON

```
U Y M J M P A R K E U O N I
G Y A M A D A M O A R E M O
I N R M O Y I K B T T P T H
G I U W A T A N A B E O H C
S N M J D G I M Y N M R S M
I R I R I N U A A U A H M H
U Y K H H A A C S M I T W S
S G O H S K I T H M O A G O
U A B D O A A P I I N T N N
Z N T R Y M H Z K G N T O G
U G O O D U U A N S N W E N
K K W O N R S U K T G A J O
I H S A Y A H G N A H W H H
U E G R S C T K R D T Y M C
```

TURN UP THE AC

Are you one of those people who go to the movies in the summer, regardless of what's showing, just so you can sit in an air-conditioned theater? If so, bring this "cool" puzzle with you. You can try and find the terms below that are all related to air conditioning before the lights are dimmed.

ADJUST

AMPS

BLOWER

BOX

CIRCUITS

COMPACT

CONDENSER

CONTROLS

COOLS

CORD

ELECTRIC

FUSE

HOOKUP

INSTALL

LIGHTWEIGHT

METAL

MOTOR

MOUNT

OUTLET

POWER

REMOTE
(control)

SELF-CONTAINED

SWITCH

THERMOSTAT

TURN ON

VENTS

VOLTS

WINDOW

WIRING

```
W T A T S O M R E H T B W A
D O E A D U N S J H L L R D
S J D W E O N A G O V H P J
T L G N N R T I W L T O O U
N L O R I J E E H C T I W S
E A U R A W R S A T N I E T
V T S L T K E P N X D H R I
K S P H N N M U G E X M X U
V N G O O O O T L N D R O C
O I W O C M T C E C I N B R
L A A K F M E T A L P R O I
T X M U L U E L E C T R I C
S P F P E V S C S V O U D W
C O O L S C X E K M O T O R
```

Tom Cruise gives one of his most endearing performances as Jerry Maguire, in the 1996 film of the same name. He portrays a sports agent who loses his job and all his CLIENTS — except for the loyal Rod Tidwell (played by Oscar winner Cuba Gooding Jr.). Tidwell has only one demand of his agent, though, and that's "Show me the MONEY!"

AGENCY

ARRANGE

ATHLETES

BONUS

BUSY

CAREER

CLIENTS

CONTRACTS

DEALS

DOLLARS

FEES

FINANCES

GAIN

HELP

INCENTIVES

LAWYER

LEGAL

MONEY

NEGOTIA-TIONS

OFFICE

PERCENT

PLAYERS

PRICE

PROPOSALS

REPRESENT

RICH

SALARY

SIGNING

SUCCESSFUL

TEAMS

TERMS

TRADE

```
G V S G C G P R I C E S L C
L V A N B O N U S O T E U L
H I L T O A R R A N G E F E
N P A V H I A U E T I F S D
T E R M S L T S T R P Y S A
N R Y U L A E A C A R E E R
S C Y O C R S T I C O N C T
C E D C P L F R E T P O C Y
I N C E N T I V E S O M U U
I T R N A E P E Y Y S G S Y
R E Y W A L G H N L A G E L
O A S E E N S A C T L L F N
M M U H G N I N G I S H P V
N S B E C I F F O U R L U P
```

FROM MYTHOLOGY

Mythology, literally translated, means "the telling of stories." And there are hundreds of mythological stories to be told, many involving gods and goddesses. But we must remember that throughout all these stories, the characters weren't only deities. That's why listed below you'll find 27 mythological monsters and lovers.

ACIS*

ALCESTIS*

ARGUS**

ARIADNE*

BAUCIS*

CENTAURS**

CERBERUS**

CHIMAERA**

CHIRON**

CYCLOPES**

ECHO*

EURYDICE*

FENRIS**

GERYON**

GORGONS**

HARPIES**

HYDRA**

LAMIA**

LAOMEDON**

MEDUSA**

NALA*

NARCISSUS*

PHAEDRA*

PSYCHE*

PYRAMUS*

SCYLLA**

SPHINX**

*lover
**monster

```
C Y F U A L A N H H O G B L
A E L A O M E D O N I A S F
F C N L A N C L X R U G S O
O A A T D M I H N C I P L C
A G R A A L D O I E L H Y X
I O I G E U Y S H B A P C F
M R P C U R R S P P L Y A E
A G H M E S U S S I C R A N
L O A G A R E Y M L E A R R
L N E M E I C T O A S M D I
Y S D B P H D P M U T U Y S
C S R R E C E I D A I S H F
S E A C I S H E C A S E N H
C H D I U C M N N E L N O I
```

BORDERING ON FUN

You can show off your **CREATIVE DECORATING** skills by trimming a **ROOM** or some **FURNISHINGS** in your **HOME** with borders. It's easy to **APPLY** a whole new **LOOK** by simply adding a **PRINT PATTERN** to a solid color or by changing the **APPEARANCE** of busy patterns with solid borders.

ACCENT

AFFIX

APPEARANCE

APPLY

BASEBOARD

BEAUTY

BEDSPREAD

CABINET

CEILING

CHEST

CONTRAST

CREATIVE

CUPBOARD

CURTAIN

DECORATING

DESIGN

EFFECT

FLOWERS

FURNISHINGS

HOME

LAMPSHADE

LOOK

MOTIF

PAINT

PAPER

PASTE

PATTERN

PRINT

ROOM

SCROLL

TAPE

WALL

WINDOW
(shade)

```
D L L A W X S E P F F N P G
E L T N I A P A I U N Y N X
C O N T R A S T R R N I I B
O R E C T T O N E G L F A S
R C C C E M I T I I F S T R
A S C A N S T S E A E V R E
T W A B H A E C M B Y N U W
I Y F I P D R A O B P U C O
N K N N B E D A H S P M A L
G G T E A E R P E T A O B F
S E U T R D A E R P S D E B
G W I N D O W U P I P E M V
S V X H K O O L T A N A H L
E F F E C T Y M V Y P T G C
```

SHAKER VILLAGE

"Hands to work and hearts to God" are the watchwords of the Shaker movement. Founded in 1776 by **ANN LEE**, Shakers lived communally and created a legacy of architecture, **FURNITURE**, **CRAFTS**, and **SONG**. Visit the Shaker Village in Canterbury, New Hampshire, by way of this puzzle.

ANN LEE
(founder)

ARTIFACTS

BASKETS

BOXES

BROOMS
(handmade)

CRAFTS

CREAMERY
(restaurant)

DESIGNS

FARM

FIELDS

FURNITURE

GARDEN

GIFTS

GUIDED

HERBS

MANU-
SCRIPTS

MEADOW

MUSEUM

MUSIC

MYSTICS

RUGS

SEEDS

SKETCHES

SONG

TOUR

VALUES

WEAVING

WORKSHOPS

```
M Y S T I C S E H C T E K S
G N O S W N M B Y B R S O L
G U R F G U B C O U O E H N
R D C I S U M V T X I E U K
E K S E C W R I A R E D H A
G E U L O O N P G L A S R Y
D M S D S R F G N V U T R W
B X A S U K C N I U I E A L
D E N F B S A R V F M K S H
M E E X F H G T A A N S M A
A U D A N O Y C E F T A O G
G L R I T P T R W F T B O I
L M A N U S C R I P T S R W
G S G W A G P G D H E R B S
```

Frank Herbert's *Dune* books rank among the classics of science fiction. In Herbert's complex fictional universe, the legislature of the ruling empire is called the Imperial Landsraad. All the important familial clans, known as the Great Houses, have voting status in the legislature. We've hidden the names of 38 of these Great Houses in the puzzle below.

ABEFOR
ALMAN
ATREIDES
BENDAU
BESKID
BROMELI

ELIOZ
EMAR
ESTILON
FENRING .
FORBINO
GHULAN

GINAZ
HAJUS
HIRADO
HYBLA
IASI
IGAL
ISFAHAN
KENRIC
MELUI
MOLAY
MOROTAI
MWAMI
NGARA
ORDOS
PALIGO
PASTRAN
PHYFE
QAIR
REJANI
TOMBE
TURENNE
VICO
VILLISH
WALLACH
XINGUS
YASU

```
H U A D N E B D O T T T Y N
P A S T R A N R O F E B A T
L O T I M A W M O I C L S B
F R G R H Z B R N M U I U V
E D E A E E B A K H E I I L
N O F M N I R O G A A L U A
R S Y E N B D M G Z L J I G
I E H O E A E E A I N H U I
N D P S R L C N S A L C S S
G V K I U N I H M T G A D A
L I H I T G R O H O I L P L
D C R E J A N I Z R L L I M
K O Q A I R E I B O D A O A
S H Y B L A K V X M R W Y N
```

MEERKATS

Meerkats are small mammals of the mongoose family that live in all parts of the Kalahari Desert in southern Africa. Meerkats may be best known through the fictional character Timon, featured in the 1994 film, *The Lion King*.

Standing on their hind legs, meerkats are about one foot tall. Some typically "guard" their underground homes while others in the group search for food. If these sentries sense trouble, they send a message of alarm to their hunting pals.

```
O S Y S S E G A S S E M S T
G W L T E E F G E E L I H W
U I B A N K H N A D N E S B
T N T K P O T I R E I S D Y
Y T D R M R G T C R D O E D
P H R E I T O N H N O H L L
I E S E R O B U I F T N B E
C F S M F G G H R D R A U G
A U T E S G R O U P N B O S
L N N H R I F O F A L A R M
L O A R E A B O U T O L T F
Y I O H H S O M E N Y B A S
C K T O T H E I R E D S A T
W A C W O T B P C W B T F U
```

It's easy to feel like a big shot when you're enjoying a ballgame, CONCERT, or other special EVENT in the COMFORT of your own PRIVATE LUXURY SUITE. The first SPORTS ARENA to introduce LAVISH suites for FANS who could afford them was the Houston Astrodome, which opened in 1965.

AMENITIES

ARENA

BALLPARK

BAR STOOLS

BEVERAGES

CARPET

CHAIRS

COMFORT

CONCERT

COUCH

COURT

EVENT

FANS

FIELD

FOOD

GAME

HOSPITALITY

LAVISH

LEASE

AREA

LUXURY

PRIVATE

SEATS

SERVICE

SPORTS

STADIUM

SUITE

TELEVISIONS

UPSCALE

VENUE

VIEW

WINDOWS

```
C B A R S T O O L S X L Y Y
W H R C N S E G A R E V E B
S T A E S N H H T A A P M A
W V V I F O O T S R R P A L
O E I S R I S E E I U E G L
D N E T E S P A V P V O N P
N U W A C I I A S E R A C A
I E V D I V T C R T L A L R
W G A I V E A I O T R D C K
K N E U R L L D N N L O N P
P U T M E E I Y P E C V P S
Y O I I S T T C I N M E N S
F L U X U R Y F O O D A R B
M P S H C U O C O M F O R T
```

WORK THAT WOOD!

In the mood to do some woodworking? If so, you're going to need some of the tools from the list below. You probably already have a **HAMMER** and a **SAW** in your **TOOLBOX**, but a **CLAMP** is helpful for holding pieces while you're working on them, and a **PLANE** can be very useful to make sure surfaces are **LEVEL**.

CALIPER
CAT'S PAW (for removing nails)
CHISEL
CLAMP
COUNTERSINK
DOWEL
DRAWKNIFE (shaves surfaces)
DRILL
FROE (for splitting wood)
GIMLET (for boring holes)
GOUGE (chisel for cutting grooves)
HAMMER
HAND ADZ (axe for trimming and smoothing)
LATHE
LEVEL
MALLET
NAIL PUNCH
OILSTONE (sharpens tools)
PLANE

PLUMB BOB (determines vertical alignment)
RASP
ROUND FILE
ROUTER
SANDER
SAW

SPOKESHAVE (makes rounded edges)
STROP (sharpens tools)
TOOLBOX
VISE

```
S K R E M M A H Z F O P K X
T C R O U N D F I L E P L C
M E E G U O G U C P F L O L
R F L W B T Z R L O I U H A
M O R L N D E R W R N M Z M
L F E O A P V R D T K B I P
E D D D I M A I E S W B R T
S F N L L L H R S O A O F M
I A A P P G S E E E R B E U
H C S L U I E T A C D F D V
C A A A N M K X O B L O O T
R N W K C L O I L N C A W U
E L A T H E P L E V E L E D
D P T C A T S P A W S A L K
```

ROLLICKING ROLLER DERBY

No one has to tell Raquel Welch just how rough-and-tumble the SPORT of roller derby can be. In the 1972 flick *Kansas City Bomber*, Raquel played K. C. Carr, a roller derby queen for the Portland Loggers. The glamorous star did her own stunts for the movie and ended up breaking her wrist during filming.

ARENA

ATHLETIC

BLOCK

COMPETE

CONTACT

CONTEST

COSTUMES

ENDURANCE

HELMETS

JAMS

LAPS

MILE

PADS

PASS

PERIODS

PHYSICAL

PLAYERS

POINTS

POPULAR

PROFES-
   SIONAL

SCORE

SKATES

SKILLS

SPEED

SPORT

SPRINTS

TRACK

TURNS

TWO TEAMS

WINNER

```
C O S T U M E S P A L O A W
M P D T M D C C R R F W L L
Y I E Y N O N L C E U O A S
T O L R R I A O D N Y N M S
L F C E I C R O M N O A S D
C H T O I O U P C I J A L A
N E W S N O D O S W P K T P
P F Y N D T N S M L B H R O
O H S K A T E S A D L J A I
P T K N A F R S E E A I C N
U U E C O M P E T E C K K T
L R T R O P S I O P Y P P S
A N P C B L C N W S K U J J
R S E C K M B S T E M L E H
```

You've probably seen the **ALOE VERA** plant serving ornamental purposes, especially in public buildings and gardens. But did you know juice from the plant is often added to cosmetics and ointments, and can be used medicinally to heal cuts and burns? This multipurpose plant, along with the names of 29 others ending with the letter "A," can be found in the diagram below.

ACACIA	POINSETTIA	SWEET PEA
ALOE VERA	RAFFIA	VANILLA
AZALEA	RUTABAGA	VIOLA
BALSA	SEQUOIA	ZINNIA
BANANA		
BEGONIA		
CAMELLIA		
CANNA		
DAHLIA		
ERICA		
FORSYTHIA		
FREESIA		
GARDENIA		
GLOXINIA		
GUAVA		
HYDRANGEA		
JOJOBA		
MAGNOLIA		
OKRA		
PAPAYA		
PAPRIKA		
PETUNIA		

```
L B A N A N A A F H A I D B
A C I R E J L K A Y A P A P
V V C A P L J A I D J L H F
X G A M I O I A H R S A L S
Y U C N J N I K T A P Z I M
O A A O O N E N Y N F A A A
T V B G I C D D S G K L P G
H A E X A A Q W R E H E A N
O B O L C M E E O A T A H O
A L O E V E R A F U G T A L
G I Z O T L C A N N A R I I
V F K P U L Z I N N I A L A
F R E E S I A I O U Q E S A
A A G A B A T U R A F F I A
```

LET'S DWELL ON "LL"

Please **ALLOW** us to **CALL** your attention to an important **BULLETIN**. This diagram is **FILLED** with words that contain a double "L." Even though there may not be a **MILLION** of them to find, it will be no **SMALL** task to **COLLAR** them all.

ALLERGY	BULLETIN	DOLL
ALLOT	BULLY	DRILL
ALLOW	CALL	FALLEN
BALLAD	CHILLY	FILLED
BELLE	COLLAR	FOLLOW
BRILLIANT	DALLY	GULLY
		JELLY
		LOLL
		LULL
		MALLARD
		MELLOW
		MILLION
		MULLED
		PILLOW
		RECALLED
		SCROLL
		SELLER
		SHELL
		SHRILL
		SMALL
		SPELL
		SPILL
		TILL
		TROLL
		VILLAGE
		WILLOW

```
I J L B P J F D J D A L L Y
O A L L O W W E R B U L L Y
T I B W U O L I E S E E I C
L B T R O L L Y L H D P M A
G U L L Y L N G S R V S D L
B L W A I O L R G I W R E L
S L O T I F N E L L A F L O
D E L L U M T L M L N O L T
H T L R E C A L L E D W I V
S I I L N G H A O A O L F D
M N P A E L M I L L O R C S
A E S U B R A L L O C G M I
L T U M T N A I L L I R B S
L E L L E B W R J I Y T S E
```

We all know how incredibly common the surname "Smith" is; all you have to do is look in any telephone directory. Did you know, however, that there are also many occupations ending in "smith" as well? Some are waiting to be discovered in the diagram below.

ANGLE   STONE   WEAPON

ARROW   TOOL   WHITE

BLACK

BLADE   VERSE   WIRE

BRIGHT   WAGON   WORD

BRONZE

CHAIN

CLOCK

COPPER

GOLD

HAMMER

HOUSE

IRON

JOKE

KNIFE

LOCK

RUNE

SHOEING

SILVER

```
I J B K N I F E W G T V I S
J S C C V J B O V J O B A C
D O N O G A W D P B O M T C
L S I L V E R S E I L K H F
B J S C A N R W S T A A E N
I R T P M U I S H H I Z C I
S G O L D R E D W N F H R K
R N N N E T F S M T W C W K
R I E P Z L V G P D R O W T
P E P D I E G E D S R R V L
O O M H W S D N O R I C R M
C H R M H U M A A E B R S G
E S F T A O W O L A F V H B
A K B B T H G I R B A A F R
```

In America, it is customary to toss white rice at weddings to wish the newlyweds a fruitful and plentiful life together. But as you'll read below, in Japan rice is not only a staple, it is a building material.

After the rice hulls sorting crop, from the out the Japanese leftover white farmers rice and kernels from take the mix them into a kind of paste. Then they mold this substance into brick-shaped blocks and they build houses that are known as "houses of rice skin."

```
K S K C O L B U I L D N L C P
L R U I I I P Y G N I T R O S
B E I B P A E K A K M X K M T
H M F K S H G E S Y K K L E K
M R Y T T T C M B E E T I H W
I A E D O I A K R H P D O T W
X F N P R V S N I T E U G M O
T A K E T H E E C N S W N O F
H F H U L L S R K E D C E R R
E T M G S E U M S H I O Y F I
M E H F N I O T H T P N F N C
P R R A L L H R A O U T T H E
M O P E D A S T P O B C S O T
M A R R T P A R E K N O W N A
J N N C D H X D D L N I L O F
```

WHAT THE DICKENS!

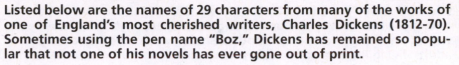

43

Listed below are the names of 29 characters from many of the works of one of England's most cherished writers, Charles Dickens (1812-70). Sometimes using the pen name "Boz," Dickens has remained so popular that not one of his novels has ever gone out of print.

ARTFUL DODGER (The)

BUMBLE (Mr.)

CARTON (Sydney)

CHUZZLEWIT (Martin)

CLAYPOLE (Noah)

COPPERFIELD (David)

CRATCHIT (Bob)

DARNAY (Charles)

DEFARGE (Ernest)

DOMBEY (Paul)

ESTELLA

FAGIN

GASPARD

HAVISHAM (Miss)

HEEP (Uriah)

JUPE (Sissy)

MARLEY (Jacob)

MICAWBER (Wilkins)

PEGLER (Mrs.)

PICKWICK (Samuel)

PINCH (Tom)

PIRRIP (Philip "Pip")

SCROOGE (Ebenezer)

SIKES (Bill)

SPARSIT (Mrs.)

SPENLO (Dora)

TINY TIM

TWIST (Oliver)

WINKLE (Nathaniel)

```
B B S P Y H R N O T R A C A
H Y E L R A M E H P B C L R
W E L B M U B C L V M L A T
H B M I T Y N I T G E J Y F
J M A H S I V A H T E U P U
Y O I K P S W O S C D P O L
K D F C O P P E R F I E L D
N Z A I A E M A L R V G E O
O S G W L W T O R Z A F C D
T E I K W C B I L S Z B G G
S K N C H G P E P N I U U E
I I S I D E F A R G E T H R
W S T P S C R O O G E P I C
T K W P I D A R N A Y U S L
```

"MELROSE PLACE"

Spun off from "Beverly Hills, 90210" in 1992, "Melrose Place" became one of the '90s most popular evening soap operas. At first, there really wasn't anything too special about a show which told of some young adults living in the same apartment complex. But once the crafty AMANDA Woodward was introduced in season two (played by the irreplaceable Heather LOCKLEAR), the series really took off in the ratings. Fans eagerly awaited her doings as well as those of MICHAEL, KIMBERLY, and the other attractive, scheming characters.

ALISON
AMANDA
BAR
BILLY

BISSETT (Josie)
BROOKE
CALABRO (Thomas)
COUPLES

GREED
HOSPITAL
JAKE
JEALOUSY
JESS
KIMBERLY
LEIGHTON (Laura)
LIES
LOCKLEAR (Heather)
LOVE
MATT
MICHAEL
PASSION
REVENGE
RIVALRY
SAVANT (Doug)
SECRET
SHOOTERS (Restaurant)
SHOW (Grant)
SHUE (Andrew)
SYDNEY
THORNE-SMITH (Courtney)
ZUNIGA (Daphne)

```
B T Z I P S L C W C N H E M
C O U P L E S O O J O Y I Y
A D N A M A H N V S A C Z D
T H I Y T S O W P E H K T G
D T G T L T O I Y A P K E Y
W I A I H R T H E K O O R B
A M E G R A E L K C O L C A
R S I N L O R B A L A C E R
J E A L O U S Y M V K U S S
L N V L J I W Y I I H O S A
G R E E D S S R L S K E M V
T O Y E N D Y S A L J E P A
B H N T N G D E A L I S O N
G T B I S S E T T P D B Z T
```

BENNY GOODMAN RECORDINGS

Clarinetist and bandleader Benny Goodman (1909-86) was known as the "King of Swing." It was his orchestra that established that variety of music, the most popular big-band jazz style of the 1930s and early '40s. How many of his hit recordings listed here do you REMEMBER?

ALWAYS

AVALON

BLUE LOU

CHINA BOY

CLOUDS

COKEY

DINAH

EMALINE

FRENESI

GOODBYE

HUNKADOLA

IF I HAD YOU

LIZA

LOUISE

MARGIE

MOONGLOW

RAMONA

REMEMBER

ROLL 'EM

ROSETTA

SANDMAN

SHINE

SMILES

SOFT WINDS

SUGAR

TANGERINE

TEA FOR TWO

TI-PI-TIN

TOPSY

WHISPERING

```
W N L E N I R E G N A T Y D
A W N M E I G R A M O N A T
T R O S E T T A C L O U D S
Z E L L V A D I S I F O T M
P M A C G G L D P F S L O I
N E V F H N N O R I B E P L
A M A M O I O E D H T U S E
M B B T W R N O L A D L Y S
D E D T O E T A M D K B L E
N R F L S P D W B Y D N O N
A O L I L S S N O O B Z U I
S E M A L I N E O U Y C I H
M D I N A H Z G R A G U S S
Z I S Y A W L A N C O K E Y
```

Polar bears, which live in regions bordering the Arctic Ocean, have pads of fur on the soles of their feet to help them walk on ice. You can learn more about the charateristics of bears by solving this puzzle.

BIG FEET

CURVED (claws)

DENSE (fur)

EXCELLENT (hunter)

FIERCE (fighter)

GRAYISH (nose)

GRIZZLED (coat)

HAIRY (head)

HEAVY (body)

LARGE (carnivore)

LONG (snout)

LOOSE (skin)

MAMMAL

ORANGE (nose)

ROUNDED (ears)

SHAGGY (fur)

SHARP (claws)

SHORT (legs)

SKILLFUL (tree-climber)

SMALL (eyes)

SOLITARY (animal)

STRONG (legs)

THICK (fur)

UNRETRACT-ABLE (claws)

WHITE (patches)

WILD (animal)

WOOLLY (coat)

YELLOW (markings)

```
K W S K I L L F U L R S I O
Y L L O O W C H E L U M S U
A S M A L L S F X W A B N N
T E E F G I B H O M U R R A
H E S C Y T T L M M E E G P
Y S H A R P L A Y T X M B E
K R R O L E L S R V C D D T
I G H O Y R I A H Y E E Y I
K S K V G S C F I V L D B H
C D A R G T I L R Z L N K W
I E G N A R O U Z I E U K D
H N X B H O C I W G N O L S
T S L V S N R I U S T R M U
Z E E E C G T E R D G P O B
```

ON THE RUN

Over the **COURSE** of this next puzzle, see if you can find the 30 words associated with **RUNNING**. Just keep a steady **PACE**, and if your **ENDURANCE** level is high, you just might go the **DISTANCE** and finish this one in record **TIME**. That is if you don't pull a **MUSCLE** and get a **CRAMP** in your writing hand.

CARBOS

CONDITION

COOLDOWN

COURSE

CRAMP

DISTANCE

ENDURANCE

KICK

MARATHON

MILE

MUSCLE

NUTRITION

OLYMPICS

PACE

RACE

REGIMEN

RUNNING

SHINSPLINTS

SPLIT

SPRINTS

STOPWATCH

STRETCH

SURFACE

TIME

TRACK

TRAINING

TREAD

WALKING

WALL

WARMUP

```
I D G C E E C A F R U S I Y
D R F H C T E R T S P H I S
P E S E N M C K E R F P T N
U C T R A C K O I G A N U M
M N O I T I D N O C I T P F
R A P D S Y T M E L R M R G
A R W A I S A K P I D C E G
W U A E D R C S T M W O L N
A D T R A I N I N G A U W I
L N C T K I O N P B L R F N
K E H O H N E A C M L S C N
I O M S P L I T M N Y E R U
N T E I I R W M U S C L E R
G O R M T C U E C A R B O S
```

Although Leonardo da VINCI (1452-1519) was known primarily as a painter and sculptor, his quest for knowledge led him to do research in many fields, such as OPTICS, GEOLOGY, and BOTANY. He was also an architect, engineer, inventor, and scientist, a true OBSERVER and researcher of life.

BARONCELLI*

BIRDS

BORGIA (Cesare; patron)

BOTANY

BOTTICELLI (rival)

CATERINA (mother)

CLOUX (residence)

GEOLOGY

LAST SUPPER*

LUTE

LYRE

MASK

MONA LISA*

NUDES*

OBSERVER

OPTICS

PARACHUTE

PIERO (father)

PUPILS

RENAIS-SANCE

SINGER

SMILES

STEAM (experiments)

ST. JEROME*

TEXTBOOK

TREE (art study)

VINCI (birthplace)

*works of art

```
I O P J L B S R H M K B R R
X U U N U D E S H X U E G E
J S P K P V E N Y B P R G C
O P I E R O V T A P M E V N
Y R L E E K O R U R O G I A
N P S A K R O S K L X N N S
M B A S D N T K O P T I C S
O S A R C S M G O V R S I I
N M O E A J Y Y B E H G K A
A I L L E C I T T O B M S N
L L L D L I H A X S R T D E
I E L O N D C U E L E G R R
S S U V V P B O T A N Y I N
A X S T J E R O M E L Y B A
```

Margaret Mead (1901-78) was an American anthropologist and writer who gained notoriety for her studies of primitive cultures. Often controversial, Mead wrote and spoke about a variety of topics, including child care and adolescence. The quote below is from an article of hers that appeared in a 1965 issue of *Redbook* magazine.

What the world needs is not romantic lovers who are sufficient unto themselves, but husbands and wives who live in communities, relate to other people, carry on useful work, and willingly give time and attention to their children.

```
T P E O P L E C N C R B V L
I V R E H T O O T I U A Y B
M U R U A V I M T T A N S A
E N I L F T T M H N U D L E
A A E G N D O U T A U W V O
N R H E L M S N B M H I P Y
D F T R D B U I N O G V M L
N T O R A S D T L R H E R G
A W T N E I C I F F U S V N
K K D F L O V E R S F C P I
R S U T H E M S E L V E S L
O L C H I L D R E N Y N C L
W K O N O Y R R A C O L I I
O A W H O A R E H T T A H W
```

If Word Searches are your FORTE, then this puzzle will surely REIN-FORCE your solving skills. The 28 terms hidden in the diagram all contain the word "FOR." One way to measure your solving PERFORMANCE is to set your watch or clock BEFORE you begin and see how long it takes you to finish.

AFFORD

BEFORE

COMFORT

CONFORM

FORAGE

FORAY

FOREIGN

FOREST

FOREVER

FORFEIT

FORGE

FORGIVE

FORGO

FORK

FORMAL

FORMATION

FORMULA

FORTE

FORTUNE

FORUM

FORWARD

INFORM

PERFORATE

PERFOR-
MANCE

PINAFORE

REFORM

REINFORCE

UNIFORM

```
C R S M A B I N F O R M A L
K P W S T M B S E G R O F I
E R E G I B R T R O F M O C
L T O R E C R O F N I E R C
B L A F F G V N F T F V M B
K T O R R O O A S E G I U N
T R E D O C R E G U R G L N
E B S N F F R M E F O R A Y
E U N I F O R M A T I O N A
O G R O F R R E U N P F F T
F O R A G E A W P R C F G N
V T N S I V I A A R O E R D
E I E O O E N U T R O F U G
P N G I E R O F D S D L W F
```

CLANS OF SCOTLAND

The clan structure of Scottish society had its beginnings in the 11th century and spread throughout the Highlands and the Lowlands, evolving into numerous branches of the original clans, each with its own distinctive tartan. Listed here are 30 well-known Scottish clans.

ABERCROMBY

AGNEW

BAXTER

BISSET

CARNEGIE

CRAWFORD

DUNLOP

FLEMING

GLEN

HAIG

HAMILTON

HEPBURN

KINCAID

KINNEAR

LAMONT

LOGAN

MACBAIN

MACDOWALL

MACDUFF

MACEWEN

MACFARLANE

MACMILLAN

NAPIER

NESBITT

PATTERSON

SKENE

WALLACE

WEIR

WHITELAW

WOOD

```
T P M M A C E W E N E K S T
E O A R P H H G E B T K K X
C L C T E I N I A B C A M N
A N M B T I G X R E T X A B
L U I E M E P L N L Y G C B
L D L E N C R A W F O R D I
A A L R C I L S N L N Y U S
W F A B E R C R O M B Y F S
O C N W A O A A T N H N F E
D Y R F G E H D L A M O N T
C O C L N E S B I T T G K N
A A O N E L G G M T P C W U
M H I W W A D I A C N I K R
U K N R U B P E H G Y M X M
```

There are 34 words that start with the letters "BR" hidden below. Use that BRILLIANT BRAIN of yours to BREEZE through the diagram and find them all!

BRACE

BRACKET

BRAID

BRAIN

BRAKE

BRAN

BRAVE

BRAWN

BRAY

BREAD

BREAK

BREATH

BREED

BREEZE

BREW

BRICK

BRIDE

BRIEF

BRIGHT

BRILLIANT

BRIM

BRING

BRINK

BRISK

BROAD

BROIL

BROKE

BRONZE

BROOK

BROOM

BROTH

BROWN

BRUNCH

BRUSH

```
U R N D G B B B S N I E N L
Z W Y N D R R R U G B Y O R
B A I I K E I O A A R O M G
B R A C E A E O T Y I W N R
B R I Z T K F M M H S U R B
B R E L H L O D V Y K L R R
B R Z E L Y B R A K E I Z O
C R N E D I R B B E G O B W
Y S O F M V A L M H R R C N
K B R A I N V N T I U B Y U
T O B K D F E A T N R F O G
O V O W D T E K C A R B D N
W Y Z R H R U H W R S I H Z
Z W E R B R I N K B U A F N
```

RED IN THEIR FLAGS

When it comes to designing one of their own, some nations look to other country's flags for inspiration. Just check out the flags of CHILE, LIBERIA, and MALAYSIA and you'll definitely see they were influenced by the USA's Stars and Stripes.

ALBANIA

AUSTRIA

CAMBODIA

CANADA

CHILE

CHINA

DENMARK

EGYPT

FRANCE

HAITI

HUNGARY

ICELAND

ITALY

JAPAN

LIBERIA

MEXICO

MOROCCO

NEPAL

NORWAY

PERU

POLAND

PORTUGAL

RUSSIA

SAMOA

SPAIN

SWITZERLAND

TAIWAN

THAILAND

TUNISIA

TURKEY

```
C A M B O D I A I S S U R O
F A Y R A G N U H G Y T A X
F O N C N N P A D U A U O D
S D U A A Y O B L L P N M C
A W N W D L L I B E R I A H
H J I A S A A A G A C S S I
M A A T L T N D F X A I L L
T O I P Z I D R N N U A A E
B C R T A E A O I Y G R P G
O I T O I N R H T U R K E Y
E X S F C W C L T O A D N P
B E U E A C K R A M N E D T
H M A Y Y U O G R N L Y G N
H G R M S P A I N U D U P X
```

54

You'll have a double dose of fun as you solve this puzzle filled with 29 double-letter edibles. From APPLE to ZUCCHINI, each term is a food that contains one set of double letters.

APPLE

BEEF

BEET

CABBAGE

CARROT

CHEESE

CHERRY

COOKIE

CURRANT

EGGPLANT

FRITTER

JELLY

LEEK

LETTUCE

MAYONNAISE

MOLASSES

MUFFIN

MUSHROOM

MUTTON

NOODLES

PERSIMMON

PIZZA

PORRIDGE

PUDDING

SCALLOPS

SHALLOT

SPAGHETTI

TRUFFLES

ZUCCHINI

```
M A Y O N N A I S E M O M Z
J G N I D D U P D Z U S B P
L C E L P P A S U I T N F C
C A B B A G E C U T T E L P
P R E B H S C A L L O P S T
E R E E S H Z C O N N S N K
R O T A I Z M Y O P F A K R
S T L N I Z R O N O R E E J
I O I P A R D I O R K T E P
M L Y S E L F F U R T I L B
M L M H E F P C B I H S E M
O A C S U J O G R D I S Z L
N H L M M Z U F G G N J U O
E S E E H C Y L L E J A Z M
```

Below is an observation by Theodore Roosevelt (1858-1919), the 26th President of the United States. His sense of activism and innovation are well illustrated by his words, as you shall see.

Far better
it is
to dare
mighty
things,
to win
glorious
triumphs,
even
though
checkered
by failure,
than to
take
rank
with
those
poor
spirits
who neither
enjoy
nor suffer

much,
because
they
live
in the
gray

twilight
that
knows
neither
victory
nor defeat.

```
N I W O T N A H T Y H D R F
E C L V U O O E T K A E A T
V I C T O R Y R N A B R H H
E K N O W S I A D W B E G G
Y O J N E U R D H E Y K E I
E T S G M F V O T D F C H L
O T H P C F N T B T A E V I
E N H G I E E O H S I H A W
K S U O I R O L G O L C W T
A Y U T S M I N O E U K I W
T A H A N E I T H E R G T I
I E M U C H V T S M E A H L
R O O P T E N I I L N V A M
Y E H F P I B M L S O O T N
```

COOKING TERMS

It's been said that the way to a man's heart is through his stomach. If that's true, then here are 38 different ways to prepare oneself for the journey.

BAKE

BARBECUE

BASTE

BEAT

BLACKEN

BLEND

BOIL

BREAD

BROWN

CANDY

CHARBROIL

CHOP

CHURN

COMBINE

CREAM

CUBE

CURE

DEEP-FRY

DICE

FILLET

GLAZE

GRATE

GRILL

KNEAD

MARINATE

MASH

MINCE

MIX

PICKLE

POACH

ROAST

SAUTÉ

SCRAMBLE

SLICE

STIR

STUFF

TOAST

WHIP

```
K P U E L D B L A C K E N M
U M C P A P A M E B L U T D
C E A E O I O W N K Y C U E
T H N R U H C A C W A E L E
L K D I I W C I C C O B C P
I B Y T B N P O D H M R T F
B B X S D M A R S A C A B R
I I D T S A O T R R E B S Y
M I N C E A U C E B G R O H
Z G E E S F S A C R C U B E
M B L T F M M L I O B K R C
H Y B A S T E L L I F U E I
H K O R Z R L D S L C X G D
T Y S G T E T U A S N W N G
```

ABC'S OF FOOD

This particular puzzle possesses an alphabetical aura. See how quickly you can round up the 28 foods beginning with the letters "A," "B," and "C." We hope this whets your appetite — for more puzzles, that is!

ALMOND	CAMEMBERT	CHOCOLATE
AMBROSIA	CARAMEL	CINNAMON
APPLE	CEREAL	COOKIE
APRICOT	CHEESE	CORN
ARTICHOKE	CHICKEN	CRAB
ASPARAGUS		
AVOCADO		
BACON		
BAGEL		
BANANA		
BEEF		
BEET		
BISCUIT		
BLACKBERRY		
BRATWURST		
BREAD		
BROCCOLI		
CAKE		

```
W  B  A  N  A  N  A  A  L  M  O  N  D  M
W  I  K  F  T  K  P  M  F  A  C  R  H  E
E  S  K  V  Y  R  R  E  B  K  C  A  L  B
G  C  M  P  I  H  E  E  V  R  S  T  S  H
A  U  H  C  M  B  U  B  A  C  O  N  M  N
P  I  O  Y  B  B  L  B  M  A  U  S  K  O
P  T  K  D  Y  R  R  E  C  E  C  U  I  M
L  N  L  F  A  O  A  H  M  E  M  G  T  A
E  E  K  O  H  C  I  T  R  A  E  A  O  N
G  S  D  B  O  C  O  E  W  I  R  R  C  N
A  B  E  R  K  O  A  V  K  U  L  A  R  I
B  E  N  E  P  L  N  O  A  A  R  P  C  C
T  R  N  A  H  I  O  N  S  M  C  S  T  B
W  G  S  D  U  C  H  O  C  O  L  A  T  E
```

Are you nimble with a THIMBLE? Have an itch to STITCH? In a haste to BASTE? Even if you're not, these quilting terms will be fun to find in the diagram.

ASSEMBLE	BORDER	HOOP
BACK	CUTTING	IRON
BASTE	DESIGN	LAYER
BATTING	FABRIC	MITER
BINDING	FILLER	NEEDLES
BLOCK	FRAME	PATCHWORK
		PATTERN
		PENCIL
		PIECE
		PINS
		PRESS
		ROWS
		RULER
		SCRAPS
		SEAMS
		STITCH
		STRIPS
		TEMPLATE
		THIMBLE
		THREAD
		TRACE
		TRIM
		UNITS
		YARDAGE

```
D N S C E M A R F N P F O C
H E H P I N S A C G M S B I
O E S D I N B G N I T T U C
O D P T A R R I T S M A E S
P L Y O I E T E N E R C K D
A E G C M T R S L D T M S F
T S L N A T C H P U I S W Y
C T S B F A D H T R R N A D
H I T E M P L A T E E R G B
W N R B M I G Y C Y D S K D
O U A O C B H S P A R C S A
R C C N N L L T G L O O M I
K O E F I L L E R L B K W Y
F P I E C E S O B T O G P S
```

Read the following passage to learn how Australia's official national day came into existence, and then find each line in the grid below.

Australia

Day

commemorates

the

landing

of the

First

Fleet

in Sydney

Cove on

January

twenty-

sixth in

seventeen

eighty

eight.

As a

national

public

holiday,

many

celebrations

are

held

around

the country

such as

civil

ceremonies

and

fireworks

displays.

```
E M J O P U B L I C V T F F
E C S U C H A S E E S H S E
T H E B O R L R R R H E L D
A S T L V J E A I O T C G S
I K H F E M A F N A T O N I
L R O D O B L N R O T U I X
A O L N N E R O U D I N D T
R W I I E U M A S A S T N H
T E D T V E O Y T Y R R A I
S R A V M I T R D I N Y L N
U I Y M T N C N A Y O A F C
A F O S E V E N T E E N M O
G C N W S Y A L P S I D S O
C Y T H G I E I G H T S W C
```

The Tempest is a successful mix of tragedy, comedy, and magic that is considered by many to be William Shakespeare's greatest accomplishment. Some scholars also believe *The Tempest* was the Bard's last play. If that's true, then this story of a magician who gives up his powers to become an ordinary man may reflect Shakespeare's own thoughts as he left London to retire to his home in Stratford-upon-Avon.

Duke Prospero was banished to a deserted island by his evil brother, but he used the magical spirits of the island to bring his enemies into his power. Instead of taking revenge, he forgives them and, freeing his magic servants, returns home in peace.

```
H R E H T O R B L S V C N I
I O Q O S F R E E I N G N T
S Z M R Y P H V T U D T O Z
L I V E C V I S A U O B L Y
A P Q P I G E R K H R Z B G
N E F S R N N E I I G N I E
D G A O T Z E S N T B D S H
S N F R D C M G G A S E P T
I E A P L A I P N C V S O D
H V C M G H E I E H W E W E
Y E J I E H S T N A V R E S
B R C V T H O I S H C T R U
I A Q U E H T F O N G E J Q
L V B D N A L S I Z I D D H
```

A FLOOD OF FLOWERS

The colorful blossoms of flowering plants are a welcome change from the drabness of the late winter months. We've planted a bouquet of 29 flowers for your solving pleasure to pluck from the maze of letters below.

ASTER

AZALEA

BLUEBELL

BLUET

CAMELLIA

CARNATION

CHRYSAN-
THEMUM

COLUMBINE

DAHLIA

DAISY

HYACINTH

IRIS

JASMINE

JONQUIL

LARKSPUR

LAUREL

LILAC

LILY

MALLOW

MARIGOLD

MYRTLE

ORCHID

PEONY

PHLOX

PINK

ROSE

TULIP

VIOLET

ZINNIA

```
D A I S Y A Y W O S L W X C
G L I U Q N O J H E I O H V
C O O Y L L C Y S N L R X I
B O L G L E A O K H Y K I O
L E L A I C R U P S K R A L
Y A M U I R N U A T S Z O E
T I C N M I A N A U M I K T
T L T K L B T M I L N N Y E
E H O R C H I D L I I N N L
U A S T E R O N L P Z I O T
L D V M T J N I E Y M A E R
B L U E B E L L M S M E P Y
X M V S K A E L A Z A V R M
S G N Z C K V J C N Z B Y L
```

Probably the most famous of Scotland's lochs, or lakes, is Loch NESS, home of the legendary and elusive Loch Ness Monster. We've hidden a total of 37 lochs in the diagram below; find them — but beware of Nessie!

AFFRIC
AILORT
ALSH
BROOM
CARRON
CLUANIE

CORUISK
DOCHART
DOON
DUICH
EARN
EINICH

ERIBOLL
ETIVE
FYNE
GARTEN
HOPE
KATRINE
LAIDON
LOMOND
LONG
LOYAL
LYON
MAREE
MUICK
NESS
NEVIS
OSSIAN
PATTACK
QUOICH
RANNOCH
SCRIDAIN
SHIEL
SLOY
TREIG
TULLA
VOIL

```
U Q E N T R L O V G I E R T
E T G V I B S I V E N Q U R
D N M U I C K T H I E L P Q
N H Y A D T T M R N L R C N
O Y O F H N E T R A G I A B
M S L F R C A M Y U H K O M
O C S R V K I O D L M C C V
L O H I H V L O Q C A R O M
C F C C A L O R U R V R R D
L A I D O N R B R Q H R U Q
S U N B R N T O H S F Q I L
D S I A N G N O L E I H S Y
I R E A C L P A T T A C K O
E S T N E E S C R I D A I N
```

ARRIVING IN ALABAMA

On December 14, 1819, Alabama became the 22nd state to enter the Union. The state seceded in 1861 during the American Civil War and became part of the Confederacy, but was readmitted in 1868. Search the diagram below for 30 cities and towns that are located in Alabama, The Heart of Dixie.

ARITON

AUBURN

BOAZ

BUTLER

CALERA

CENTRE

CLIO

DAPHNE

DELTA

ELBA

EUTAW

FOLEY

GENEVA

GUIN

HOOVER

HUNTSVILLE

JASPER

KINSEY

LANETT

LAPINE

LEEDS

MOODY

NORMAL

OZARK

REFORM

SEALE

TROY

VANCE

WALDO

YORK

```
W H E N H P A D L U A T A V
A A U N O T I R A Z T Y K T
D C T G O E Z G N S N H O G
Z L U U V R I A E R U Z E D
K I N S E Y O R T N A Z N D
N O F L R C E N T R E I I E
O P T E J P N S K U C V P L
A U C F S J V A B B N B A T
B E I A F I C M V U O M L A
S T J B L Y F T R A R J L Y
F D E L A E S S Z O Y C D O
M T E E U L R J N A F O M B
W K J E S O W A L D O E R F
S F L R L F G B F M I D R K
```

Ray Kroc opened the first McDonald's RESTAURANT on April 15, 1955, in Des Plaines, Illinois, and by 1959, Chicago became the home of the 100th. When he died in 1984, at the age of 81, there were 7,500 franchises worldwide. Today there are more than 31,000 of the fast food restaurants, with roughly half of them in foreign countries.

AUTOMAT

BEANERY

BISTRO

BUFFET

CABARET

CAFE

CANTEEN

CANTINA

CLUB

COFFEE SHOP

COUNTER

DINER

DRIVE-IN

EATERY

GRILL

HOTEL

INN

KITCHEN

LODGE

LOUNGE

LUNCHROOM

MESS

MOTEL

PUB

RESTAURANT

REST STOP

SALOON

SNACK BAR

SUSHI BAR

TAVERN

TEA ROOM

VENDOR

```
B T B G E N P U B S N E Y G
R N R C M T O U L L I R G C
A A A E O N F O N R E V A T
B R B B N F D E L N H B C C
K U U I E I F R A A A S A L
C A L T H A D E I R S F N A
A T C E C S B S E V B T T V
N S C O T M U T S S E M E K
S E V Y I O N S A A H I E E
L R E T K U M T R M O O N G
E G N U O L V O H R O C P D
T G D C D F O P B I S T R O
O M O S S M O O R H C N U L
H Y R E T A E C A N T I N A
```

CATTLE COLLECTION

For those solvers old enough to remember the probing question "Where's the Beef?", we finally have an answer — it's right here! You can find all the beef you want by searching the diagram below for 32 breeds of cattle.

ANGUS

ANKOLE

BARKA

BORAN

BUSA

CHARBRAY

DEVON

DEXTER

EVOLÈNE

FINNISH

GASCON

GLAN

GLOUCESTER

HEREFORD

HIGHLAND

HOLSTEIN

JAULAN

KERRY

KILIS

KURDI

LOHANI

MALVI

NELORE

NIMARI

OROPA

PONWAR

RED POLL

SALERS

SANTA GERTRUDIS

TEXON

VOSGES

WAGYU

```
S A N T A G E R T R U D I S
R C E I X P N I E T S L O H
E L K E O A P T N I M A R I
L F I N N I S H N A R O B G
A N W G N E Y A Y P H R X H
S A U N C E L R E D P O L L
R S N U H U L O R L P P L A
U I O X A H B O V E O A W N
Y L X J R O F I R E K K V D
G I E C B E V X D E V O N B
A K T U R L T N O C S A G A
W H S E A A E X C G L C V R
E A H M Y A G D E G A Y T K
V J T Y W D R S I D R U K A
```

So you think you only know one language? You may be speaking French without realizing it! For example, if you've had apple pie with ice cream on top for dessert, you've eaten pie **A LA MODE.** Look for these French terms that have made their way into the English language.

A LA CARTE

A LA MODE

AU GRATIN

BISQUE

BON VOYAGE

BRAISE

CABARET

CAFE

CAMISOLE

CANAPÉ

CHIC

CRAVAT

CREPE

CROISSANT

CUL-DE-SAC

FLAMBÉ

FONDUE

GOURMET

MARINADE

MAYONNAISE

MOTIF

NAIVE

OMELET

PÂTÉ

PENSION

PURÉE

QUICHE

REGIME

SALON

SAUTÉ

SUEDE

VOGUE

```
O E T R A C A L A V S M F B
E L T A V A R C Q P A T I R
P O F N B F G O U R M E T A
E S E R I E Q R I L Y R O C
R I T S S T E N C S U A M H
C M U U Q E A A H N S B B R
H A A E U D N R E E R A O Y
I C S D E O S B G A U C N A
C T N E I M M E I U G G V T
M O E S D A I S V S A L O N
F T N L L L E G I I E A Y V
U E E F E A U L E P A N A C
P A T E R M R C B R S N G Q
R E Y M A Y O N N A I S E L
```

NAME THAT WORD

"The question is," said Alice in *Through the Looking-Glass*, "whether you *can* make words mean so many different things." Try and find these 46 words that are also names of people.

ABBEY	NORM	TERRY
AMBER	PATSY	VICTOR
APRIL	PATTY	VIOLET
ARCH	RICH	WADE
AUGUST	ROBIN	WARD
BASIL	RUSTY	WARREN
BERYL	SALLY	WILL
BILL	SANDY	
BLOSSOM		
BOBBY		
CAROL		
CHARITY		
CRYSTAL		
DAWN		
DEAN		
DUKE		
EARL		
FAITH		
FERN		
GABBY		
GALE		
HERB		
HOMER		
HOPE		
IRIS		
JACK		
JUNE		
LANCE		
LANE		
MARK		
MILES		

```
A U G U S T N P F P I B B B
I P Y L E C N A L O R A C C
L F R L P D E K E I I D N K
R A O I G R A V D D S N P A
E I T E L A G W J A W A C R
V T C S C W I L L W T T B C
M H I H Y A U L G S E F L H
I L V D A R Y I Y R E M O H
L A N E U R C B R R Y P S O
E A G S H E I Y N O E I S Y
S A T J K N V T K Y B B O B
M Y G U W N W T Y C B I M B
V U D N O R M A R K A C N A
H B R E H L R P D G J J H G
```

"I" ADJECTIVES

On an ICE-COLD day, it's IMPORTANT to bundle up! An IDEAL outfit for the chilly outdoors includes a jacket, a pair of gloves, and a scarf. The list below is filled with adjectives that begin with the letter "I."

ICE-COLD

IDEAL

IDENTICAL

IDLE

IDYLLIC

IGNORANT

IMMEDIATE

IMMUNE

IMPACTED

IMPATIENT

IMPERFECT

IMPERIAL

IMPORTANT

IMPROMPTU

IMPULSIVE

INANE

INDIRECT

INFORMED

INNATE

INSTANT

INTENSE

INTERNAL

INVERSE

IRONIC

ISOLATED

ITCHY

IVORY

```
O D E O E T A N N I D E A L
I E C I L L Y D I E Y H A C
V M F E D A A I T H T I I I
N R I I S L T C C R I N N
T O N I M P A T I E N T A O
T F S M M P I D P T C I N R
N N T V M E E M E A N O E I
A I A I T T I R H I D E L N
R C N T A Y N R F D L S D D
O S T L R A E S R E V N I I
N L O O L O V T O M C E C R
G S V L I M P R O M P T U E
I I Y V E N U M M I P N C C
E V I S L U P M I D H I O T
```

CHARMING

Charm bracelets can represent one's fondest memories, hobbies, or personal milestones in a fun and fashionable way. Here's a puzzle that's full of charm — or should we say charms?

AIRPLANE

ANCHOR

ANGEL

BABY

BALLERINA

BEAR

BOOTIES

BUTTERFLY

CRAB

CROSS

DOLPHIN

FISH

FOOTBALL

FROG

GOLF CLUB

HEART

HORSE

JOGGER

LION

MONKEY

MOON

PANTHER

PHONE

SEAL

SHELL

SKATE

STAR

STORK

SUNSHINE

SWAN

TURTLE

UNICORN

```
B B P B J J P U Y U G G M W
T A N C H O R A R E N O H P
M R L S T G N S K L K E R Y
D C I L K G L K R T A N B F
B F C Y E E N A O R M A O W
E Y Y L F R E T T U B O C M
A S B O O T I E S T T E O T
R W R C D F N N K B G J D N
T A I O S I S A A W M O N K
E N T Y H G O L F C L U B L
U F M S E A L P Y P R O G L
S M N B L N I R H F S O F W
M U R C L L O I B L K W S L
S E R E H T N A P H R J L S
```

LEND A "HAND"

You've got to hand it to this clever puzzle. Each word in the list can either precede or follow the word "hand" to form a new word or phrase. Feel FREE to start circling anytime!

BACK	CART	FIRST
BALL	CLASP	FREE
BEFORE	CRAFT	GRIP
BOOK	DECK	HOLD
BRAKE	DOCK	KERCHIEF
BREADTH	FARM	KNIT
		LENS
		LONG
		MAIDEN
		ME-DOWN
		MOWER
		OVER
		PRESS
		PRINT
		PUPPET
		RAIL
		SECOND
		SHAKE
		SHORT
		SIGNAL
		SOME
		SPRING
		STAGE
		STAND
		TRUCK
		UNDER
		WRITING

```
T D U E L I E P V O W T E C
E U S L P I G L F A R M E M
N K A S E B A C K O O B H E
M B A P V N T R H S B R L U
G L L R G K S S E R P M O W
C N K I B N H M E D O W N I
O C S N E D I A M W N T G H
V P W G I M D T E F F U O U
E U D F E T N R I A L L K P
R P D F H N O U R R D O C K
O P R C I I C C N N W E T S
F E I H C R E K A H S A C W
E T M R B P S T L R T H R K
B N G L G L S T L M T T O T
```

TREASURE HUNT

Although the BOOTY you seek in this treasure hunt includes GOLD, SILVER, and JEWELS, your true reward will be finding all of the 29 terms that are associated with sunken treasure submerged in the diagram.

AIRLIFT

ANCHOR

ARMOR

BARGE

BARS

BOAT

BOOTY

BUOY

CACHE

CHART

CHINA

COINS

CORAL

CORROSION

DEBRIS

DIVER

DREAM

FLEET

GOLD

JEWELS

METAL

MONEY

MUDDY

RELIC

SHIP

SILVER

VESSEL

WATER

WRECK

```
B B R B A R S C J Y C K R H
G O C O A H O W V A H D C J
W C O A G R O H C N A N H D
R I R T A R G H U I R N U B
E I R L Y T E E R W T E W L
C D O E U P V C J M Y I Y A
K H S P V A I A I R L I F T
F B I L T L M H O E I J C E
B M O N E Y I M S V P I O M
R U N R A W R S N I O C T U
R D W D O A E H G D R E A M
P D L O R V T J M S E B T O
V Y Y O U B A N V L J E E R
I K K Y G N W L F P A I E D
```

On March 7, 1986, the Steger International Polar Expedition set out to reach the North Pole by dog sled. Endeavoring to make their journey without resupply, the team planned to depend solely on the provisions they carried with them from the beginning. Fifty-five days and more than a thousand miles later, the expedition reached their destination. Below, find the names of 31 sled dogs who helped to accomplish this feat.

BANDIT

CAPONE

CAPTAIN

CHESTER

CHOCOLATE

CIARNUK

COWPUCK

CRITTER

ETUK

FANG

FUZZY

GOOFY

HUNTO

JAKE

JUNIOR

LEIF

MITT GRABBER

MONGO

MUGSY

NUMPUCK

PISTON

RAVEN

SCARFACE

SEQUOIA

SLIDRE

SMARTY

SNICKERS

SPOT

TARSALIK

TIGAWAK

YEAGER

```
P T S J E L E Z D D K S A U
M I T T G R A B B E R C S V
W D S E C I E O G N O M R S
V N K T H N P F V W R Z E A
S A G O O F Y J P I J A K N
J B J P C N K U N R A I C U
F H A S O S C N R C L O I M
G C C K L K R I P A C U N P
K M S I A E E O S P V Q S U
U F D O T W G R E T S E H C
T R A T E C A F R A C S N K
E T I N K T E G F I E L O W
Q R M U G S Y U I N W B M G
C G H H F U Z Z Y T R A M S
```

QUOTESEARCH

Elected to the Senate in 1952, Arizona Republican Barry Goldwater (1909-1998) was decisively defeated by Lyndon Johnson in the 1964 presidential election. A staunch conservative, he is credited by many with remaking the Republican party, and he served in the Senate until his retirement in 1987. Below is Goldwater's definition of a conservative.

A conservative...

has a

philosophy

based

upon

proven

values of

the past.

When

we seek

answers

for the

problems of

today

we look

to the

past to

see if

those problems

existed.

Generally,

they

have. So

we ask

what was

the answer?

Did it

work? If

it did,

let us

try again.

```
K S A E W H E N G M E D D A
I I M K O O L E W X F I W E
L S R E W S N A I K O D V T
P R O B L E M S O F R I O O
V P S T R B T P A S T T O N
A A H A T E O A S A H H V F
I E L I D O H R V E E A S F
Y L E U L K D R P D A V A V
Y F T N E O E A D E N E W C
S I U E M S S E Y S S S T D
V E S V N T O O C A W O A I
S E W O R K I F P B E P H D
W S C R U W E B G H R B W T
D A U P O N I A G A Y R T I
```

IT'S A HOOT

The large eyes and inquisitive call of "hoo-hoo" have earned the owl the reputation of being old and wise. You can show your wisdom by circling these kinds of owls.

BARKING

BARN

BLEWITT'S

BOOBOOK

BOREAL

CHESTNUT

CRESTED

EAGLE

FISH

FULVOUS

GREAT GRAY

HUMES

ITOMBWE

LAPLAND

LONG-EARED

MANED

MASKED

MOTTLED

PYGMY

RUFOUS

SCOPS

SCREECH

SNOWY

SOOTY

STRIPED

STYGIAN

TAWNY

URAL

WINKING

WOOD

```
Y N O L D T S N O W Y W V B
Y M D L H C E E R C S O O D
L A P L A N D T M T R O B E
F N R C G E U U Y U B D L D
T E L G L N R G F O H G E E
C D C T T A I O O D A P W K
I R T S K A U K B E I Y I S
D O E A N S E A R R H G T A
M H W S W Y R R T A D M T M
C P B C T N F S G E B Y S T
N L M O T E Y M B G E F I S
H R O P E C D W I N K I N G
S S T S W N C S U O V L U F
H S I F P B A G V L A R U C
```

St. Patrick's Day is celebrated March 17 to honor the patron saint of Ireland. Solve the puzzle below to learn about the shamrock, both how it became the symbol of Ireland and a traditional practice related to it.

When St. Patrick went to Ireland to preach to the heathens, he used the three-leafed clover — a shamrock — as a tool to help them understand the doctrine of the Trinity. In honor of him, Irishmen wear shamrocks in their hats on St. Patrick's Day.

```
D E S U E H B N K I D A H P N
A S I R I S H M E N P R N A O
Y A K I D T H V A H L E V T R
S T P C A A T L E H T V L R J
P E I I O H E M R A B O C I C
A L E N I R T C O D O L T C L
S N E T I H M V N T D C O K O
A K H H R R T A O B E N F J V
X E C E P M T P H O F T H E W
M H E I R S R O N S A I I N H
E T E R R E S R I R E A M U E
H S H E A T H E N S L R B L N
S I D C K S A K C O R M A H S
O N H I D N U P H G R I M E T
U C I V E O T T N E W A R E W
```

The NFL's Raiders have won the Super Bowl three times, twice as a team from Oakland (1977, 1981) and once after the team was moved to Los Angeles (1984). Now, however, they are back in Oakland. Here are some of the streets that can be found in the new old home of the Raiders.

ADAMS

ALICE

ATHENS

BROADWAY

BRUSH

CASTRO

CLAY

FALLON

FILBERTT

ISABELLA

LAKESIDE

LEE

LENOX

LINDEN

MARKET

MONTECITO

MYRTLE

NORTHGATE

PALM

PERKINS

SAN PABLO

SYCAMORE

VALDEZ

VALLEY

VERNON

WARWICK

WAVERLY

WEBSTER

WILLIAM

```
N C N Z E D L A V W P R Y C
E O N O N R E V G A D A M S
X C L S R X O O L W L L O W
B O I L L T L M E C A L T D
P K N L A B H B A K N E E M
W B D E A F S G E C P B K Y
K R E P L T K S A T Y A R R
M O N T E C I T O T W S A T
R A X R I D H Y C R E I M L
S D I W E E W A V E R L Y E
H W R L N H S U R B D P S E
N A Y S L T X G O L C N E V
W Y F R R I F S N I K R E P
P G I O U B W Y L F S F D P
```

SEA SURVEY

Believing he could reach the East by sailing west, Christopher Columbus left Palos, Spain, on August 3, 1492, with his three ships, the *Santa María*, the *Niña*, and the *Pinta*; land was sighted on October 12. Navigate through the grid upon these seas that many a vessel has traveled.

ADRIATIC

AEGEAN

ANDAMAN

ARABIAN

AZOV

BALTIC

BANDA

BARENTS

BERING

BISMARCK

BLACK

CARIBBEAN

CHINA

CORAL

DEAD

IONIAN

IRISH

JAPAN

JAVA

KARA

LIGURIAN

MARMARA

MEDITER-
RANEAN

NORTH

OKHOTSK

RED

SALTON

SARGASSO

SULU

TASMAN

TYRRHENIAN

WHITE

YELLOW

```
G N T L A R O C T A S M A N
L J A V A K D W C I P A N C
D U T E H G N I R E B R D N
W L T O N E T I H W P M A A
G U T C A A S V O J T A M E
V S U Y I H R S T N E R A B
K K E R R T A R A B I A N B
K C D P U R L A E G E A N I
Y A E B G O H A Z T S A N R
E L R A I N E E B O I M S A
L B S A L T O N N S V D D C
L S R K C R A M S I B N E S
O G U R C H I N A P A J A M
W N I R A G I O O B U N D K
```

VERBS GALORE

We hope that you'll SMILE after checking out the theme of this puzzle! In the list below, you will find 36 5-letter verbs.

AMBLE

ARGUE

AVERT

BASTE

BREAK

CLOSE

DRIFT

DRIVE

EVOKE

FLOAT

GRAZE

HOVER

KNEAD

LUNGE

LURCH

NUDGE

PAINT

PIVOT

PLEAD

REACH

REACT

SHOUT

SMILE

SPEAK

STAMP

STAND

STOOP

TASTE

TEACH

TRAIN

UNTIE

VOUCH

WRING

WRITE

YEARN

YODEL

```
T B N V R H C U O V K H E E
U U C D C B E N H A D G T G
L L O A M B L E E O N K C I
R I E H H C K P E U V N A H
M T W C S O S C L O S E E S
F H R A V E R T Z E Z A R G
I U L E D O Y S I L A D Z W
L S A R V B H T F I R D P R
H T T R A I N A O M H M O L
I O A S G U R N E S A G U T
G R T O D U A D T T D N N O
I E S G L N E W S O I I Z V
K A E R B F Y O A O A R T I
Z E S G B R Z W T P M W W P
```

MONEY MATTERS

When it comes to money, the best thing to do is earn some, spend some, and save some! CHECK out this puzzle because we've hidden 31 terms related to what "makes the world go round" in the diagram below.

BALANCE

BANK

BOND

BUDGET

CHECK

COIN

COST

CREDIT

DEBIT

DEBT

DIME

DOLLAR

EURO

INCOME

INFLATION

INTEREST

INVESTMENT

LOAN

LOSS

MORTGAGE

MUTUAL FUND

NICKEL

PENNY

PRICE

PROFIT

QUARTER

RAISE

SALARY

SALES TAX

STOCK

WAGE

```
B V K B M C N T S O C T P W
L A M N I T H I B O R U H N
A I A R A I S E B E E I I O
S O M C U B I O C S D T K I
L P X S P E N N Y K I E B T
P O L A T D A D C F T U N A
N R S X K L O P O O D E F L
A T O S A L A R Y G M T D F
D Q W B L T P U E T R E K N
I D X A F V S T S T O C K I
M O R T G A G E C I R P I O
E R Q F Q E V P L F B A A C
N U V N D N U F L A U T U M
L E K C I N T E R E S T M Q
```

PROVERB PROBE: VIPS

"Power can corrupt," admits an anonymous wit, "but absolute power is absolutely delightful." When you've circled this cast of influential people, the leftover grid letters will form a proverb about the use of power as a test of character.

BEGUM
BEY
BIGWIG
CALIPH
CHIEF
CZAR

DESPOT
DUKE
EARL
EMIR
GOVERNOR
HERO

HEROINE
IMAM
KHAN
KING
KINGPIN
LORD
MAYOR
MOGUL
MONARCH
NIZAM
PASHA
PEER
PRESIDENT
PRIMA
   DONNA
RANEE
SHAH
SHEIK
SHOGUN
STAR
SUZERAIN
TOP BANANA
TYCOON
VIZIER

```
B E G U M M I F Y G R A T S
O T E D R O L N O O C Y T P
U O E N W N I V S C H I E F
H P K T A A E O K N H E R O
A S U Z E R A I N M R O C W
N E D A N C N A H K A M A A
N D A O N H E K I N G Z L N
O M R I M E G N I B V U I A
D A A E H I G M I A G U P N
A Y Z M A P T G H O L K H A
M O C H I O W Y M R R I H B
I R S N V I Z I E R A E A P
R A N U G O H S I B E H H O
P R E S I D E N T T Y S S T
```

There are certain spices that are immediately identified with certain types of food. Where would Italian spaghetti sauce be without GARLIC? As soon as you hear of Indian food you think of CURRY. Other seasonings are more universal and are used with almost any kind of food — SALT and PEPPER, for example. If you can find all 32 spices and seasonings below, you'll really be cooking!

ALLSPICE
ANISE
BASIL
CARAWAY
CARDAMOM
CAYENNE
CELERY SEED
CHILI
CHIVES
CINNAMON
CLOVES
CORIANDER
CUMIN
CURRY
DILL
FENNEL
GARLIC
GINGER
MACE
MINT
MUSTARD
NUTMEG
ONION
PAPRIKA

PARSLEY
PEPPER
SAFFRON
SAGE

SALT
SHALLOT
TARRAGON
THYME

```
W F M O M A D R A C U R R Y
E M Y H T O L L A H S R C B
B O M I N T L R G I C E G F
N A D L I S A B R V L G E F
F D K R P W I R E E W N M V
C O R I A N D E R S A I T F
I M C Y R T I Y N A I G U P
N E A K S P S M W G G N N U
N N F C L E A U U E A O A G
A N E F E P L P M C R I N W
M E N D Y P T F T F L O D G
O Y N N C E R V F I I L T K
N A E Y I R G A H N C W I P
I C L O V E S C O V W A B D
```

TV viewers can either praise or blame "Survivor," which debuted in 2000, for the proliferation of "reality GAME shows" in the U.S. One thing that makes some of these programs different from traditional game shows is that VIEWERS watching from home can often play an active role in deciding who the winners will be by VOTING. These votes, usually cast by phone, can be used to eliminate an unpopular player, or help one's favorite participant win.

ADVENTURE

ALLIANCE

AUDITION

BETRAYAL

CAMERAS

COMPETITION

CRITICS

DRAMA

EMOTION

ENDURANCE

ENEMIES

FAME

FIGHTS

FRIENDS

GAME

HOST

LOSER

MONEY

PRIZE

PRODUCER

RATINGS

ROMANCE

RULES

STRATEGY

STUNTS

SURPRISE

TWIST

VIEWERS

VOTING

WINNER

```
B C W P H R E W A N G S C B
M O N E Y C T W I S T R U Z
R A T I N G S S I N V P S Z
L A Y A R T E B U I N V F C
G A M E D I M T E A O E O H
P O E T M V S W A T T M R O
R M I E V F E S I R P R U S
I E N D U R A N C E T A L T
Z E C N S F G Y T C S S E H
E W R N O I T I D U A D S G
R W I E A I T H D D R N M I
U I T O S I T D R O E E W F
G N I S O O L O A R M I E A
B C C N W O L L M P A R V M
E B S F V P W F A E C F B E
```

CRUISE SHIPS

Finding the names of these cruise ships just might inspire you to plan your own HOLIDAY at sea.

HOLIDAY

HORIZON

INFINITY

IRIS (The)

JUBILEE

LOFOTEN

MAASDAM

MELODY

MERCURY

MINERVA

MISTRAL

MONTEREY

NARVIK

NOORDAM

NORDLYS

NORWAY

OCEANIC

ORIANA

PARADISE

RYNDAM

SAPPHIRE

SEAWING

SUMMIT

SUN BAY

TOPAZ

TRITON

VICTORIA

WALRUS

```
Y J L P V S Y D O L E M A H
A U K F T R I T O N J V T T
B B I I U L O R I A N A E T
N I V C E W M M I N E R V A
U L R P A I R O T C I V V H
S E A W I N G O N H G F E O
M E N J M B P L P T T S N L
A S I E Z A M P A T E U A I
D A Y R Z Y A W R O N R A D
N H I L B S D S A W T L E A
Y C P N D O R V D S W A W Y
R N O Z I R O H I A L W J Z
C I N A E C O M S U M M I T
J Y P B G E N N E T O F O L
```

UNCLES, YES...ANTS, NO!

Having a family picnic some weekend soon? Here's a puzzle filled with things to bring along, so you might want to keep this list handy to use as a checklist just so you don't forget anything.

BASKET

BLANKET

CAMERA

CHARCOAL

CHICKEN

CHIPS

COOLER

FORKS

GRILL

HAMBURGER

HORSESHOES

HOT DOGS

ICED TEA

KETCHUP

LEMONADE

MUSTARD

NAPKINS

ONIONS

PICKLES

PLATES

RADIO

RELISH

SALAD

SANDWICHES

SODA

SPOONS

TABLE

TOMATO

TONGS

WATERMELON

```
S E L K C I P B O N I O N S
N N R T I A U N A L C D P A
G E I E N S M O R D O O S N
R N S K G A C E K E O A I D
I N G N P R B S R N L S O W
L S O A W A U F S A E I C I
L T D L T L N B D O R L S C
A A T B E E D E M M L O P H
E B O H K M K D U A C U S E
T L H C H O R S E S H O E S
D E I G R N T E A C I I T K
E H H O T A M O T B P D A R
C U H M R D H E P A S A L O
I W D D W E K C S G W R P F
```

COLOR THEM YELLOW

The study of flags is known as vexillology, from the Latin *vexillum* meaning flag or banner. Hopefully you won't be vexed as you study the diagram below and locate 28 countries whose flags contain the color yellow.

ANDORRA

ANGOLA

BELGIUM

BENIN

BOLIVIA

BRAZIL

CAMEROON

CHAD

COLOMBIA

ECUADOR

ETHIOPIA

GABON

GHANA

GUYANA

JAMAICA

LITHUANIA

MALI

MOZAM-
BIQUE

PALAU

ROMANIA

RWANDA

SENEGAL

SPAIN

SWEDEN

TOGO

UKRAINE

VENEZUELA

VIETNAM

```
B A C I A M A J U A S L N Y
O S N K T R B N I N E B A G
L P M C R O B E L A N L K A
I A K O C W G I R Y E W D B
V I D L Z A Z O T U G N B O
I N G O U A M R Z G A E N N
A A H M R A M E J W L L J W
T U A B N N N B R G R Z A M
G H N I S E T H I O P I A P
W T A A V D I U D Q O Y N J
V I E T N A M A L I U N G A
C L M Q U H U W J M O E O B
H R L O V C G Z I O A O L N
S W E D E N I A R K U N A U
```

The word "philosophy" is derived from the ancient Greek *philosophia*, which roughly means "love of wisdom." Many philosophers have dedicated themselves to finding the one natural element basic to all nature and being, while others have been concerned more with social and political problems. We've hidden the names of 31 noted philosophers in the grid below.

ARISTOTLE

BACON (Francis)

BERLIN (Isaiah)

BURKE (Edmund)

CONFUCIUS

DESCARTES (René)

DEWEY (John)

EPICURUS

HEGEL (Georg W. F.)

HOBBES (Thomas)

HUME (David)

KANT (Immanuel)

KIERKEGAARD (Søren)

LOCKE (John)

MAIMONIDES

MALLY (Ernst)

NIETZSCHE (Friedrich)

OCKHAM (William of)

PASCAL (Blaise)

PLATO

PYTHAGORAS

REID (Thomas)

RYLE (Gilbert)

SARTRE (Jean-Paul)

SCHOPEN- HAUER (Arthur)

SOCRATES

SPINOZA (Baruch)

THALES

VICO (Giambat- tista)

VOLTAIRE

ZENO

```
S  S  P  I  N  O  Z  A  V  B  S  Y  O  E
E  C  E  P  O  E  Y  L  L  A  M  B  C  H
T  M  H  T  N  L  L  S  R  C  M  K  K  C
R  N  U  O  A  Y  U  T  H  O  A  I  H  S
A  V  A  H  P  R  R  A  L  N  I  E  A  Z
C  R  I  K  U  E  C  H  A  I  M  R  M  T
S  U  I  C  U  F  N  O  C  D  O  K  V  E
E  V  I  S  O  U  Y  H  S  G  N  E  Z  I
D  P  L  A  T  O  P  T  A  B  I  G  Y  N
E  S  E  B  B  O  H  H  P  U  D  A  N  I
K  R  G  V  O  L  T  A  I  R  E  A  N  L
C  D  E  W  E  Y  Z  L  S  K  S  R  A  R
O  V  H  I  P  U  M  E  E  E  G  D  A  E
L  M  N  W  D  D  S  S  H  G  F  U  E  B
```

Bruce Springsteen is known as the BOSS, but even he likely has to answer to someone (his wife Patti?). Here's a list of people in authority. Some may be more intimidating than others, but they all command our attention.

ABBOT

ADMIRAL

BARON

BISHOP

BOSS

CHANCELLOR

CHIEF

COACH

COUNT

DEAN

DIRECTOR

DOCTOR

DUKE

HOSTESS

JUDGE

KING

MAESTRO

MAGISTRATE

MANAGER

MARSHAL

MOGUL

MONARCH

NAVIGATOR

PREMIER

PRINCIPAL

QUEEN

RULER

SHERIFF

SQUIRE

TEACHER

```
M O G U L E C M N S N U F V
O O N F M A G I S T R A T E
C H I E F B P D T C C Q E O
O S K T Q I M I U L O L S D
U O M U P D R R C J H A N G
N N E R O L L E C N A H C J
T E A C H E R C H S I S S H
N M T V S E A T H S N R L H
Q O I Q I B I O H Q O A P S
R N E M B G S R B U R M S R
S A E O T T A F J I A O E Q
O R T S E A M T M R B L E A
P C K S E K U D O E U F M B
K H S M A N A G E R L M V R
```

"To be or not to be . . .," six of the most well-known words in drama, come from Shakespeare's most enduring masterpiece. It is the story of a man who knows what he wants to do, but somehow can't make himself do it.

The ghost of Hamlet's father tells him that he was murdered by the present king, Hamlet's uncle. Hamlet vows revenge, but is surprised to find that he can't bring himself to do it. Only when he himself is dying is Hamlet able to kill the king.

```
H E C A N T R I B I U S K Y
Z A R B D E R E D R U M B O
V B U L V L Y V G R I Y N G
U Q E J L P N P V T N V N
F N N T N S I R C H I O G I
L G C O I K I Z E V W Y S Y
E V J L E S K G Y S X T V D
S U T H E W H E N H E W A S
M T T D R O I A K L V N G I
I O O E S Q M U M I Z I T Z
H D F T L V T A J L L O U Q
Z O I K M M H I M S E L F U
K I N G V F A J R E H T A F
Z T D U O H T H A T V Y S O
```

Jerry Lewis was born Joseph Levitch on March 16, 1926, in Newark, New Jersey. A man of many hats, Lewis has thrived as a comedic actor (both in his popular partnership with Dean Martin and as a solo act), film director, and philanthropist (he received a Nobel Prize nomination for his work as a spokesman and major fundraiser for the Muscular Dystrophy Association).

Jerry Lewis is revered as a comedic genius in France, but he is much admired here in the United States as a dedicated fundraiser for medical research. Lewis himself realizes, however, that comedy, like acting, is a lifelong calling: "When the light in the refrigerator goes on, I do twenty minutes."

```
N H L Y F K A A T H G I L Y F
F D M R J B D L C L E H T U B
R E F R I G E R A T O R N O O
I R R E H S D C U D I D E Y D
S I O J O C I E J B R N T I I
M M T R W D C S T A I N G I N
U D T Y E G A E I I E E N I O
C A F M V V T S K W N G O E S
H C R A E S E R T I E U L S A
H O A V R R D R U U L L E E S
F M N T H I M S E L F T F H E
M E C A L L I N G D U S I T T
T D E H T N E H W N A K L N A
Y I Z T R E A L I Z E S A I T
M C C N Y D E M O C L E W I S
```

Nothing compliments good food better than a glass of wine. Craving oysters? Make sure to have a bottle of CHABLIS on ice. On the other hand, if you're a meat-eater, RIESLING is the perfect choice to accompany a veal casserole.

ALBANA

ARBOIS

AUSONE

BAROLO

BORDEAUX

BUAL

BURGUNDY

CANARY

CHABLIS

CHAMPAGNE

CHIANTI

CLARET

LILLET

MACON

MALAGA

MARSALA

MEDOC

MONICA

MOSELLE

NAHE

PERNOD

PORT

RIESLING

ROSÉ

SACK

SAKE

SHERRY

SOAVE

TAVEL

VERMOUTH

XERES

```
S B U M M U Y G E O P Y N V
D H A A B A I P B K E K C M
E T E R A L C O E L R G E C
V G S S N C R O L N N D I S
A C K A M D I E N H O N K I
O R H L E T S N Y C D S H L
S E B A R O L O O I L A U B
H T U O M R E V T M P M U A
E X P Y I P C N T B U R G H
R O S E I S A C K E G A T C
R I E S L I N G V U L T T O
Y S R K H O A A N A B L A T
V L E C A M R D M E B B I V
Y M X Y A S Y H N T A V E L
```

The saying that circulated through the country in the mid-1800s was "Go west, young man, and grow up with the country." It was attributed to an editorial by Horace Greeley, but it actually originated from another source.

"Go west, young man," was first said by John Soule, editor of the *Terre Haute Express*, in eighteen fifty-one. Horace Greeley simply popularized the statement in his own paper, *The New York Tribune.* The phrase caught on and Greeley was given credit for it.

```
H G R E E L E Y W A S D W T
E J O L R S C I E C A R O H
H T D W H R I T G L Y U T G
T H E N E W D H N H E W E U
F M Z D N S Z E N N T E R A
O I I G E E T S F I N E R C
W T R M V R S T S O X G E G
N O A I I W R A Y P R A S N
P N L B G G I T R O T I D E
A A U C N D F E E H A U T E
P N P U B I S M Y L P M I S
E D O Y F S A E O D U E M A
R Y P T I Z W N R Y J O H N
Z F G N I O B T K C I A S T
```

The Greek playwright Sophocles is remembered as one of the greatest literary figures of the ancient world. Here is his opinion of hardheaded people.

I beg

you, do

not be

unchangeable.

Do not

believe

that you

alone

can be

right.

The man

who thinks

that, the

man who

maintains

that

only

he has

the power

to reason

correctly,

the gift

to speak,

the soul —

a man

like that,

when you

know him,

turns out

empty.

```
Y Y N Y L I K E T H A T T N
E L B A E G N A H C N U O O
M T N Z Q O M F E R M T M S
L C A O L A L Y H P B E A A
I E M A N S T W T E S H I E
W R E W O P E H T C E O N R
T R H V M C A J A H V U T O
U O T E E T Y N H I O M A T
O C N A Y I B D T Y E I I N
S D J O W E L K N R B H N E
N O U W D G G E B I C W S A
R L U O S E H T B G N O L P
U Q H I Y W H O T H I N K S
T H E G I F T A H T R K T Y
```

In Ireland during Maytime revels, the fairies would appear, casting mists over travelers and displacing familiar landmarks. To avoid trouble, the Irish stayed close to home. If they had to travel, they wore their coats inside out, to confuse the fairies. Other fairy superstitions are described below.

Families kept a close eye on young children, because fairies had been known to abduct some, leaving changelings behind. As a precaution against fairy shenanigans, parts of Ireland still find people who put food and drink on the doorsteps to appease the mischief-makers.

```
S T U P S L B B E C A U S E
G N I V A E L L A T P E K H
N E A T A R I I D N I F T T
I R O G H B T R T L C A P M
L D T E I E I S I S G I R I
E L N L F N S M O A D R E S
G I W P K G A A I F F Y C C
N H O O I F S N E E B B A H
A C N E H R S Y E P E A U I
H B K P E T E S G H P S T E
C S D K I O O L I N S A I F
E O A U N L W N A K U L O A
K M H Q C P D H N N M O N T
T E S P E T S R O O D D Y R
```

Are you a free spirit? A **FLAMBOYANT NECKTIE** may suit your taste. Perhaps you're the **SOLID** and straightforward type. If so, a sober **KNIT** or a nice neat **PAISLEY** tie might fit the bill. A tie can express the inner you as well as be a fashion statement.

ABSTRACT

BOLO

BOW TIE

BROCADE

CHECKERED

CLIP-ON

CRAVAT

DESIGNER

FLAMBOYANT

FLORAL

FOULARD

GEOMETRIC

JACQUARD

KNIT

LEATHER

MEDALLION

NARROW

NECKTIE

PAISLEY

PATTERNED

PLAID

PLAIN

PRINT

REP

REVERSIBLE

SILK

SOLID

STRIPED

WESTERN

WIDE

```
F O U L A R D W P N R P E K
F L Q E D P J E F L D D L N
L O V A E R M S P L A I D I
A B S T R A C T D C O I C T
M V Q H E J Y E O T E R N N
B J G E K L N R L N A I A D
O W U R C R B N O V R M E L
Y O E Y E L S I A P N P I M
A R I T H N L T S O I K T C
N R T Y C L G O P R L Q W K
T A K T A N L I T I E I O J
P N C D B I L S S G D V B D
N P E R D C I R T E M O E G
G M N J A C Q U A R D B R R
```

QUOTESEARCH

John F. Kennedy (1917-1963) was the youngest man ever elected President. In his short time in office, Kennedy proved his mettle and won the United States respect by refusing to back down to the Soviet Union during the tense days of the Cuban Missile Crisis. The passage below is from Kennedy's inaugural speech, which he delivered in Washington, D.C., on January 20, 1961.

Let every

nation

know,

whether

it wishes

us well

or ill,

that

we shall

pay any

price,

bear any

burden,

meet any

hardship,

support

any friend,

oppose

any foe

to assure

the

survival

and the

success

of liberty.

This

much

we pledge —

and more.

```
A A W R E H T E H W L B A N
S N N Y H S B E A R A N Y A
U A D D T T O D L N V E N T
P N T T M A V P Y E I D A I
P Y U V H O H F P R V R Y O
O F L I B E R T Y O R U A N
R O O L L I S E V E U B P L
T E G D E L P E W R S I L B
A B Y N T W M Y H U H A I L
O O D W E H S G M S H N L T
M F V I V B M U D S I I C H
S U C C E S S R E A R W L I
L E C I R P A W W O N K T S
Y N F H Y H Y N A T E E M I
```

SOMETHING'S FISHY

Found in warm waters around the world, the **SWORDFISH** is a large predatory fish with a long, swordlike bill at the top of its snout. It's great for grilling, so when buying, make sure to look for bright flesh with tight swirls (like rings on a tree trunk). Keep in mind, though, that its skin can't be eaten. Don't **FLOUNDER** around as you reel in these 28 edible fish from the diagram below.

ANGELFISH

BARRACUDA

BASS

BLOWFISH

BLUEGILL

CATFISH

FLOUNDER

GOLDFISH

GROUPER

HADDOCK

HALIBUT

HERRING

MARLIN

MINNOW

PERCH

PIKE

PIRANHA

ROUGHY

SALMON

SHARK

SNAPPER

SOLE

SUNFISH

SWORDFISH

TARPON

TROUT

TUNA

TURBOT

```
T E H N U T R T A R P O N E
R U Y O O E U N T A K T D F
O W B W K S G R O U P E R K
U L L I G E U L B M O O D R
G B P C L N M T W O L R D A
H A A F H A I U H N T A T H
Y S I R R A H R E C L N S S
F S I L R D D E R A R I N I
H S I F T A C D H E F E A F
G N N W N K C N O D H W P W
K E R U B U A U R C L P P O
W L T G B R S O D O K P E L
W O N N I M W L A A W Y R B
P S F P H S I F D L O G K I
```

COOKED OR RAW

CAULIFLOWER is a variety of **CABBAGE** with fleshy flower stalks. See if you can find this crispy white vegetable, along with a variety of other foods that can be eaten cooked or raw, in the puzzle below.

APPLE

APRICOT

BLACKBERRY

BLUEBERRY

BROCCOLI

CABBAGE

CARROT

CAULIFLOWER

CELERY

CHEESE

CHERRY

CUCUMBER

DATE

GARLIC

GREEN BEAN

GREEN
 PEPPER

MUSHROOM

ONION

OYSTER

PEACH

PEAR

RAISIN

RASPBERRY

RED PEPPER

SPINACH

STRAWBERRY

TUNA

```
H B R O C C O L I A K A R U
C T T E Y P E A C H E E S E
A U O C P S C N B S P S P T
N N C A B P T H E P R E A T
I A I U E L E E Y A L H R
P T R L M R A P R R U G E A
S E P I P B D C N R R G W S
L P A F G E E R K E A Y W P
A T C L R Y R R E B E U L B
C P A O N I O N B W E R O E
A E R W A H B A N A T R G R
D Y R E L E C I L R A G R R
C H O R A I S I N T D R C Y
U H T N M O O R H S U M M H
```

Take a guided tour through the streets of Vienna, Austria, one of the great music capitals of the world. Its rich cultural life is matched only by its rich pastries and strudel. If you ever visit this city, you might sit at a sidewalk cafe on one of the streets below as you enjoy a tasty treat and solve your favorite puzzles!

AKADEMIE
ANNA
BÄCKER
BALL
BANK

BAUERN
BRAND
BRÄUNER
BREITE
BURG

CANOVA
FICHTE
GLUCK
HAARHOF
HANSEN
HEGEL
JOHANNES
KRUGER
KURRENT
LEHÁR
MAHLER
MAIS
MUSEUM
NAGLER
PLANKEN
RAHL
RATHAUS
ROSEN
SEILER
SINGER
SPIEGEL
STADION
WALLNER

```
C J A L H A R E N L L A W N
S G M O E K I J A V O N A C
S T N B G M C L M M A J F C
P B A U E R N U E G O U I B
M L A D L L R E L H A M C S
L K A K I M N E A G A H H R
E K N N U O R N L R A R T R
A A E E K R N S P I E G E L
B H S T N E R R U K E G T S
U U N I S N N J C A U S R I
M G A E E U H A A R H O F N
M A H R R A B N K E S T T G
M N I B U R G N T E S N A E
E R R S W B R A N D D T R R
```

You're probably familiar with the Victorian rhyme, "Something old, something new, something borrowed, something blue." It's a popular superstition that many brides-to-be follow before they walk down the aisle. The passage below explains some more wedding superstitions.

A bride who dreams of fairies the night before her wedding will be thrice blessed. A groom who carries a small horseshoe in his pocket will always be lucky. Finding a spider on a wedding gown by the bride is considered a token of happiness.

```
B E D I R B A A L L A M S A
E K W W C G S M A E R D S N
L D T H R I C E D S E P S G
U O I O O F F A I R I E S H
C B O R M C T F E D T H E B
K M L S B F A D E Y K R N U
Y A L E M E I R B P W G I I
W L T S S S H N R E N K P U
E W E H N S W T D I D B P I
B A K O N O E D D I E F A T
L Y C E G G I D E F N S H B
L S O F O N E K O T A G R Y
I K P N G W H R K W I L L L
W O B L A R E K H N Y F C D
```

THREE-SYLLABLE SUSTENANCE

Here's some food for thought: What could a BANANA and a TORTILLA possibly have in common? Well, for one thing, like all 30 of the words listed here, they are foods which contain three syllables!

ANCHOVY

APRICOT

ARTICHOKE

BANANA

BOLOGNA

BURRITO

CANNOLI

CAVIAR

CEREAL

COCONUT

CRANBERRY

CUCUMBER

GRANOLA

HAMBURGER

HAZELNUT

LASAGNA

LINGUINE

LOLLIPOP

MACAROON

NECTARINE

PAPAYA

PINEAPPLE

POPOVER

POTATO

SALAMI

SPAGHETTI

TANGERINE

TOMATO

TORTILLA

ZUCCHINI

```
M Y V O H C N A N G A S A L N
P A B E H A L I N G U I N E G
X A C A K O M R E B M U C U C
V S P A N O L B C A T T N R T
H O P A R A H A U A A A M P S
A O R A Y O N C E R N H I O A
Z G C L G A O A I R G N U P L
E Z U C C H I N I T E E O I A
L A O Y R R E B N A R C R L M
N N T S T O M T P P I A E L I
U G I V M S T P T R N V V O O
T O R T I L L A C I E I O L T
T L R B P E K R M C Q A P T G
E O U K T O T A T O P R O V M
V B B C O C O N U T T O P V Y
```

IN AND AROUND COVENT GARDEN

Formerly England's largest fruit and vegetable market, today Covent Garden is a popular shopping and entertainment complex, complete with many stores and individual stalls that sell high-quality goods. Take a stroll through 29 streets in and around one of London's biggest tourist hotspots.

ADELAIDE

AGAR

ARNE

BEDFORD

BURLEIGH

DRYDEN

EARLHAM

ENDELL

EXETER

FLORAL

GARRICK

HENRIETTA

JAMES

KEAN

KEELEY

KEMBLE

KING

LANGLEY

MACKLIN

MERCER

NEAL

NEWTON

PARKER

ROSE

SHELTON

STUKELEY

TOWER

WEST

WILD

```
E A D B U R E C H C K G M G
M X N R N N A T N T E A X
O S E M A J O G E O N R C K
P G D T S W P T A D R L K U
K A Y F E T D C L I H E L Y
L B R R C R U I C E E J I M
E U D K O E W K N L H K N A
Y R T F E C G R E W E S T H
N L D Y K R I Y E L G N A L
K E M B L E D I A L E D A R
B I W B T M A R N E P Y A A
O G N T S U O N X D P Y P E
U H A G O L N X P N B X W O
H C K B F N R O S E C W D Y
```

Prized for their SUGAR, syrup, and shade, maple trees must be one of the most popular trees in the world. Almost everywhere you go you can find some variety of maple. CHALK maples, for example, are plentiful in the southeast United States. And North America doesn't have a monopoly on maples either — MIYABE'S maple is native to Japan.

AMUR

ASH-LEAVED

BALKAN

BLACK

CHALK

CORAL-BARK

CRETAN

FERNLEAF

FIELD

FORREST'S

FULL MOON

HEDGE

HERS'S

ITALIAN

LIME-LEAVED

MIYABE'S

MOUNTAIN

NIKKO

NORWAY

OREGON

PURPLE

ROCK

SCARLET

SILVER

STRIPED

SUGAR

SYCAMORE

TARTAR

VINE

```
R D E P I R T S I L V E R A
C O E V N Y Y A O H D R M K
W N C V I C A F C P E V B F
B A L K A N O O M L L U F M
M T F M T E E R P F W L I F
K E O B N H L R A K G Y E K
H R R S U N U E K L A H C I
E C D U O P L S M B B A T S
D A L G M N Y T E I L A A N
G T E L R A C S N B L N R I
E R I E W D O H S I N P T K
O M F R Y S U G A R K K A K
S H O E I R E N Y L E F R O
F N T N L D E V A E L H S A
```

STARRY, STARRY NIGHT

Astronomers study them, sailors navigate by them, poets are inspired by them, lovers dream under them, and children wish upon them. How boring the night sky would be without stars. Listed below are 28 of the brightest stars in the heavens, as seen from the Earth. SIRIUS, the Dog Star, is the brightest one of all.

ACHERNAR

ALDEBARAN

ALGOL

ALIOTH

ALPHERATZ

ALTAIR

ANTARES

ARCTURUS

BELLATRIX

BETELGEUSE

CANOPUS

CAPELLA

CASTOR

DENEB

DUBHE

EL NATH

FOMALHAUT

MERAK

PHECDA

POLARIS

POLLUX

PROCYON

REGULUS

RIGEL

SCHEDIR

SIRIUS

SPICA

VEGA

```
A H L P X I R T A L L E B H
I A S X S U I R I S E Z T Y
A L L E P A C H E R N A R E
C I C A S T O R S O N M I H
I O R R U R A U U L E C D B
P T H R I T L E E C D A E U
S H U G N U P A G P L N H D
U S E A G P H H L D E O C X
M L D E H O E E E D K P S U
E O R F T L R B T C U U U L
R G O H S A A G E V D S U L
A L T A I R T M B E V A X O
K A G O A I Z N O Y C O R P
F O X N D S H C N F P D C Z
```

KENNEL CLASS

Take your dog to the **KENNEL** for **OBEDIENCE** classes. If you **TEACH** him to **BEHAVE** when he's a pup, you'll have a loving and loyal **COMPANION** as your **REWARD**.

BEHAVE
BREED
CALL
COACH
COAT
COLLAR
COMMAND

COMPANION
DISCIPLINE
DOWN
EXERCISE
FETCH
HEEL
KENNEL

LEASH
LESSON
LOYALTY
MASTER
NAME
OBEDIENCE
PATIENCE
PEDIGREE
REGISTER
REWARD
SCHOOL
SHOW
STAY
TEACH
TRAINER
VOICE
WALK

```
X B C S V L M D F H S A E L
A K H R E V Y Y R N C C P E
N O L N N C T K M A I A B G
W B N W I O L P L O W P O V
F E O V L A A E V A H E B C
K D S V P T Y N M V W D R B
A I F I I C O M P A N I O N
D E F E C S L L A C N G K X
A N N C S R E T L S F R N C
D C A E I R E G I S T E R H
E E L M D D H X P V T E C C
E A K P M T L R E N I A R T
R C O N C O L L A R E D Y E
B M L O O H C S N T D D O F
```

A PUZZLER'S PROFILE

Calling all **EXPERT** solvers! This puzzle lists many of the attributes that you possess. As you find them in the diagram, see how many traits are **SUITED** to you.

ABLE

ADEPT

ARTFUL

ARTISTIC

BRIGHT

CAPABLE

CAREFUL

CLEVER

COMPETENT

CREATIVE

CURIOUS

DEFT

DETERMINED

EAGER

ENDOWED

EXPERT

FACILE

FITTED (for)

GOOD AT

INVENTIVE

NEAT

ORGANIZED

PATIENT

PERSISTENT

PRECISE

QUICK

SKILLED

SUITED (to)

TALENTED

THOROUGH

```
M W S D N R A D E T T I F Q
P A T I E N T R E P X E U F
Q V N V S T P O T W A W D A
Z A E C Q U I C K F O O A C
B L T H O R O U G H U D H I
C R S A T M C I S K E L N L
L E I H L A P R R T N C E E
T S S G B E E E U G I A S
A I R L H G N R T A C T T K
D C E D A T M P E T S L I
O E P E V I T N E V N I M L
O R G A N I Z E D D L T V L
G P Z E L B A P A C S R B E
Q K D E F T L U F E R A C D
```

Early games of baseball were played with a different set of rules than are used today. Here are some differences that existed during the years 1840 to 1859.

In early baseball, a fielder put a runner out by hitting him with the ball. Home base and the batter's plate were two separate spots, and the lineup included a fourth baseman. There was no difference between fair and foul balls, and the umpire sat in a rocking chair behind the catcher.

```
S E S E A F I E L D E R A P
E I Y R P U E N I L B W I L
P H B I T S W F B C G A H A
A K T P W R F H L R N T S T
R S U M O E R O C K I N G E
A F O U R T H M U W T A R E
T I N E S T B E M L T D F H
E B N P V A Y I E W I R A T
P C O C L B H L B E H I N D
E T H L L S I E R C N A D N
S W S Y A U T E N A A H T A
L A B T B W D R M T E C H L
V S I W E R E E G C A N E N
A N D E S H S H D H D T I K
A O N E A A T T R E N N U R
E L L A B E H T H R A D G P
```

READ MY FACE

Facial expressions can reveal what a person is privately feeling. The list below contains 29 feelings and emotions that can be detected by the expressions on one's face.

AMAZEMENT

ANGER

ANGUISH

APATHY

BOREDOM

CALMNESS

CHAGRIN

CONCEIT

CONCERN

DISGUST

DISTRESS

DREAD

EAGERNESS

ENVY

FEAR

GAIETY

GRIEF

GUILT

HAPPINESS

HEARTACHE

INTEREST

LOVE

PANIC

REGRET

REMORSE

SADNESS

SORROW

SURPRISE

WORRY

```
R E G R E T V E L T C Z H P
G S F V L S S E N M L A C A
W A O I S Y E E O V P A E N
S L U F T S M D R P Y Y R I
C G U E R E E T I E C N O C
H H I O Z R H N Y H T A P A
A A M A O T E W D V D N O L
G E M B H S A C M A I G I D
R A E F S U R P R I S E O T
I L I I I G T V D Y T R I O
N N I R U S A W O R R O S Z
F E I R G I C O N C E R N Z
D R S R N D H F Y U S A O M
C W W E A G E R N E S S D W
```

The United States has Independence Day on July 4, and Canada celebrates a somewhat analogous holiday on July 1 — Canada Day. For an explanation, read below and then solve the puzzle.

On this day in eighteen sixty-seven, the British North America Act came into being. This was the first step toward Canadian independence. It united Upper Canada (which became Ontario), Lower Canada (which became Quebec), New Brunswick and Nova Scotia in a British dominion.

```
K I A P L H T F R S S I H T
C N N V E M A C E B Q X O K
I T A D O T W M F U G W N W
W O W D E N S V E C A E T Y
S E U H A P D B A R E M O T
N D A Y I N E N D M I A N X
U P P E R C A N A D A C T I
R H R A N D H C D C W T A S
B T M E I T E S R E V C R E
B R W A X B S T I E N A I V
E O N T H I S R I T W C O E
I N S C O T I A I N I O E N
N O I N I M O D W F U R L T
G H S I T I R B A Q H T B H
W A S T H E N E E T H G I E
```

"BOX" TOPS

You'd better hope you're in shape because it's time to step into the ring and go a few rounds — with this puzzle, that is! Listed below are terms, all of which can be followed by the word "box." Find all 35 and you'll score a knockout!

BALLOT

BREAD

CARDBOARD

CEREAL

CIGAR

DROP

ELECTRICAL

FLOWER

GEAR

GIFT

GLOVE

JEWELRY

JURY

LETTER

LOCK

LUNCH

MATCH

MONEY

MUSIC

PENALTY

PENCIL

PILL

POST OFFICE

PRESS

SAFE-DEPOSIT

SALT

SAND

SENTRY

SHOE

SOAP

STORAGE

STRONG

TINDER

TOOL

WINDOW

```
J  L  E  D  P  F  M  J  W  L  P  A  O  S
E  T  L  J  G  R  Y  G  B  O  M  H  O  T
W  H  L  I  C  N  E  P  S  C  D  C  I  F
E  C  F  P  P  W  N  T  N  K  I  N  U  L
L  T  M  V  G  N  O  R  T  S  D  U  I  O
R  A  G  I  C  F  M  S  U  E  L  L  D  W
Y  M  C  K  F  J  T  M  R  N  L  A  F  E
S  L  B  I  T  O  O  L  Y  T  E  A  V  R
S  A  C  A  R  D  B  O  A  R  D  O  A  N
P  E  N  A  L  T  Y  H  B  Y  L  E  V  C
O  R  G  D  U  L  C  R  V  G  G  N  T  Y
R  E  E  A  R  U  O  E  U  N  S  N  L  W
T  C  J  S  H  O  E  T  L  J  T  S  A  N
G  V  T  I  S  O  P  E  D  E  F  A  S  B
```

In 1903, when the Binney & Smith company sold the first boxes of Crayola® crayons to schools, there were only eight colors: BLACK, blue, BROWN, GREEN, ORANGE, red, VIOLET, and YELLOW. Currently, the company offers a choice of 120 colors, some of which are listed below.

ALMOND

APRICOT

BLACK

BROWN

CANARY

CERISE

DENIM

EGGPLANT

FERN

GOLD

GRAY

GREEN

INDIGO

MAGENTA

MANATEE

MAROON

MAUVELOUS

MELON

ORANGE

ORCHID

OUTER SPACE

PEACH

PIG PINK

SALMON

SEPIA

SHADOW

SHAMROCK

SILVER

SUNGLOW

VIOLET

WHITE

WISTERIA

YELLOW

```
D V W O L G N U S H A D O W
N I O P V M G H G I H E O I
O O H K S M A U V E L O U S
M L L C P M I N E D G V O T
L E F E R T O U A I L U E E
A T A O M O K K D T T O R R
V C C P R C R N N E E R G I
H K P A A I I A R I M E A A
Y P M L D R L S N E P L E K
R E B O M P P O B G F G S W
A T N E G A M K R S E P I A
N I D G C L W A O T P P R P
A H E E A T Y T W O L L E Y
C W F S E C N D N N H N C F
```

GOING ONLINE

Remember the days when getting on line meant you were ready to pay for your groceries? Or when the only mail you received was delivered by the postman? Here is a collection of terms that should be familiar to all you INTERNET surfers out there.

ATTACHMENT

BLOG

BROWSER

CHAT ROOM

CLICK

DIALUP

DOT-COM

DOT-GOV

DOT-ORG

DOWNLOAD

E-MAIL

E-ZINE

HYPERLINK

INTERNET

JPEG

LINK

LOG OFF

LOG ON

MODEM

ONLINE

PASSWORD

POP-UP

PROGRAM

SPAM

UPLOAD

VIRUS

WEBSITE

WORM

ZIP FILE

```
G G H M A P S E B L J U P F
R O E L U K D D L V I R U S
O N M L P N P R O G R A M N
T L A O L I L O G O F F M N
O I D A O L N W O D A S P E
D N Z I A R U S E T K K R J
O E K N D E T S T B H E Z E
T W G T P P K A V N S M L N
G E O E C Y C P H W O I M I
O R I R P H O K O C F G T Z
V Z B N M J B R T P L Y O E
M O D E M W B O I I U I O L
G R N T M H D Z N B M P C W
L T Y Y B G L K F Z H E V K
```

WHAT'S NEW?

It's been said that "Everything old is new again." That certainly applies to these cities and towns that are all preceded by "New." A quick look at the list will reveal that they're all in New Jersey, New Hampshire, or New York.

BERLIN (N.Y.)

BOSTON (N.H.)

BRIGHTON (N.Y.)

BRUNSWICK (N.J.)

CASTLE (N.H.)

CITY PARK (N.Y.)

DURHAM (N.H.)

EGYPT (N.J.)

HAMBURG (N.Y.)

HAMPTON (N.H.)

HARTFORD (N.Y.)

HEMPSTEAD (N.Y.)

HOPE (N.Y.)

HYDE PARK (N.Y.)

IPSWICH (N.H.)

LISBON (N.J.)

LONDON (N.H.)

MILFORD (N.J.)

PALTZ (N.Y.)

ROCHELLE (N.Y.)

RUSSIA (N.Y.)

SHARON (N.J.)

SQUARE (N.Y.)

SUFFOLK (N.Y.)

UTRECHT (N.Y.)

WINDSOR (N.Y.)

WOODSTOCK (N.Y.)

YORK (N.Y.)

```
C G C Y K R A P E D Y H N G
W I H I F K E L T S A C H R
A M Q I T R L D U R H A M U
G K R N A Y N O T H G I R B
N B C U O O P F F D N N H M
W K Q I T D O A A F R O C A
D S R S W R N E R O U B I H
M W O O D S T O C K H S W A
C B I L Y S N H L P S I S M
P E G Y P T E U Q U N L P P
A K N M I L F O R D E A I T
L B E R L I N W S B Z P D O
T H C E R T U O S H A R O N
Z Y F K G U R N L L F I D H
```

QUOTESEARCH

American theatrical producer, director, and playwright George Abbott (1887-1995) began in the theater as an actor. During a career that spanned eight decades, he was celebrated as a co-author, director, or producer for over 100 Broadway plays. The passage below is a quote from Abbott about acting.

People wouldn't know a good actor if they saw one, but they can recognize a good part If you have a good part in a hit, your whole life will change, you will become a success. You will play the same part all the rest of your life under different names.

```
G U K R U O Y E G N A H C U
O S P L A Y T H E A U Y T T
O N H L V H Y Y O O E C S R
D D A D E E E Z Y W L P E A
P H V R I H M F K D P C F P
A Y E H T F I O F Y O U R D
R S A T W L F T C G E O W O
T R U W H O L E N E P D G O
A B W C G K N I R D B Y V G
L I B L C O Z F W E L U K A
L L L I W E F I L U N U N N
T I H A N I S E S D O T O F
W F S N A M E S E U B Y W W
U E M A S N D R R O T C A N
```

BATTER UP!

Just like major-league teams, Little League baseball has its own WORLD SERIES. It's held every summer in Williamsport, Pennsylvania, where the league was founded in 1939. Step up to the plate and search for the 33 terms we've hidden in the diagram below that are all related to this youthful sports organization.

AT BAT

BALL

BASES

BENCH

BOYS

CATCHER

COACH

DRILL

FIELDER

GAME

GEAR

GIRLS

HATS

LEVELS

LINEUP

MANAGER

PARENTS

PITCHER

PLAYER

POSITION

PRACTICE

ROSTER

RUNNER

SCHEDULE

SCORE

SHORTSTOP

TEAM

TRYOUT

UMPIRE

UNIFORM

WARM-UP

WORLD SERIES

YOUTH

```
M A N A G E R E Y A L P S P
F G L W I L C S T A H V E Y
O E L S R U H I P R W U L M
Y F I E L D E R T O Y I G N
R B R Y S E E B R C N O P P
U S D O F H V L A E A O U O
N Y L U C C D E U S T R V T
N O I T I S O P L D E S P S
E B I H E F M A U H U S O T
R P A R E N T S C M G E A R
U N I F O R M T P H R B G O
E E I C B D A I E O T A L H
S L O V R C R D C A M L W S
R N H C N E B S M E M L V N
```

QUOTESEARCH

Epictetus, a Greek philosopher and teacher, left no writings. However, his views were passed on by his star pupil, Flavius Arrian. Read Epictetus' ancient words of wisdom before finding each line in the diagram.

If you

would

cure

anger,

do not

feed it.

Say to

yourself:

"I used

to be

angry

every day;

then

every other

day; now

only every

third or

fourth day."

When you

reach

thirty

days,

offer a

sacrifice of

thanksgiving

to the

gods.

```
Y A D Y R E V E W H A N L S
L R E E O E M T H I R T Y W
O P G N I V I G S K N A H T
S N Y N S E K E O D D E F T
A T N U A R P Z O D N X O H
Y D W E Q Y H N C Y S B E I
T A F L H O O S O G E P C R
O Y A D H T R U O F N I I D
T N E S D H Q S T E F W F O
H O N L Y E V E R Y X E I R
E W Z K E R S M O H E R R E
S R I H W W O U L D E H C A
Y O U R S E L F I S I J A C
N A H C R O H T R E Y L S H
```

Besides being one of the leaders of the American Revolution, Benjamin Franklin (1706-90) was an abolitionist, author, diplomat, inventor, journalist, philanthropist, public servant, publisher, and scientist. He was also well known for his many quotations, including the one below.

It is the man and woman united that makes the complete being. Separate, she wants his force of body and strength of reason; he, her softness, sensibility and acute discernment. Together they are most likely to succeed in the world.

```
E E H T S E K A M A P K S S
T F L O N N N S T S C I H S
E O P N S E P A R A T E I G
L R O T S O M T M I H H S O
P C B O D Y A N D E S T E O
M E D G K D I O R T H F N Y
O O M E N H T G N E R T S P
C F T T E Y O A T I C S I W
P W R H L C W U M R E S B B
C G T E U E C T D N T O I I
F N K R A A C U T W O R L D
I I F A D S F F S K I Y I I
L E A N D W O M A N E A T T
T B A Y H S U N I T E D Y U
```

SHADY CHARACTERS

This is a collection of colors called seismic shades — because they all vibrate with explosive color. Give yourself a GOLD star for finding them all!

AMETHYST

BRASS

CANARY

CERISE

CHARTREUSE

CHERRY

CITRON

COBALT

COPPER

CORAL

CRIMSON

EMERALD

FLAME

FLAMINGO

FUCHSIA

GOLD

GRAPE

JADE

LEMON

LIME

MAGENTA

MANDARIN

PEACOCK

POPPY

PUMPKIN

RUBY

SAPPHIRE

SCARLET

TANGERINE

TEAL

TURQUOISE

VIOLET

```
L A R O C A N A R Y U R N G
F A K G Y J U K I K S D O I
L Q E V Q B E Q C S L I M E
H Y J T E C U O A H S E F
P M R D F Q M R G R C C L T
C U A R J L B A A A H A U Q
R J M N E P A R G A M R E F
I T C P D H C M R E Q L M P
M L O O K A C T I U N E E C
S A P P H I R E O N J T R I
O B P P S E N I R E G N A T
N O E Y U R S V N I L O L R
U C R S T E L O I V S L D O
A M E T H Y S T Q I U E T N
```

In preparation for your next trip, you can scan through the 32 items in the word list so you will remember to pack everything you need.

BELTS

BLOUSE

BOOKS

BRUSH

CAMERA

CHECKS

CLOCK

COAT

COLOGNE

COMB

FILM

HOSIERY

IRON

ITINERARY

JACKET

MAKEUP

MAPS

PAJAMAS

PURSE

RAZOR

ROBE

SHAMPOO

SHIRTS

SHOES

SLACKS

SLIPPERS

SOCKS

SWIMSUIT

TICKETS

TIES

TOOTHPASTE

WATCH

```
G Y K S L I P P E R S L T K
T H A P S B P J Y S Z I T E
T C P U E K A M C Z U I B O
J Y J R H C T A W S E O H S
F S R S K C O S M S R K L A
G Y U E A O E I K M A P S B
L R T M I L W C S O Z L K U
B A E E T S A P H T O O T S
M R J P N L O M A E R B E H
A E F O S G B H M J C I A U
S N R I T N O M P S A K H N
J I G Y L A C L O C K M S S
E T J A E M T A O C L W A Z
S I Z F B O T T I C K E T S
```

PLAY BASQUE-BALL!

Jai alai originated with the Basque people and is similar to our GAME of handball. The BALL is made of rubber and covered with goatskin; the CESTA is a hand-held basket made from reeds. The traditional Basque BERET was part of the uniform until necessity in the form of a ball traveling upwards of 150 mph finally convinced players to switch to a helmet.

AIRE
APRON
ARRIMADA
AUPA
BALL
BERET
CAROM
CATCH
CESTA
CHIC CHAC
CHULA
CORTADA
COURT
DEJADA
DELANTERO
ENCESTAR
ENTRA
FOUL
FRONTON
FUERA
GAME
GANCHO
HOOK
LATERAL
PALA
PARADE
PELOTARI
PERFOR-
    MANCE

PIDO
POINTS
RALLY
RESTADOR
SASH

SCREENING
SERVE
SHARE
TEAM
ZAGUERO

```
S E S E I O R E T N A L E D
C H I C C H A C O D I P Y M
O C F P R N M P A L A L A B
S O O E A E A J P L L F K A
A R E U F I E M E A U N O E
S T P O R D T N R B R H K B
H A E E R T C E I O C A C E
O D L N C E T M D N F E D R
O A O O S A U A A J G R S E
K M T T L T T G S H A R E T
E I A N T S N C A K G N R P
P R R O E E I I H Z T S V U
B R I R G C P M O R A C E T
T A H F O U L Y A P R O N N
```

120

Mark Twain was a novelist, essayist, and public speaker known for his quick wit. He would pause, puff on his cigar, and then — beware!

Mark Twain loved to deflate pomposity. When a self-righteous hypocrite bragged that his dream was to go to the Holy Land to recite the Ten Commandments on Mount Sinai, Twain dryly replied, "Why not stay here in Boston and keep them?"

```
U L A N D K E E P L I C T O
E Y O V R G H O T S A W W M
T C X V U I M Q A S A B A Z
I V O G E P G U I I O R I B
R J D M O D O H N S K V N K
C N E S M Y T E T A L F E D
O S I Z L A O O W E Q K T E
P T L E H V N T N H O H Y G
Y A P T R M V D Q Y E U Q G
H Y E Z O E W N M H H N S A
C H R U J O H A O E T W A R
S I N A I S E L F G N H O B
E T I C E R Y V T H E T E N
A B L I D R Y L Y U O Q S M
```

GEM STATE COUNTIES

IDAHO is known as The Gem State, not only because of its lovely setting in the midst of forested mountains and snow-capped peaks, but also because of the wealth of precious and semi-precious stones mined there. We've listed 28 of the state's 44 counties below.

ADAMS

BANNOCK

BEAR LAKE

BINGHAM

BLAINE

BOISE

BONNER

BUTTE

CAMAS

CANYON

CARIBOU

CLARK

CUSTER

ELMORE

FRANKLIN

FREMONT

GOODING

IDAHO

JEFFERSON

JEROME

LATAH

LEMHI

LEWIS

MADISON

ONIEDA

POWER

TETON

VALLEY

```
O G W E P U F T E T O N A V
L B M S M U F R E M O N T E
P G N I D O O G A S N B T T
B O H O H M R B R N J Y L T
B O W B L M N E I A K V E U
R N N E C F F Y J R U L W B
B V M N R F E F B T A K I I
R H O M E L V K C T E C S N
I N A J L R P C A N Y O N G
A B L A I N E H M L T N Y H
L D V D S W Y T A R R N E A
D S A D E I N O S I D A M M
G H C M T I L A I U L B E R
O F L G S H K R A L C N N B
```

PETERS AND PAULS

Peter and Paul get equal time in the limelight in this puzzle of notables who have one of these first names. See how many you recognize as you locate and loop their surnames in the puzzle diagram.

ANKA

BOYLE

CEZANNE

FALK

FINCH

FONDA

FRAMPTON

GAUGUIN

HARVEY

HENREID

HOGAN

HORNUNG

LAWFORD

LORRE

LYNDE

MARSHALL

MCCARTNEY

MUNI

NERO

NEWMAN

O'TOOLE

REISER

ROBESON

SCOFIELD

SCOLARI

SELLERS

SIMON

SORVINO

TORK

USTINOV

WEIR

WINFIELD

```
L G N U N R O H M R I E W A
C E Z A N N E M E G B B K G
T F H H I O O S U F O N D A
M O A V I S I T O N A S E U
N T R D P E I P P W I K L G
I O V K R B D D I M R L S U
S O E O H O V N O B A R C I
S L Y C N R F N Y H L R O N
H E N R E I D W S L O S F A
F I L Y E N T R A C C M I M
F A R L N R A S U L S A E W
H A D T E M R G U B O Y L E
Y K L P R R L O O M N T D N
B G E K O T S S L H M L B L
```

"WESTERN" PLANTS

Many of the plants in this puzzle are probably sporting cowboy hats. That's because they're all "western" plants. In other words, each of the terms below can be preceded by the word "western" to form the name of a variety of plant.

AZALEA

BALSAM

BIRCH

BROME GRASS

BUCKEYE

CATALPA

CEDAR

COFFEE

CRAB APPLE

DAISY

DOGWOOD

DROPWORT

HEMLOCK

LARCH

MUGWORT

PEONY

PINE

PITCH PINE

PLUM

POPPY

RAGWEED

RED LILY

SAGE

SAND CHERRY

SPRUCE

SUGAR MAPLE

TAMARACK

WALLFLOWER

WHITE FIR

```
E E E B P E O N Y B T S L E
E Y C E R D D R O P W O R T
H E R U F O I A A N P G A D
G K E R R F M D E G D O K Y
P C D K E P O E H L W C P S
M U L T W H S C G C A E M I
U B I F O P C H E R R Z E A
G H L M L P E D A A A I A D
W C Y U F M G M N B P S B O
O R M E L P A M R A G U S O
R A K O L T S Y T P S D F W
T L C M A S L A B P C A C G
A K N P W C A T A L P A L O
A P I T C H P I N E N I P D
```

124

"BLUE" TUNES

Movies don't get much darker and more bizarre than David Lynch's *Blue VELVET* (1986). The film's title is taken from Bobby Vinton's song by the same name, which is sung by Isabella Rossellini's character, Dorothy Valens, in the movie. Here we've listed 32 song titles that begin with the word "Blue."

ANGEL

AUTUMN

AVENUE

BAYOU

CHAMPAGNE

CHRISTMAS

COLLAR MAN

EDEN

EYES

GARDENIA

HAWAII

JAY WAY

JEAN

MONDAY

MONEY

MOON

ON BLUE

RIVER

SHADOWS

SIDE

SKIES

STAR

SUEDE SHOES

SUNDAY

TAIL FLY

TANGO

THURSDAY

UMBRELLA

VALENTINE

VELVET

WATER

WINTER

```
E T B T A N G O T S J L W U
G D M O N D A Y U R E V I R
R J V A E E R E N A A I B A
E E M D Y V D F M V N C K T
I V I Y E E E U E G O A S
S S T L S E N I T N E L A V
A W V H I H I G U U L L W W
M E O S U T A H A E Y A U W
T E B D Y R J W R P T R H W
S U N D A Y S B A E M M W Y
I L O K W H M D R I T A E G
R B O Y Y U S E A D I N H I
H N M T A I L F L Y O B I C
C O C N J B G L B M T R T W
```

EUROPEAN MUSIC FESTIVALS

In any one year, there may well be more than 100 music festivals throughout Europe, from **ATHENS**, Greece, to **EDINBURGH**, Scotland, to **WARSAW**, Poland. So no matter where you are on the continent, you stand a good chance of being able to attend at least one.

ATHENS

BATH

BAYREUTH

BERGEN

BERLIN

BRIGHTON

BUDAPEST

BUXTON

DRESDEN

EDINBURGH

ESTORIL

FLORENCE

GRANADA

HELSINKI

ISTANBUL

LUCERNE

MUNICH

PESARO

PRAGUE

RAVENNA

SALZBURG

SPOLETO

STRESA

VERONA

VIENNA

WARSAW

WEXFORD

ZURICH

```
A I F O I T D P W Z W H D B
L N S L S R S A R A W C R U
O T E L O P S N N A D I E D
I T F F C R V N E E G R S A
L G X G A L E L T H S U D P
K E A W R V R N T T T Z E E
W E G L A A O O C U R A N S
P H G R U B N I D E E E R T
B O C B U B A A S R S B E O
U R T I E B N T D Y A E C R
X A W R N N Z A H A G R U I
T S G M E U L L T B O L L L
O E L I B P M N A S D I K T
N P V Y P Y H E L S I N K I
```

One of the most accomplished Americans in history, Benjamin Franklin was a writer, scientist, printer, and philosopher. The passage below provides a glimpse of Franklin's humor and wisdom.

Were it have no life

offered objection from

to my to a its

choice, repetition of beginning,

I should the same only

asking

the

advantages

authors

have

in a

second

edition:

to correct

some

faults

of the

first.

```
T C E R R O C O T Z O L E B
E S L M N V O O I T S V C N
Y E R E A J B D E Y A T I W
A G V I X S J R R H U S O L
C A L O F F E R E D T G H A
H T S P L S C H W B H F C Q
J N R E P E T I T I O N O F
W A V R C A I L K R R U D N
I V J Y Y O O X U J S Q L E
E D I T I O N W N A Z I U S
F A O K Y O M D J Z F R O M
T M G N I N N I G E B M H M
Y C M N R W E L J W E A S P
T D A S K I N G Y X L A I C
```

IN THE BEGINNING

In this puzzle, look for 30 types of people who can be considered to be in a learning stage.

AMATEUR

APPRENTICE

BEGINNER

CADET

CHILD

FLEDGLING

FRESHMAN

INFANT

INGÉNUE

INITIATE

LAYMAN

LEARNER

NEONATE

NEOPHYTE

NEWBORN

NOVICE

NOVITIATE

PLEBE

RECRUIT

ROOKIE

RUBE

STARTER

STUDENT

TENDERFOOT

TRAINEE

TYRO

UPSTART

YOKEL

YOUNGSTER

YOUTH

```
O R O E R E N N I G E B R E
T I U R C E R N O T E M O C
R S C B Y I I R Y V N P O Y
A T A F E T T H E E I L K O
T A D M I O P N W N A C I U
S R E A R O Y B E Y R D E T
P T T U E F O K M R T A N H
U E U N N R U A U P P A E A
D R I D N E N B R N F P T L
H C F L E D G L I N G L A H
F H H B T N S N I Y E S N O
B I E L O E T A I T I V O N
K L A M A T E U R Y O K E L
P D T B Y F R E S H M A N I
```

COLORADO GHOST TOWNS

CENTRAL City is one of Colorado's finest surviving ghost towns. While there you can visit Teller House to see the legendary "face on the barroom floor." Don't get spooked while looking for these Colorado ghost towns.

ALDER

ALMA

ALPINE

ALTA

ALTMAN

ANACONDA

BONANZA

CENTRAL (City)

COMO

CORONA

CROOK

ELKTON

EUREKA

FAIRPLAY

FREELAND

GILMAN

GOLD HILL

GOTHIC

LULU (City)

MARBLE

OHIO (City)

OPHIR

PEETZ

PITKIN

RICO

RUBY

SCHOFIELD

SHAVANO

TOMBOY

TOMICHI

TUNGSTEN

VICTOR

WARD

```
L N A H N K G P I T K I N D
G A C T R E A H D C B H N T
W M W E L N L L O I P C R S
V T D B O A E K K H A I N M
A L R R O I N T T T C M B Z
A A O G F A V P S O M O C E
M C T O M B O Y F G N T L U
L R H L C S H A V A N O A R
A C I D D L I R N C V U R E
S G O H T R U Z O H I O T K
R E N I P L A D N O C A N A
I M M L U O Y W N Z T E E P
D N A L E E R F K O O R C A
F Y H D V G E F T H R U B Y
```

A MOUNTAIN OF MINERALS

ALABASTER is a translucent, whitish variety of **GYPSUM** (soft mineral) used for statues and vases. There are 29 minerals or varieties of minerals waiting to be unearthed in the diagram.

ALABASTER	HORNBLENDE	QUARTZ
APATITE	MALACHITE	SILVER
AZURITE	MICA	SULFUR
BAUXITE	OLIVINE	TALC
BERYL	PYRITE	TOPAZ
CALCITE		
CINNABAR		
COPPER		
CORUNDUM		
DIAMOND		
FELDSPAR		
FLINT		
FLUORITE		
GALENA		
GOLD		
GRAPHITE		
GYPSUM		
HALITE		
HEMATITE		

```
E G E G O T C G Y P S U M X
T M A L A C H I T E D U Z T
I A R L Y R E B N N D R M O
R P C E E G X O N G P O P
O A P I P N G M U E A L A A
U T P D M P A R T Z I B L Z
L I E S O I O I A V D A A U
F T G Y D C C I P G U B R
Z E D N E L B N R O H X A I
E T I T A M E H U M S I S T
Z I R C N C R F F D N T T E
C R T A E I H A L I T E E E
L Y M C U A L O U T Z N R F
F P U Y N Q G F S I L V E R
```

The most commonly used letters in the English language are E, T, A, O, N, R, and I, in that order. Please NOTE: All 37 words below contain only those letters.

AERATE

ANTE

EATER

ENTREE

ERRANT

ERRATA

INITIATE

INNATE

INNER

INTENT

IRATE

IRON

IRRITATE

NARRATE

NINE

NONE

NOON

NOTE

ORIENT

RAIN

RATE

RATIO

RENT

RETAIN

RETINA

RETORT

ROTOR

TAINT

TATTOO

TEETER

TENET

TENOR

TENT

TIARA

TINT

TITAN

TONER

```
E A O I N A A T I N R R R E
N R O I T I R T E O N R I T
O E N I T N E R T R A T E N
T I O R A N A O I I N A N T
O R E E E R T N E A R A O
E R I T I R A E I T E R T T
T A T N O O N R T O N O A N
A R T R E N O N I A T N E T
R T R E T E E T A T I R R I
R O E N R T O R T T R N A N
A T N R N R T E E A A R T E
N N E I T N A R N T T R E N
E I T A N R A T I O E O I N
I N N A T E E T A B R A R O
```

TENOR ROLES

In the opera *I Pagliacci* (The Clowns), the part of CANIO — a favorite role of many great tenors — is all the more poignant as he is compelled to make others laugh while his heart is breaking. One of opera's most famous arias, *"Vesti la giubba"* is a highlight of this tenor role.

ADOLAR
ADORNO
ALTOUM
ANDREA
AVITO
BANKS
BENVOLIO
CANIO
CHRISTIAN
CORENTINO
DANCAIRO
ERNANI
FAUST
GENNARO
GUIDON
HANEGO
HEROD
LORIS
LUIGI
MELCHIOR
MERRILL
NADIR
NANDO
NICIAS

NOLAN
OBERON
OTHELLO
OVLOUR
ROMEO
RUDOLPH

SAMSON
SIEGFRIED
TRISTAN
TURIDDU
TYBALT

```
T G N A I T S I R H C S T S
Y S E N I C I A S K N A B T
B V U N U K E D E O A M O H
A B H A N E G O A R N S T P
L G A B F A F R O D D O I L
T I N A D I R N A L O N V O
B E N V O L I O S N R L A D
G S L A I T E N I C E H A U
N U L G N P D A R H H N D R
E O I E A R L T O F C D F B
D U R D C T E S L A I L F N
L O R E O U I I I R O M E O
C R E U B N L R U O L V O M
V O M G B O O T H E L L O R
```

Abraham Lincoln, our 16th president, remains a hero in the minds of many people because he preserved the Union during the American Civil War and brought about the emancipation of slaves. Poet Carl Sandburg (1878-1967) spoke these words in an address to Congress marking the 150th anniversary of Lincoln's birth.

Not often
in the
story of
mankind

does
a man
arrive
on earth

who is
both
steel and
velvet, who
is as
hard as
rock and
soft as
drifting
fog, who
holds
in his
heart and
mind the
paradox
of terrible
storm and
peace
unspeakable
and perfect.

```
F X O D A R A P I F U Y H O
A F H H E A R T A N D F T H
M T W S W T D D S F T G R A
A O G T S T W P N K N H A R
N V O O F T E R R I B L E D
D D F R R A U V T T K S N A
P M N M K O O F L B N N O S
E H I A R R I V E E H F A P
R C B N K R S O T G V T S M
F L A D D C I F V H F S O I
E D O E S T O R Y O F P N B
C D K A P T H R S L V H D T
T U S G O F W E M D I A I X
E I D N A L E E T S A P M C
```

El Paso, TEXAS, is located on the Rio Grande opposite Juárez, Mexico. In a region of cattle ranches and cotton and vegetable farms, the city is a port of entry as well as a commercial, industrial, financial, and mining center. We HOPE you enjoy your armchair tour through these 37 streets.

BEECH
BYRON
CHAPEL
CHASE
CROSS
DEBORD
DOLAN
DONWAY
DORSET
EDISON
ELKTON
FORT
HARDY
HOPE
JORDAN
LAMAR
LARIAT
MARICOPA
MARSH
MENLO
MESA
MONTANA
MYRTLE
NEVADA
OCHOA

OREGON
OSAGE
PAISANO
PIONEER
POCANO
POPLAR

REVERE
TEXAS
TOLUCA
TREMONT
VULCAN
WELCH

```
V T R O F L T W E L C H T G
U K E L K T O N Y I A U O L
L D V J R S L P A S E M Y Y
C E E A S X U E I D N D A E
A G R B B P C M P O R W P R
N A E Y O P A I S A N O T T
A S R C G R B I H O H E J A
T O A M I A D L D J X C E I
N N H C E E B N W A U L S R
O G O C U N O N S D T A A A
M P M M O G L M A R S H H L
A D A V E N H O Y L U S C P
S S O R C R L M C U O L S O
G D O R S E T I G T K D F P
```

BEFORE OR AFTER "SCHOOL"

A **FINISHING** school is a **PRIVATE** institution for young women that focuses on cultured behavior and social graces. The list below contains 31 entries that either precede or follow "school" to form new words or phrases.

BOARD

BOOK

DANCING

DISTRICT

ELEMENTARY

FINISHING

GRADE

GRADUATE

GRAMMAR

HIGH

HOUSE

INTERMEDIATE

JUNIOR (high)

MASTER

MEDICAL

MIDDLE

MILITARY

MUSIC

NIGHT

NURSERY

PAROCHIAL

PREP

PRIVATE

PUBLIC

ROOM

SUNDAY

SYSTEM

TEACHER

WORK

YARD

YEAR

```
U T O K D A F G R P A O J H A
J K C U G R A D U A T E R I S
K R K I Y N A R R R O I N U J
P O E D R Y I O H O U S E R T
M W O T E T P H B C O T A H A
P L M B S E S K S H A M G A H
B A U Y R A T I L I M I P P I
M S S P U C M P D A N C I N G
Y G I F N H R E R L U I Y Y H
L A C I D E M G A I H H F V N
I R D K N R A E Y I V L U G B
N H D N E L E M E N T A R Y S
Y P N T U Y U M Y K G A T N P
D U N S Y S T E M I D D L E M
C I L B U P U L I E W L D L O
```

HOME ON THE RANGE

PIONEER life had its perils and hardships, but the freedom to raise families and crops in the new FRONTIER was the reward. Can you find all the BUFFALO, WAGONS, and other terms below that are related to the Old West?

ADVENTURE

BEARS

BEAVERS

BUFFALO

DEER

EXPEDITION

EXPLORERS

FISH

FORT

FRONTIER

GAME

HORSES

INDIANS

LAKES

LAND

MOUNTAINS

OREGON TRAIL

PACIFIC OCEAN

PIKES PEAK

PIONEER

PRAIRIE

RABBITS

SANTA FE TRAIL

SCOUT

SURVEY

TRADERS

TREK

TURKEY

WAGONS

WATER

WOLVES

```
G V P R A I R I E L A N D S
S L I A R T N O G E R O N L
R R K B C O R E T A W I M L
A D E B T I S O H G A T T I
E H S I F E F Y F T G I B A
B S P T T R I N P O D L R
V E E S R N I U C I N E E T
Y V A E A N O Y T O S P I E
E L K V D M E R L N C X D F
V O Y I E K U A F E E E U A
R W A M R R F S D E E V A T
U N A U S F S E S R O H D N
S G T T U O C S E K A L S A
O X V B R E X P L O R E R S
```

ECCENTRICITY

Eccentricity is defined as "a deviation from what is ordinary or customary." Everyone's ECCENTRIC sometimes, but some folks are more DIZZY and QUAINT than others. Circle all the descriptive words in this puzzle without getting too FOOLISH!

BALMY

BARMY

BUGGY

CRACKED

CUCKOO

DAFFY

DAFT

DIZZY

DOTTY

DREAMY

ECCENTRIC

FLIGHTY

FOOLISH

GIDDY

GOOFY

LOCO

LOONY

NUTTY

PECULIAR

PIXILATED

QUAINT

SAPPY

SILLY

SPACEY

STRANGE

UNUSUAL

ZANY

```
N Y Y B U G G Y D Z Z O P Y
B A R M Y N A Z S T E P R D
M Y A I L U U M E L X D E D
Y E Y E C A P S Y D S K C I
P F K Q O G B O U R C T C G
P L F G L O S T R A N G E B
A I O A C P K F R I L Q N E
S G X O D F O C A L B H T C
T H L I N O H U U R Z R D
Y T F S L Y Q O G C S F I A
E Y H I S A T G K E Y Z C F
K Y S L D O T T Y P Z K F T
R H L L A K I E U Y F O O G
T T N Y M A E R D N T S G H
```

BUSY HANDS

Have you ever stopped to consider all the tasks our hands can perform?
Coupled with the ingenuity of the human brain, it's what separates us
from the other living things on Earth.

APPLAUD
BUILD
CLASP
CLEAN
COLOR
COMPOSE
DIRECT
DRAW
DRINK
DRIVE
FEED
FIGHT
GESTURE
HAMMER
HIDE
HOLD
KNEAD
KNIT
MOVE
OPEN
PAINT
PARE
PLANT
PRAY
PRUNE
SCRATCH
SCULPT

SHAPE
SIGN
SKETCH
SOOTHE
SQUEEZE
TICKLE

TWIDDLE
TYPE
WASH
WAVE
WRAP
WRITE

```
A K C K N I R D P A R E P E
V R H G B S A G R E V I R D
D P E Z E E U Q S A D F U I
F A T M N S V T W T W E N H
T I N K M G T W I D D L E P
N N G O P A I U C I G N S F
D T V H Y E H S R R D A O T
Q E D A T I C K L E L E P S
E B R U N R E E H C I L M H
R P O P A O M T H T U C O O
V G A T L L O C I C B L C Y
N R C H P O P H S R D U Q Y
W H L R S C E P Y T W A S H
W S N M Q Y N O A C M E O H
```

The Bay of FUNDY is New Brunswick's largest. Its tides, which are the world's highest, usually keep the bay's harbors free of ice in winter. A small portion of the northwest corner of the bay's coastline fronts the U.S. state of Maine. In this puzzle, you will find some geographical highlights of this Canadian province.

BIG BALD (mountain)
BLACK (Mountains)
BLUE (Mountain)
CAINS (River)
CAMPOBELLO (Island)
CANAAN (River)
CHALEUR (Bay)
COSTIGAN (Mountains)
FUNDY (Bay of)
GRAND (Lake)
GREEN (River)
KEDGWICK (River)
KENT (Hills)
MACES (Bay)
MIRAMICHI (Bay)
MISCOU (Island)
NASHWAAK (River)
OROMOCTO (Lake)
PALFREY (Lake)
PLEASANT (Mountain)
PORTAGE (Island)
SALMON (River)
SERPENTINE (Mountains)
SHIPPEGAN (Island)
SQUAW CAP (Mountain)
ST. CROIX (River)
ST. JOHN (River)
TOBIQUE (River)
TODD (Mountain)

```
I K C I W G D E K E Y H B E
M S K Y H S D R U D C I S G
J A A G E C D Q N L G S T A
B L A C K R I U P B E N J T
I M W F P B F M A C A S O R
T O H C O U C L A S E D H O
C N S T H K D M A R D D N P
U A A T N A G E P P I H S A
S O N G O L L E B O P M A C
P E C A I P N E E R G M K W
K U M S A T A E U L B P C A
N P C A I N S T C R O I X U
G R A N D M C O E H H H F Q
I Q E O R O M O C T O N E S
```

Pearls are composed of over 90% calcium carbonate and, like all carbonates, they will dissolve in strong vinegar and other weak acids. This occurs slowly because of their hardness, but if pulverized, they will effervesce and dissolve quickly. A famous use of this fact is noted below. Note: A sesterce is an old Roman coin.

Cleopatra once made a bet with Marc Antony that she could spend ten million sesterces on one amusement. She won by making the most expensive drink in history. Having in her earrings two of the largest pearls in the world, she threw one of them into vinegar and drank it when the pearl dissolved.

```
E X P E N S I V E P Y D D R F
E D L R O W Y N O T N A H E B
H I C V I I A R T A P O E L C
I U D F L N H D R A N K I T T
S N I O L T H A T S H E C D H
T E S O I H G S G N I R R A E
O E S W M E C N O G A I M N M
R O O T N L A W I M N U L P O
Y T L I E A E R N K S I H W S
N N V W T R I D I E A H V R T
O I E U H G C N M D A M D A R
W M D T H E P E A R L S Y E H
E E E D D S N P S B E U H B H
H H K A X T O S F O E N O N O
S T M E D R S E V S I T T C T
```

DIG THIS!

The most fundamental characteristic of jazz music is IMPROVISATION. An artist's ability to change and experiment is what gives jazz its sense of urgency and immediacy. As with most movements, jazz has spawned its own jargon. Below you will find 34 words related to this dynamic music genre.

ACCENT
AVANT-GARDE
BALLAD
BEAT
BEBOP
BIG BAND

BLOW
BLUES
BREAK
BRIDGE
CHART
CHORUS

COMBO
DIXIELAND (jazz)
EIGHT
FUSION
IMPROVISA-TION
JIVE
LICK
LINES
MODERN (jazz)
NOODLE (ramble musically)
PROGRES-SIVE (jazz)
REED
RHYTHM
RIFF
SCALE
SCAT
SIDEMAN
SOLO
SPACE
SWING
TENOR
UP-TEMPO

```
O B M O C H W E G D I R B A
S O C H O R U S A E M P U G
C E B A T A E L I N R D N G
A F U E V Y L G L O J I V E
T W N L A A H O G I W X F U
E O I D B T N R D S N I M F
R C L O P M E T P U A E F G
K L D O R S E N G F I L S F
S N B N S I D E M A N A C V
E E R I A B H C W J R N A K
B C V E R B H C F H M D L X
L E A I D A G A D L D E E R
O I M P R O V I S A T I O N
W M X T S P M E B R E A K A
```

GLITTER, GLISTEN, OR GLOW

Polish up your searching skills by finding the 28 terms that make up this word list. They are all items that are radiant in one form or another.

AGATE

BEADS

CANDLE

COALS

CROWN

CRYSTAL

DIAMOND

EMBERS

EMERALD

FIREFLY

FIREWORKS

FLASHLIGHT

HALO

HEADLIGHT

ICICLE

JEWELS

LANTERN

LIGHT BULB

METALS

MICA

NEON SIGN

RHINESTONE

RUBY

SEQUINS

SPARKLERS

SPOTLIGHT

STAR

TINSEL

```
L E S N I T S L A T S Y R C
S B J R I R H Y H A L O C P
K L A U E T H G I L T O P S
R E M B W K I N I I A B K I
O M M Y R L Q G I L N D C M
W E I F H H H I S P D I G Q
E R C S F T I S E C C A B T
R A A N B I N N I L R M E Y
I L F U R I R O E A D O A H
F D L B U E A E G S E N W O
S B Y Q G E T N F T T D A N
N J E W E L S N A L H O C C
K S L A T E M G A E Y K N E
B E A D S P A R K L E R S E
```

BEAUTIFUL STAINED GLASS

Stained glass isn't just for church windows anymore. You'll find it's used in items such as jewelry, mobiles, and mosaics. Get the LEAD out and begin searching for these terms which are all related to this elegant art form.

ANTIQUE

CATHEDRAL

CHAGALL (Marc)

COLORED

CURVES

DECORATIVE

DESIGN

EDGES

ELABORATE

ENAMEL

FIGURE

LA FARGE (John)

LAMP

LEAD

LIGHT

MIDDLE AGES

PAINT

PATTERN

PICTURE

PIECES

PUTTY

ROUAULT (Georges)

SCENE

SHAPE

SHEETS

SHINE

SOLDER

SPARKLE

STRIPS

TIFFANY (Louis C.)

WINDOW

```
W E S R E T W S N G I S E D
D I D N M I H E W D L D N S
L Q E G N I E G G D M F A E
M C C D N L D M I R A I M C
S E O E K F G D P L A E E E
M W R R O U A U L T P F L I
M A A U B S T N R E T T A P
O P T G T T M N U H A C R L
S B I I Y C S Q I M H G D K
H E V F U T I F F A N Y E V
E D E R R T I P G C P W H S
E G V I N E L A B O R A T E
T E P A H S L Q I R P M A L
S S M S O L D E R O L O C O
```

CONNECTIVE

Conjunctions are words that are used to connect other words, phrases, or clauses. Take a quick grammar lesson as you find these 31 conjunctions.

AFORE

AFTER

ALBEIT

ALSO

ALTHOUGH

BECAUSE

BEFORE

BOTH

DIRECTLY

EITHER

ERGO

EXCEPT

HARDLY

NEITHER

ONCE

ONLY

PROVIDED

RATHER

SAVE

SEEING

SINCE

STILL

THAN

THAT

THEN

UNLESS

UNTIL

WHAT

WHEN

WHETHER

WHILE

```
L T A L T H O U G H Y A A N
T A Y O S L A G R O I F L R
E X N T L V Y U R S T O A R
E C N I S P N S P E X R R F
E S T E I T H E R O F E B T
W S N B I R V Y O T H U P D
Y F U L O A L S V T H E N C
L S Y A S T S R I N C A X B
O S S L C H H E D X X S N Y
W B I E D E N H E F Y B E R
B Y R P L R B T D I L O H D
U I W I R N A E R C N T W P
D T H I G H U H V V O G C G
O W G V T A H W L E R N N R
```

Many Africans look upon the hippopotamus with fondness, and some hippos have even become folk heroes. The most celebrated was a hippo known as Huberta. She made a 1,000-mile trip across Africa, visiting local villages, being met with parades and food, and grazing in parks and roadways until her death.

In the nineteen twenties, Huberta the hippo wandered across drought-stricken South Africa. She was wel-comed because people noticed that rain often followed her arrival, so she was seen as a spirit sent to relieve the drought. When she died, all of South Africa mourned.

```
T H G U O R D E R E D N A W E
H V N O T I C E D S R I A A C
W H U B E R T A T U T O S S E
M P T D S S O R C A V N P S H
I I A U V E O T I C E E I E S
O L R D O P P I H E H T R E A
L W H E N S H E T B H A I N C
D G H N L E T E K G R T T A I
M E G R A I N R U R N S N S R
K F W U A I E O I E H E E I F
S U F O N B R V W C L S T N A
O O V M L D A T E A K P F W W
W A S W E L C O M E D E O F A
B T A H T U O S F O T T N E S
H L T D E L A F R I C A W N P
```

HAMMER IT OUT

Archaeologists speculate that the first hammer was a mere stone. After several million years, early man learned to fashion hammerheads out of harder and more durable metals. A handle was attached to gain mechanical advantages and to protect the hands. Of course, new materials required a harder tool to work with, and thus the hammers listed below were born.

BALL-PEEN

BEETLE

BLACK-
   SMITH'S

BOILER-
   MAKER'S

BRICK

CHIPPING

CLAW

CROSS-PEEN

CUTLER

DROP

ELECTRIC

ENGINEER'S

FRAMING

JACK

MACHINIST'S

MALLET

PILE

PNEUMATIC

RAISING

RIVETING

RUBBER

SLEDGE

SPALLING

STEAM

STONE

TACK

TILE SETTER'S

TRIP

```
S T S I N I H C A M C T A I
L K B R A R C H I P P I N G
E S R E E N I G N E I B V I
D M G G N K T J C U T L E R
G B G N I M A R F V R A E U
E E N I I C M M N E V C C W
E E E L K T U E R L N K N K
M T I L E S E T T E R S D G
M L U A T P N V E C L M N R
D E K P S E P P I T B I W E
C R R S T L L K C R S T O B
S T O N E L C L I I J H J B
T R I P A I A C A C R S T U
C D F B M W K R W M V D V R
```

Knoxville, named after the first Secretary of War Henry Knox (1750-1806), is Tennessee's third largest city. It is the home of the Tennessee Valley Authority (TVA) and the main campus of the University of Tennessee. In 1982, the city was host to the World's Fair. If you were to stroll through this famous town, you would be sure to see many of the 37 streets listed below.

AILOR
ARTHUR
BLOUNT
BOOKER
CANSLER

CENTRAL
CHARLES
CHURCH
CLARK
CLINCH

COMMERCE
DALE
DENMAR
DEPOT
EUCLID
FOREST
FRONT
GRAND
HANNAH
HENLEY
HILL
JACKSON
LAUREL
LOCUST
MARKET
MIMOSA
MULVANEY
RAMSEY
SEVIER
STATE
TRAVIS
TULIP
WALL
WALLACE
WALNUT
WESTERN
WHITE

```
M J N R W R Y L R U H T R A
A T L O E R I R E M A E E I
S F O K S I A G C R L K C L
D R O P T K V M H S U R A O
C O M M E R C E N T R A L R
B N U B R D N A S E W M L C
C T L N N L C A J U D S A J
S H V Y E F E C U C H E W H
I T A Y O T W A L L L Y H E
V N N R W A S O M I M A C D
A O E U L H I L L D N A R G
R S Y N O E I A B N D C U K
T S U C O L S T A T E N H V
K T U L I P B H E L A D C N
```

MARVELOUS MAKEUP

Everyone wore eye makeup in ancient Egypt — men, women, and children of all classes. Green was the color of choice back then and it is still a stylish shade of eye shadow today, as are these others.

APRICOT

AVOCADO

BAMBOO

BISQUE

BRONZE

BURGUNDY

BUTTERCUP

CAMEL

CARIBBEAN BLUE

CHARCOAL

CLOVE

COFFEE

DUSK

EGGPLANT

EGGSHELL

EMERALD GREEN

GOLD

HAZELNUT

HONEYDEW

KHAKI

KIWI

LAVENDER

LEMON

MAPLE

MOCHA

OYSTER

RUST

SEA BLUE

SILVER

SNOW

TAUPE

TEAL

TURQUOISE

TWILIGHT

WILLOW

```
G W C T W I L I G H T D B T R
M S R I O S Y M P N V N U Y P
Z N E U L K I D A Q O R T S W
B O D P L E T L N P Q M T N K
I W N B I G P T V U L A E T E
S F E P W G E R O E G E R L T
Q O V D G S K I K C R R C S Z
U F A E Y H S W T G I A U E U
E U L B A E S U D E V R P B A
Z B F K M L N L V O C U P H E
N K I W I L A O C R A H C A E
O Y S T E R L A H T G O L D F
R R Y Z E C D S L E M A C B F
B B A M B O O F P M R I T Q O
D H E U L B N A E B B I R A C
```

Cinco de Mayo (Spanish for May 5) is a Mexican holiday that commemorates the Battle of Puebla, which took place in 1862. In this decisive battle, the Mexican army defeated French forces who were attempting to take control of the country. Many people think *Cinco de Mayo* is Mexico's Independence Day, but Mexico actually declared its independence from Spain on September 16th, 1810 — more than 50 years earlier.

Cinco de Mayo is a day of celebration in Mexico that has become a festive holiday in parts of the United States as well. Cities with large Mexican-American populations celebrate the day with festivals that include music, dancing, and food.

```
X W E I N M E X I C O F Y A
P W S L A V I T S E F L E S
C H I E C C E D U L C N I E
W I L C I N C O D E Y O S T
Y F S L R T T O L B F B N A
L E T U E G I E C R O S O T
M S G H M W B C M A Y O I S
E T H R A R S A H T A H T G
X I O O A T D A N E D R A N
I V L T H L V E M D A T L I
C E I E H N H O T P F T U C
A O D D U T C T N I S O P N
N A A N F E I I I M N T O A
Y G Y O B U V W B W C U P D
```

CAR PARTS

Even those who claim they know nothing about cars are probably familiar with these automobile items.

AXLES	OIL GAUGE	SPARK PLUG
BRAKE	PISTON	THROTTLE
CARBURETOR	RADIATOR	TIRES
CHAINS	RADIO	WHEELS
CHASSIS	SEAT BELTS	WINDSHIELD
CLUTCH		
CUP HOLDER		
CYLINDER		
ENGINE		
EXHAUST FAN		
FENDERS		
GAS TANK		
GEAR		
GLOVE BOX		
HUBCAPS		
MOTOR		
MUFFLER		

```
O I D A R O T A I D A R W S
G G E X G L O V E B O X I E
A B N E X H A U S T F A N R
S N I A H C S L E E H W D I
T P G U L P K R A P S C S T
A M N F A R U R T G Y L H G
N E E C K B E E B F H R I W
K K B W R L G D E S O A E S
C U X A F U P N L T E K L I
H L C F A R D I T O A L D S
K H U G O E V L S R H Y X S
T M L T R P E Y B T A P A A
W I O S C Y E C I I O E U H
O M Y R C H D D A P R N G C
```

"GOOD" VIBRATIONS

Whenever you feel good **AND READY**, feel free to circle the 33 entries in the list that can follow the word "good" to form new phrases. We suspect there's a good **CHANCE** you'll find them all based on your fine solving skills rather than just good **LUCK**!

AND READY

AS GOLD

BEHAVIOR

CHANCE

CHEER

CITIZEN

COMPANY

DEAL

DEED

ENOUGH

EVENING

EXAMPLE

FAITH

FORTUNE

FRIDAY

GRACES

HEALTH

HEAVENS

HUMOR

IDEA

LOOKS

LUCK

MANNERS

MORNING

NEWS

OLD DAYS

OMEN

RIDDANCE

SAMARITAN

SPIRITS

TIDINGS

TURN

WEATHER

```
E N O U G H V O M E C S P L
N C I S Y A D D L O G S A G
U L H W D D E E M R T E P R
T D O E A V M E I I D C A A
R U K N E O N D R F Y N O C
O O R N R R D I C H A N C E
F I I N D A P X N T D I I S
S N I V N S G N I D I T T R
G N D C A G H R W X R I I H
G S E I N H A E O U F S Z F
K K A V A M E X A M P L E Z
C O M P A N Y B N L U D N K
U O H S R E N N A M T H M K
L L B H R E H T A E W H U B
```

STATE YOUR VOCATION

We hope you enjoy this geographical job listing in which the name of each U.S. city is also the name of a vocation.

ARCHER (Fla.)

BAKER (Ark.)

BISHOP (Md.)

BREWER (Me.)

BUTLER (Ga.)

CARPENTER (N.C.)

CLOTHIER (W. Va.)

COOK (Minn.)

DRESSER (Wis.)

DRIVER (Ark.)

FARMER (Ohio)

FISHER (Ark.)

HELPER (Utah)

HUNTER (N.Y.)

MARINE (Ill.)

MATADOR (Tex.)

MILLER (S. Dak.)

MINER (Mo.)

PAGE (Ariz.)

POTTER (Kans.)

RANGER (Tex.)

SENTINEL (Okla.)

SHEPHERD (Mich.)

SHIPMAN (Va.)

SINGER (La.)

SQUIRE (W. Va.)

SULTAN (Wash.)

TELLER (Alas.)

VICARS (W. Va.)

```
T D A D O H N R C G T K A I
E R Q A U E S V I P S L G L
L I Q N H B T U O K E E R F
L V T D A B U T L E R N A I
E E K K R H T M C T N I T S
R R E P L E H D A V A T D H
M R M G R E H C R A M N R E
V I C A R S P P P R P E R R
C K N I T A F E E O I S E E
N U U E A A N N N H H S G W
  I Q G I R D D G T I S S N E
S A S M B D L O E E R U I R
P S E M I L L E R R I A S B
D R K O O C Q D I O Q S M L
```

We hope this next bit of news won't disappoint you breakfast lovers out there, but Thomas' English Muffins® don't come from England at all — they come from New Jersey! They're made at 930 RIVERVIEW Drive in TOTOWA, the address they share with Entenmann's® baked goods.

ACORN

BOGERT

BOYLE

CARROLL

CHARLES

CHERBA

CHURCH

CREWS

CROSBY

DEWEY

GARFIELD

GORDON

GRANT

GREENE

HIGHVIEW

HUDSON

LINDEN

MAIR

MEADOW

MINNISINK

MITCHELL

RAPHAEL

RIVERVIEW

ROSENGREN

SCRIVENS

SUTTON

TOTOWA

TRACY

UNION

YOUNG

```
M I T C H E L L O R R A C I
W I D G L C D U H T S C I E
H P N Y M B R I N D E O A F
P Y O N R B G E A I F R I B
N B E T I H B C W W O N Y O
O T T W V S H U D S O N B G
T L T I E A I D E P N T S E
T D E A R D L N N E V C O R
U W N L V E G E K O W H R T
S N E V I R C S A Y D E C M
Y S E F E N I U C H U R C H
C M R N W O D A E M P B O W
E A G O M H R E M T N A R G
G N U O Y T D K N S S W R V
```

No, this is not a list of fast-food locations. Rather, the diagram below is filled with cities and towns in the U.S. whose names begin with "MC."

MCADOO (Pa.)

MCAFEE (N.J.)

MCALLEN (Tex.)

MCBAIN (Mich.)

MCBEAN (Ga.)

MCBEE (S.C.)

MCCALL (Ida.)

MCCLOUD (Calif.)

MCCLURE (Pa.)

MCCLUSKY (N.D.)

MCCOMB (Miss.)

MCCOOK (Neb.)

MCCOOL (Miss.)

MCCORKLE (W. Va.)

MCCORMICK (S.C.)

MCDONALD (Ohio)

MCDO-NOUGH (Ga.)

MCEWEN (Tenn.)

MCFARLAND (Calif.)

MCGILL (Nev.)

MCGRAW (N.Y.)

MCGREGOR (Iowa)

MCGUFFEY (Ohio)

MCHENRY (Ill.)

MCINTIRE (Iowa)

MCKEE (Ky.)

MCLAUGHLIN (S. Dak.)

MCLEAN (Va.)

MCRAE (Ga.)

MCROBERTS (Ky.)

```
L S Y E F F U G C M C K E E
L N A E B C M C C L U S K Y
A K H W R O D R O M H E I A
C H G U O N O D C M R L H H
C W R D G B N L B I D M F B
M C A F E E A I T N E C M S
D C D R R U E N A E L C M D
M Y T M G M I L B B G O C L
L S S H C C R C K I C R E A
L O L C M A M U L R B M W N
A I O C F N L L O I O I E O
N O R C M C C L O U D C N D
K A M C C L U R E D D K C C
E M C C O M B Y R N E H C M
```

Trying to ROUSE a couch potato friend out of a TV trance? Here's a list of ways you can get their attention. And just remember these words from Vince Lombardi (1913-70), one of the most successful coaches in the history of professional football: "If you aren't fired with enthusiasm, you will be fired with enthusiasm."

ACTIVATE
ANIMATE
ASTOUND
DISARM
ELECTRIFY

ENRAPTURE
ENTICE
ENTRANCE
EXCITE
FASCINATE

FIRE
GALVANIZE
IMPRESS
INFECT
INFUSE
INSPIRE
INTEREST
INTRIGUE
KINDLE
MOVE
PIQUE
QUICKEN
ROUSE
SHARPEN
STIMULATE
STIR
THRILL
TICKLE
WAKEN
WHET

```
D G I N F U S E I M O V E I
W M A S E H E N X M G M N N
H M R L A C F R B C K U T S
E W O R V E U Q I P I S I P
T T P O C A N S U F T T C I
A E A T N I N T R I G U E R
N L N V I Y F I R T C E L E
I K I D I M N M Z A E K S L
C C M N N T L U R E N U E D
S I A R E U C L I A O C L N
A T T R O C O A I R S W E I
F C E N R A P T U R E I S K
S S E R P M I E S N H Q D E
T X F G Y A N E K A W T H U
```

AWARDS

Besides the Oscar, there are other awards bestowed for excellent performances in other industries. Solve the puzzle below and learn about four other special honors.

"Apparel Annie" is a bronze statue for outstanding promotion in the apparel industry, and "The Winnie" is a bronze statue for best fashion design. "The Barney" is a cartoon-engraved silver box for the best cartoonist, and "The Edgar" is a bust of Edgar Allan Poe for the top mystery story.

```
Z F T H E A P P A R E L E T C
R A G D E F O R E V L I S T V
E S C B O X F O R S T U M S T
N H N A L L A M T H B P M E S
G I F U R R H O E A O E L B E
R O F E U T A T S E Z N O R B
A N D T H E O I F W I Z D O E
V B E R B P L O I F N D N F H
E L R O A D R N N A D U M F T
D E Y O R G N I N I U Y D A N
I R R G N I D N A T S T U O G
V A O D E Z I E S T T T X B I
L P T I Y E E F E M R W A H S
A P S Z I A U R H H Y O D N E
S A V S S Z Y A L S T D W Y D
```

Can you guess the answer to the classic conundrum below? Hint: Ponder this "weighty" problem as you solve the puzzle.

Two
twins
we are,
and let
it not
surprise,

Alike
in every
feature,
shape,
and
size;

We're
square
or round,
of brass
or iron
made,
Sometimes
of wood,
and
useful
found in
trade;
But to
conclude,
for
all our
daily
pains,
we by
the
neck are
often
hung in
chains.

```
E U H E M Z D A I L Y B E W
S S A R B F O B R M S S E W
I E Z A Y F Q S Q U A R E E
R F Z K E O R Y T L E D H D
P U N C R R R R L O F T E N
R L Q E V E A O S N G Z S D
U N T N V D U E Z T I H N N
S O O E E R M X W S H A P E
N R N W N I G N U H X A A R
I I T Z T O R R O U N D I U
A R I E O F W O O D Z R N T
H O M J M D Z A L I K E S A
C O N C L U D E B U T T O E
S N I W T Q T N I D N U O F
```

This puzzle will leave you feeling very productive. As you can see, each entry is a term related to producing something. DEVELOP a plan of action and surely you'll find every last one.

ACHIEVE

ASSEMBLE

BUILD

CARVE OUT

CAST

CHISEL

COIN

CONCOCT

CONFIGURE

CONSTRUCT

CONVERT

CREATE

DELIVER

DEVELOP

DEVISE

ERECT

EXECUTE

EXTRUDE

FABRICATE

FASHION

FORM

GENERATE

GROW

HATCH

INVENT

MAKE

MINE

MINT

MOLD

PROCESS

PRODUCE

RAISE

REFINE

SET UP

SHAPE

YIELD

```
E K F Y B E P R O D U C E Y
C H I S E L T S A C O N U I
O P V D P U T E S N I T D N
N N O I H S A F S F N L V T
F A B R I C A T E I I C M C
I T V R H T R R M U V I O E
G R E I E U U C B S N E L R
U E E T C X P O L E V E D E
R V E T A R E N E G X L D V
E N X S O E V C R V E U H I
P O N C I K R O U I R F A L
A C E G I A W C Y T B A T E
H S F O R M R T X S E E C D
S W C O I N V E N T I U H U
```

Atoms are the smallest particles of elements, which consist of electrons centered on a nucleus of protons and neutrons. Here you're looking for 26 elements that start with some letters from the second half of the alphabet.

NEON

NICKEL

NIOBIUM

NITROGEN

OSMIUM

OXYGEN

PALLADIUM

PHOSPHORUS

PLATINUM

PLUTONIUM

RADIUM

RADON

RHODIUM

SELENIUM

SILICON

SILVER

SODIUM

SULFUR

TERBIUM

THORIUM

THULIUM

TUNGSTEN

URANIUM

XENON

YTTRIUM

ZINC

```
S D Z X E N O N P H G S Y A
M D S Z R Y E L O P A U B R
N T E C D T U T L E A K E P
E O L A S T C A H M S V S E
K N E G O R T I N U L P O C
G R N N Z I N C R I L E D C
H U I M N U M O S B P I I R
T U U U C M H U C O A D U H
M Y M I Y P E Y I I L F M M
U L E R S D M Y L N L H U U
I Z G O X Y G E N U A I A I
M R H H I N K Y S M D R S B
S P E T A C H B D O I L U R
O N M U I D A R H D U M L E
E P F N O D A R Y I M D V T
```

IT'S ABOUT TIME

If you have a time LIMIT, don't let another minute LAPSE before you begin solving this puzzle. The list below contains 30 entries which, when combined with "time," form compound words or phrases. So keep an eye on the CLOCK to make sure your time hasn't EXPIRED.

AND AGAIN

AND A HALF

BILL

CAPSULE

CARD

CHART

CLOCK

CONSTANT

CONSUMING

DEPOSIT

DRAFT

EXPIRED

HONORED

IMMEMORIAL

KEEPER

LAPSE

LIMIT

LOCK

NOTE

OF DAY

PIECE

SAVER

SCALE

SHEET

SHIFT

SIGNATURE

TESTED

WARP

WORN

ZONE

```
S C S A E A S C A L E W R E
B I L L O B O Z H L O C K I
H T G N Z C C W P A I K M L
O F H N T O O A O U R M B T
N I A G A D N A T R E T I C
O H T D E T S E T M N S A T
R S E R T A U I O A O I F E
E L D E V E M R T P F F S T
D W E E C K I S E F D P Y O
X H R E E A N D A H A L F N
S I I E L O G P D L Y R L U
R P P K C O L C R S M C D G
B E X I N R Z A A A X K E H
R K E L U S P A C B W F D K
```

Casey STENGEL, "The Old Perfesser," is the only person to manage a baseball team to five consecutive World Series championships (1949-53). He did it while at the helm of the New York Yankees. The Boston Red Sox, on the other hand, hadn't won a World Series since 1918; that is until manager Terry FRANCONA led his team to their historic 2004 victory.

ALSTON (Walter)
ANDERSON (Sparky)
BERRA (Yogi)
CARRIGAN (Bill)
CHANCE (Frank)

COX (Bobby)
FRANCONA (Terry)
GASTON (Cito)
HARRIS (Bucky)
HERZOG (Whitey)

HOUK (Ralph)
HOWSER (Dick)
HUGGINS (Miller)
JOHNSON (Davey)
KELLY (Tom)
LA RUSSA (Tony)
LASORDA (Tommy)
MACK (Connie)
MARTIN (Billy)
MCGRAW (John)
MCKECHNIE (Bill)
MCKEON (Jack)
MURTAUGH (Danny)
PINIELLA (Lou)
SOUTH-WORTH (Billy)
STENGEL (Casey)
TORRE (Joe)
WILLIAMS (Dick)

```
M S S W S O U T H W O R T H
K M C G R A W U N X O Y N O
E C N A H C G L Z A J O E A
L K A X R G I A C K T R W D
L E P M I R U U U S R A G R
Y O L N M E I A A O F O N O
N N S G C A L G T R Z O O S
K H O U K L D L A R U S S A
S A T R E S X N E N U M N L
H R U I C T C H A G A M H K
O R N S H O W S E R N M O X
H I Z X N N X O T I R E J A
P S M A I L L I W Z C E T R
N O S R E D N A E R J G B S
```

Dwight D. Eisenhower's popularity as a World War II hero and his promise to end the Korean War helped him achieve the Presidency in 1952. Although the 34th President was reserved in style and rather soft-spoken, he was not without a sense of humor. Here's a sample of his wit.

In nineteen sixty, a reporter reminded Dwight Eisenhower that his next birthday would make him the oldest man to serve in the Oval Office. He replied, "I believe it's a tradition in baseball that when a pitcher has a no-hitter going for him, no one reminds him of it."

```
E V R E S T D W O U L D Y S
X S D N I M E R A L G O I T
Y Y W O X S O R A O T H I M
D A I O T R E B I N T F I D
E A G N Y P E N A A O H H A
I M H Y O S G M H M R M A W
L E T R A D I T I O N A S T
P V T B O D E H F N W K A C
E E N V U V H F O L D E S T
R I A N O H I T T E R E R N
T L P I T C H E R X H R D A
N E E T E N I N N I E T L S
M B W H E N A H X H B N N T
I I E H T M I H E B L D I I
```

"Y" IN THE USA

When they need a place to let off some steam, Arkansans travel to YEL-LVILLE. Well, that might not be true, but one thing that is true is that the 36 U.S. cities and towns contained in the list below all begin with the letter "Y."

YACHATS (Ore.)
YACOLT (Wash.)
YAKIMA (Wash.)
YAKUTAT (Alas.)
YALE (Iowa)
YAMHILL (Ore.)
YAMPA (Colo.)

YANCEY (Tex)
YANKTON (S. Dak.)
YAPHANK (N.Y.)
YARBO (Ala.)
YATES (N. Mex.)
YAUHANNAH (S.C.)
YAWKEY (W. Va.)

YAZOO CITY (Miss.)
YEADDISS (Ky.)
YEAGER (Okla.)
YEDDO (Ind.)
YELLVILLE (Ark.)
YELM (Wash.)
YEMASSEE (S.C.)
YERMO (Calif.)
YESO (N. Mex.)
YODER (Wyo.)
YORK (Pa.)
YOST (Utah)
YOUNG (Ariz.)
YPSILANTI (Mich.)
YREKA (Calif.)
YUBA (Calif.)
YUCAIPA (Calif.)
YUCCA (Ariz.)
YUKON (Fla.)
YULAN (N.Y.)
YULEE (Fla.)
YUMA (Colo.)

```
N U S S I D D A E Y T A R Y
G W R B A S A N E A O B A A
O Y Y Y A C O L T C T U T Z
D E P P K K L U Y H H Y S O
D M M S U V K R Y A R B O O
E A Y Y I A W A N T W A Y C
Y S A L Y L N N M S D K G I
E S L R R C A M D I I G E T
R E E R E H P N O T K N A Y
M E G Y K G I V T N V A E A
O L D N A Y A M H I L L Y T
S U B O U M C E A C M U O E
E Y P M Y O U L Y A W Y R S
Y Z A C C U Y A P H A N K P
```

In honor of *Cinco de Mayo*, this puzzle contains the names of *treinta* (that's 30 in *Español*) cities of Mexico.

ATLIXCO

CABORCA

CHAPALA

COLIMA

DURANGO

EMPALME

GUASAVE

GUAYMAS

IRAPUATO

LA PAZ

LERDO

LINARES

MÉRIDA

MONCLOVA

NAVOJOA

ORIZABA

PACHUCA

REYNOSA

SABINAS

SALTILLO

TAXCO

TEPIC

TIJUANA

TULA

TUXPAN

URUAPAN

VALLES

VERACRUZ

ZAPOPAN

ZITÁCUARO

```
P O A A C S N A P O P A Z T
T A X C O T E A Y E V I U C
V V A R Z Y L L P O T X X O
A E P O E A E M L A P M E L
X S R B P Y D C C A S E Y I
U R U A P A N U N R V R N M
X P H C C O A O R P V I A A
S C E U M R L N S A D D V T
A I G H O I U L A A N A O L
N P X C N Z Z I U M G J I
I E V A S A U G U T J G O X
B T R P P B O D R E L I A C
A E A A T A I R A P U A T O
S A L U T X G U A Y M A S N
```

VERBS REDUX

Can you CIRCLE all 33 6-letter verbs in the diagram below? We INVITE you to give this puzzle a try!

AFFECT	DIRECT	HURDLE
CIRCLE	EMBARK	IGNITE
CONCUR	ENDURE	IMPACT
DEBARK	FILLET	INVITE
DEBATE	GAMBLE	JANGLE
DECIDE	GOBBLE	JIGGLE
		JOSTLE
		LAUNCH
		MUMBLE
		MUTTER
		NESTLE
		NUZZLE
		OBJECT
		OFFEND
		ORDAIN
		REMAIN
		REMIND
		SPRINT
		STARCH
		STRIVE
		STROLL

```
S P R I N T K R A B M E J B
E I M P A C T R N I A D R O
L L U T C E F F A S L E J B
D J B U C R L I H B L C K S
R E U M M I U G C D E I L T
U K B I U D I N N V G D C A
H E P A T M R I U A G E I R
I N V I T E M T A Z J N R C
J U Z I E E E L B Z E C H
I B S T R O L L O P M L L P
G E J U K T T L B A O B E V
G R D Z S P S F I B E M G L
L N K O F F E N D F O A Z V
E U J R U C N O C G K G H T
```

In 1892, plants with violet-like flowers were discovered growing in Tanganyika (now Tanzania) in AFRICA by Baron Walter von St. Paul Illaire. A perennial PLANT with OVAL LEAVES, FUZZY petals, and PINK, PURPLE, or WHITE in color, they were soon renamed African violets for their resemblance to violets and their country of origin.

AFRICA

BLOOM

CLUSTER

CUTTING

DAINTY

FLOWER

FUCHSIA

FUZZY (leaves)

GREENERY

GROW

LEAVES

LOBES

LOVELY

MOISTURE

NURTURE

OVAL (leaves)

PINK

PLANT

PURPLE

REDDISH

ROOTS

SEEDS

SHAPES

SHOWY

SMALL

SOIL

STALK

STEMLESS

SUNSHINE

WHITE

WINDOW BOX

```
F Z K U X P L A N T G C M F
E L L Y Y O U Z Y R D I E U
O V A L B L B R E T S U L C
A U T E Y L E W P R F C M H
C L S Z I N O V O L V U Y S
I Y Z O E L V O O D E T S I
R U S E F F T B M L N T H A
F E R U T S I O M I E I O U
A G D F A S L L A M S N W A
P C S D E E S D L U E G Y V
E W M P I N K E R U T R U N
L E A V E S S P O G I O Z W
O H S U N S H I N E H W R O
S Z V K H P L Y G R W R G I
```

Born Philip Dormer Stanhope, Lord Chesterfield (1694-1773) was noted in his time for his polished writing style, his diplomatic skills, and his sense of honor, but he is remembered now chiefly for his *Letters to His Son*. It was in them that Chesterfield transmitted a father's advice to his son, Philip, on civility, manners, and the social graces in hundreds of letters written between 1737-1768. Below is a quote from one of his letters.

Learning is but the necessary acquired by much learning, the reading books; more knowledge of the world, is only to be acquired by reading men, and studying all the various editions of them.

```
K M K N N L M Q E H T T U B
T Q M E T L W F G R E V Y O
H F I C N Q O R N G B R T T
E O R E A C Q U I R E D B Y
W E D S B A Q B Y A T D G L
O G H S I L O E D A M E F N
R D W A W G D I U R F R U O
L E A R N I N G T H E I O S
D L G Y T G A I S T E U Y I
K W M I B C N Q N H H Q I Q
T O O O R F E B T R K C H T
Q N O U R D M L H G A A U F
S K M M Y E L O F T H E M M
S U O I R A V L N U M B L N
```

TWO IN ONE

Although the words below may seem unrelated, they all have one thing in common — each is comprised of two smaller words. See how quickly you can find them all.

ASPHALT

CANDID

CARROT

CARTON

CASHMERE

CATNIP

DENOUNCE

ENDEAR

ERRAND

GIGANTIC

GRIMACE

IMPACT

IMPLORE

KINDRED

MANDATE

MARKUP

MENACE

NOTICE

PADLOCK

PANTRY

PATRIOT

PLUMMET

PRIMATE

RAMPART

RAPPORT

REDDEN

ROTTEN

SADDEN

```
T H A P P L T R A P M A R D
Y O S R R O L L H G D K S L
R H R G I G A N T I C A R M
T C M R M K H G E O D M H A
N O T R A C P I L D H M P R
A A E U T C S D E R D N I K
P G N R E M A N D A T E S U
R H D Y E P D E G D K T R P
O C E N N M N D R R G R U T
T G A M A O H T I O K O T C
T C R T U R T S M D L P G A
E U O N N S R I A E N P I P
N E C M L I C E C C A A M M
T E M M U L P U E E H R C I
```

GOBBLING PILGRIMS

In 1621, the Pilgrims enjoyed their very first Thanksgiving meal, and since that time, Americans have continued the tradition of a big Thanksgiving Day dinner. This puzzle tells why we celebrate the holiday on the day that we do.

The first
Thanksgiving
was celebrated
by the
Pilgrims
after
they
harvested
their
first crops.
Thereafter,
a day
was set
aside to
prepare
a feast
and give
thanks. In
nineteen
forty-one,
Congress
passed
a law
declaring
the fourth
Thursday in
November
as our
national
holiday.

```
V A R T S R I F E H T A D T P
S O R H H S U P T H R I E H T
W S D E T A R B E L E C S A W
R A S R B E N F O N L D S N L
U E L E P M O K I M A E A K S
O W T A R U E Y S B N T P S O
S W R F R G A V P G O S H I L
A E N T A D N I O V I E O N B
S F H E S I L O R N T V L K G
I T E R E G D E C L A R I N G
D Y U A R T H B T I N A D N H
E H A I S T E S S A W H A B G
T S M D Y T A N R T H E Y F S
O S O B A N D G I V E L Y W H
H E N O Y T R O F N R N T Y N
```

STREETS OF HOLLYWOOD

"Hooray for HOLLYWOOD" goes the song, and anyone who's ever enjoyed a movie or TV show will agree. Listed here are some of the streets in this capital of America's entertainment industry.

ALTA VISTA

BARTON

CAHUENGA

CARLOS

CITRUS

COLE

EL CENTRO

FORMOSA

GORDON

GOWER

GREGORY

HAROLD

HOLLYWOOD

IVAR

JUNE

LA BREA

LAS PALMAS

LELAND

LODI

MELROSE

MONROE

ORANGE

OXFORD

SANTA MONICA

SELMA

SEWARD

SUNSET

TAMARIND

VAN NESS

VINE

WESTERN

WILCOX

WILTON

YUCCA

```
F D F D N A L E L O C G P B
O R T N E C L E S O R L E M
R F D O W I L C O X J U N E
M C L T D N I R A M A T O I
O V O L H O L L Y W O O D A
S S R I C M T G R E G O R Y
A E A W C A R L O S L A O D
Y L H M V T H L S T R E G O
U M S I L N E U S E E R M X
C A S U O A N G E R W B O F
C T C T R S P N N O A N O
A E R M E T I S N A G L R R
W A C T J V I V A R R A O D
B C R B S X S C V L B O E F
```

ROYAL DISCIPLINE

It is surely forbidden to spank a king, but what if the king is a child? Here's how the English dealt with that problem in the 15th century.

Henry VI became king of England at the age of nine months. His first royal decree, signed with a thumb print, named Dame Alice Butler the royal nurse and gave her official permission "to chastise him reasonably from time to time."

```
K N O I S S I M R E P H R H
S H T V N N D T S D G G O B
F I N Y A H T I W T K D Y L
D M P R I N T R E H E V A G
H R K N E S E S S C H I L E
B E T E A L R H R E C N A I
M A V H G W T E E I W U T A
U S C S E N E U F I F R O S
H O E T O R C F B L S S T I
T N M M F R O M T I M E I E
T A A T A G E Y G G N A M H
G B D M N C D N A L G N E T
M L U I E V E C I L A D A T
V Y K Y V D W B T N K P A A
```

Looking for a name for a soon-to-be-born baby girl? Here are some "B"-eautiful names from which you can choose. All the names "B"-gin with the letter "B." There are 33 for you to find in the diagram "B"-low.

BABETTE

BAILEY

BARBARA

BEATRICE

BECKY

BELINDA

BELLE

BENITA

BERNADETTE

BERNICE

BERTHA

BESS

BETH

BETSY

BETTE

BETTY

BEVERLY

BIANCA

BILLIE

BLAIR

BLANCHE

BLOSSOM

BOBBI

BONITA

BONNIE

BRANDY

BRENDA

BRIANA

BRIDGET

BRIGITTE

BRITTANY

BROOKE

BUNNY

```
D N B Y E C I R T A E B B B
B B E N I T A E B T A I L G
K R L C S M T C T R D A A O
B R I G I T T E B O N N I E
L Y N T E N D A B C E C R K
O K D B T A R V H A R A S O
S C A O N A A E K N B A B O
S E T R Y D N H B A T C D R
O B E V E R L Y T I B B O B
M B G M L L D H N R L L R H
E E D D I N T O O B E L L E
S T I U A E B Y N N U B I E
T S R R B E T T Y T M E R E
O Y B E S S H S N I N G E O
```

Founded in 1968 by Coretta Scott King, The King Center is the official memorial that is dedicated to Dr. Martin Luther King Jr.'s legacy. Located in Atlanta, more than 650,000 visitors from around the world have come to the center to see exhibits that depict his life and teachings, as well as to visit the King Center's library.

On the third Monday in January, Americans across the country will celebrate the national holiday honoring the life and work of Dr. Martin Luther King, Jr. On this day, we remember the man who fought for freedom, justice, and equality for all.

```
L C M E A R E B M E M E R N
C E A E Q M H F L O Y J D Y
E W R H K U Y O D L G D F R
L Y T T D F A E N N I R O A
E A I S R S E L I O I W J U
B D N S E R H K I J R U N N
R W H O F O U G H T S I O A
A M E R I C A N S T Y C N J
T T O C L T H N I A F O T G
E F R A E J A C D O D U H K
N A M E H T E N R W N N I C
D R I H T A O A E H O T S G
B A W R N M L U T H E R H C
B Y A D I L O H H R T Y K E
```

PAPER PRODUCTS

Almost everywhere you turn there is some kind of paper product. In fact, we're willing to bet that at this very moment there is something constructed from paper right before your very eyes!

BLOTTER

BOOK

BROCHURE

CARD

CARTON

CHECK

CONFETTI

COUPON

CURRENCY

DIPLOMA

ENVELOPE

FOLDER

FOLIO

JOURNAL

KITE

LABEL

LETTER

LICENSE

MAGAZINE

NAPKIN

NEWSPAPER

PAMPHLET

PASSPORT

PATTERN (dress)

RECEIPT

STAMP (postage)

STREAMER

TABLET

TISSUES

WRAPPER

```
O W M D S N F H G L E B A L
C R R A E T S J Y A G M T I
Y A U V G P A S S P O R T S
C P R R P A A M S L K T O I
R P E T C E Z T P I E C E R
C E T R O C N I T F H N M F
U R T I U N D E N E V J O O
R E O E S H A O C E R L C L
R M L R L S C K L J D N C I
E A B D R H U O O E J V O O
N E W S P A P E R O B M U T
C R E T T E L M S B B T P A
Y T A B L E T L A N R U O J
E S N E C I L N A P K I N Z
```

MARKING YOUR PLACE

It's rather safe to say that a bookmark is one of the more self-explanatory devices out there. Whether it's store-bought or HANDMADE, FANCY or plain, anything slipped between the pages of certain reading materials, such as a BOOK of puzzles, with the purpose of marking the PAGE where the reader or solver left off can be deemed a bookmark.

AGATE

BOOK

BRASS

BRONZE

CARDBOARD

CHROME

COLORFUL

COPPER

FANCY

HANDLE

HANDMADE

LACE

LITHOGRAPH

MONOGRAM

NEEDLEWORK

PAGE

PAPER

PHOTO

PLASTIC

RIBBON

SATIN

SHAPE

SILK

SILVER

THIN

WOOD

WOVEN

```
N E E D L E W O R K Z Z H A
D T K D S F C W E T A G A R
R P V S A C U A V D F M N A
A W A N R M S O L F N Y D O
O R C G G R D C I T S A L P
B Y G R E C M N S O A I E R
D A D P L Z O G A E T S L O
R E P M M B N L I H I O Y K
A O M S B L O O O D N K H E
C T H I N C G G R R E P A P
D D R E M O R H C B F K H L
O W V K C A A D W G O U B Z
O O I Y P U M F D C Z O L I
W A S H A P E Y G V V P K M
```

The classic TV series "Star Trek" originally aired on NBC from 1966 to 1969. Although only 79 episodes were produced, the show gained a legion of devout followers (commonly known as "Trekkies") and spawned three successful spinoffs: "Star Trek: The Next Generation," "Star Trek: Deep Space Nine," and "Star Trek: Voyager." All of the shows feature a host of colorful characters, 31 of which can be found in the diagram below.

BARCLAY (Reginald)
BASHIR (Dr. Julian)
CHAPEL (Christine)
CHEKOV (Pavel)
CRUSHER (Dr. Beverly)
DATA
DUKAT (Gul)
JANEWAY (Kathryn)
KIRK (James T.)
LAFORGE (Geordi)
LAREN (Ro)
MCCOY (Dr. Leonard "Bones")
NEELIX
NERYS (Kira)
O'BRIEN (Miles)
PARIS (Tom)
PICARD (Jean-Luc)
PULASKI (Dr. Kate)
QUARK
RAND (Janice)
RIKER (William)
SCOTT (Montgomery "Scotty")
SISKO (Benjamin)
SPOCK (Mr.)
SULU (Mr.)
TORRES (B'Elanna)
TROI (Deanna)
TUVOK
UHURA
WORF
ZIMMERMAN (Dr.)

```
W E O E X J P U L A S K I Z
H X G Q L Z I V L R K H D X
J S I U U I C G B U N S J Z
Q U L L S M A J A H S I I X
B F S I E M R A S U K S J S
L D R S Q E D D H R E K I R
E A J O H R N E I R B O N E
P D Q S W M Y K R A U Q S H
A C U Y L A F O R G E I K B
H R H R W N T C C R A C H F
C P N E R A L U S C O T T R
G M N N K A O T V P M R A W
P A B U Y O N D S O O G R D
J J D D G I V D Q I K T C L
```

DID YOU KNOW?

If it wasn't for one of his pupils, we would not be aware of the teachings of Socrates (470-399 B.C.) Read on to learn why.

Socrates, philosophers, word of

one of never his teachings.

the most wrote The only

famous down a knowledge

Greek single we have

```
V L E K L Y U A N S D K G F
L S Y P T L F N O E T O R W
A P G B P N N W T N U E E I
A S W N H O E O E S V O A P
P A T K I E A D S E L F T K
B L U Y L H U F N M W A P G
Y T A G O T C L N O R P I N
H E N T S E T A R C O S B I
I I V P O E G D E L W O N K
S M F A P D O N C T A K E N
Y T P O H F A M O U S F N I
F F G R E E K Y I H R I C H
B B I N R N W T S O M E H T
O F H I S Y O Y M U M B K C
```

of his

thinking

today

comes

from

notes

taken

by his

great

student

Plato.

ACT YOUR "AGE"

Here we give COVERAGE to some words ending in "AGE." We're sure you'll MANAGE to find them all in the diagram.

ADAGE

ADVANTAGE

BAGGAGE

BEVERAGE

BREAKAGE

CARRIAGE

COURAGE

COVERAGE

DISPARAGE

FORAGE

FUSELAGE

GARAGE

GARBAGE

HOMAGE

LEVERAGE

LINEAGE

MANAGE

MARRIAGE

MESSAGE

MORTGAGE

ORPHANAGE

PASSAGE

RAMPAGE

SAUSAGE

STAGE

STORAGE

USAGE

VINTAGE

VISAGE

```
C N U E U R H O M A G E E V
N E S T G P C O V E R A G E
E G A P M A R T G U L B A G
G A G E R T T A V G I K N A
A R E G G I R N B G N P A L
R E G A R A P S I D E C M E
O V G N G O I B R V A E V S
T E G A K A E R B R G C K U
S L A H T V V A R A E O N F
A K R P E N G I S A M U O O
P D B R E G A S S E M R L R
F N A O A G A V V A S A K A
P G G G E P D T D O G G U G
E N E L E S A U S A G E T E
```

SIGN ON for adventure as you hunt for these terms which are all synonyms for the word "enlist."

ADMIT

APPOINT

ASSIGN

ATTRACT

CALL UP

CONSCRIBE

DRAFT

EMPLOY

ENGAGE

ENROLL

ENTER

GATHER

HIRE

INCORPORATE

INDUCT

INITIATE

JOIN

LEVY

LIST

MOBILIZE

MUSTER

OBLIGE

OBTAIN

PLACE

PROCURE

RECORD

RECRUIT

REGISTER

RESERVE

SECURE

SERVE

SIGN ON

TAKE ON

VOLUNTEER

```
D R L M U S T E R L D F M C
G R L P K C E T F A R D J A
P R O C U R E R O F O E O D
L K R D U L E B V B C N I M
H L N C E H L E T E E G N I
E I E V T I Z A T T R A C T
O S Y A G I I E C N T G O M
Y T G E L N N Z T O U E R N
O N Y I V T G I O N H L P J
L I B N E R U I T G S I O Z
P O D R J R E T S I G E R V
M P L A C E R S I S A H A E
E P R E C S N O E K A T T T
T A R M C O N S C R I B E J
```

THE WORLD OF FAIRY TALES

According to a 2004 poll of 1,200 children in Great Britain, the most popular fairy tales are (in order) "Cinderella," "Sleeping Beauty," "Hansel and Gretel," "Rapunzel," and "Little Red Riding Hood."

ACCOUNT

ADVENTURE

BATTLE

BOOK

CASTLE

CHARACTERS

CREATURES

DUNGEON

EMPEROR

ESCAPE

FABLE

FANTASY

FOREST

HAPPY
   ENDING

HERO

JOURNEY

KING

LEGEND

LITERATURE

MAGIC

MAIDEN

MONSTER

MYTH

OGRE

PALACE

PRINCESS

QUEEN

QUEST

RESCUE

REWARD

STORY

TREASURE

VILLAIN

```
N H A C C O U N T L N I S E
R F J H T Y M A I D E N C E
E O H A A E L T S A C A P R
W P M R F P E C B V L A O Q
A M S A J R P M T A C L U N
R D B C A O M Y P S T E I F
D L V T S E U Q E E E T H V
E Y U E L R Q R K N R R L O
L R U R N E U D N O D O O E
E O Y S A T N A F E O I R F
G T R E A S U R E G Y B N O
E S S E C N I R P N K I N G
N R R A H O M K E U C S E R
D C I G A M P A H D V H Y E
```

180

WHAT A DRAG

Get your **HELMET** and your **GOGGLES**, polish up your **FUNNY CAR** or your **DRAGSTER**, and head on down to the **DRAG STRIP**, because it's time to do some drag racing! It'll take great **SPEED** to win the **RACE** — just be sure you wear your **SEAT BELT** and avoid the oil **SLICK**!

BENCH (racing)

BURNOUT (pit)

CHUTE

CLUTCH

DIGGER

DRAGSTER

DRAG STRIP

DRIVER

FUEL

FUNNY CAR

GASSER

GOGGLES

HELMET

HOT CAR

HOT ROD

KILL BUTTON

PIT

PORTING

POWER

RACE

ROLL BAR

ROLLER (start)

SEAT BELT

SLICK

SPEED

STAGING (area)

THROTTLE

TIRE

TORQUE

TOWER

TURNOFF (road)

WEIGH-IN

WHEELIE

```
R B H C N E B B W K F C I P
Q F F O N R U T H K U U M R
F G N I T R O P E I N D E E
O Q H O N R H L E L N R D L
N O W O Q C O A L L Y E L L
H E U U T H R D I B C V P O
R T E U Y U I A E U A I L R
E K L W R T N C C T R R R S
W C T E H E L M E T K D E P
O I T I B R G C S O O L S E
P L O G S T A G I N G H S E
V S R H I R A G I G F I A D
N B H I U R M E O D V N G Y
N H T N D R A G S T E R I T
```

Let's go to London! Ride the Underground and get off at Tower Hill station to visit the Tower of London. Then it's on to Marble Arch station for lunch in Hyde Park. Want to see some tennis? Get off at Southfields to visit **WIMBLEDON**. Ride on the London "tubes" and you'll pass through these stations.

ANGEL

BARKING

BOW ROAD

BRENT (Cross)

CLAPHAM

EALING

EDGWARE

EUSTON

FAIRLOP

HIGHGATE

KEW GARDENS

KINGSBURY

LEYTON

LIVERPOOL (Street)

MILE END

MORDEN

OLD STREET

PIMLICO

QUEENSBURY

ST. PAUL'S

UPNEY

VICTORIA

WATERLOO

WATFORD

WEMBLEY

WEST HAM

WIMBLEDON

```
U P N E Y D A O R W O B M Y
M E D G W A R E C C T S K D
T B A R K I N G I G E L E R
C L A P H A M L T T E U W O
H K O D A F M B P A R A G F
F I M O C I A A L L T P A T
N N G S P N T I E E S T R A
M G A H O R N N R T D S D W
O S L T G G E L E L L O E E
R B S K M A O V T R O M N S
D U A I R O T C I V B P S T
E R O B A D N E E L I M Q H
N Y R U B S N E E U Q K E A
Q A N G E L E Y T O N R K M
```

GODS & GODDESSES

Egypt, Sumer, Babylon, Canaan, Asia Minor, Persia, and Arabia were once part of ancient West Asia. The mythology of this area encompassed the collection of gods and goddesses below.

ALITAT	ATTIS	HADAD
AMUN	BAAL	HAOMA
ANUBIS	BASTET	HAPI
ASHUR	ENKI	HORUS
ASTARTE	ENLIL	IMHOTEP
		INANNA
		ISIS
		KHEPRA
		MAAT
		MARDUK
		MITHRA
		NINURTA
		OSIRIS
		PTAH
		SEKER
		SERAPIS
		TELIPINU
		THOTH
		VAHAGN

```
O N N A S H U R E K E S E A
M P R E L L K L I L N E S H
V H E A M I T U A K G T A O
S L G L N P T R D R A K R L
R V U A P D R A S R H T K T
O N N A T U D V T R A G A E
S N H B P A R E I R V M D L
A P T A H E T L M M U A D I
R N S H P S T A I N A N H P
P A U I A I V O T P G A I I
E S E B K R T P H T O H T N
H O E N I I M R R M I N K U
K N E H B S E R A P I S I S
M G S U R O H T K H R O E O
```

CALILFORNIA CITIES

California, here we come! We're off to the "Left Coast" to visit the most populous state in the U.S., which is home to some of the nation's largest cities, including **LOS ANGELES**, **SAN DIEGO**, **SAN JOSE**, and **SAN FRANCISCO**.

ARCADIA

BANNING

BARSTOW

BRAWLEY

BURBANK

CONCORD

FREMONT

FRESNO

GARDENA

HAYWARD

LODI

LONG BEACH

LOS ANGELES

MERCED

MODESTO

NAPA

NORWALK

OAKLAND

ONTARIO

RIVERSIDE

SACRAMENTO

SALINAS

SAN DIEGO

SAN FRANCISCO

SAN JOSE

VALLEJO

VISALIA

```
A I D A C R A A P G S V Y V
Y N D R A W Y A H F L D A U
E S V O B E V D R O C N O C
D U I H L F R E S N O Y C T
Y L S W B A M A K T B L S R
K L A W R O N O N T A R I O
I R L O N G B E A C H V C B
B B I T E S M E D I E H N S
D N A L K A O A S R E V A A
E J E N R N B T S O A R R N
C S L C N D A I S L J G F I
R N A E A I D B L E S N N L
E S O C P E N E R E D O A A
M Y D S A G J G N U H O S S
B A R S T O W V T J B G M W
```

SENDING SIGNALS

The MESSAGE this puzzle is sending is to SMOKE out these SECRET terms from the diagram. Afterwards, you can toot your own HORN!

BANNER

BILLBOARD

FLAG

BASEBALL

CANDLE

FLARE

BEACON

CODE

HORN

BEAM

DRUM

LAMP

BELL

FIREWORKS

LIGHTS

LOUDSPEAKER

MESSAGE

PENNANT

PILOT

RAILROAD

SEARCHLIGHT

SECRET

SIREN

SMOKE

TELEGRAPH

TOM-TOM

TOWER

WHISTLE

```
T M B A S E B A L L T R H H
A H L K E A W P T O L I P U
T M G A L F M H N U I E P T
C D B I N A L R I D E B S
F R A I L R O A D S H K O F
F U T W L H N S R P T T D G
M M F N D L C K A E S L U N
F N O C A E B R G A N I E U
D O N T D N G O A K S N G C
P A F O M E N W A E I I A B
H U C W L O N E C R S N S B
S I R E N G T R P C D G S U
U W T R A L E I H L M A E B
G B L N D T K F E E K O M S
```

STREETS OF PRINCETON

Not too far from Philadelphia is Princeton, New Jersey, a borough with its own rich history. Princeton UNIVERSITY, located there, has evolved together with the area over the years. Street names like CAMPUS and VARSITY reflect this. HARVARD and YALE, longtime rivals, are graciously named in the list below.

ACADEMY

CAMPUS

COMMONS

ENGLISH

FACULTY

FITCH

FORRESTAL

HARVARD

HAWTHORNE

JUNIPER

KEAN

KING

LAFAYETTE

LIBRARY

LILAC

MAGNOLIA

MIMOSA

NASSAU

OBER

POOR FARM

PURITAN

QUAKER

RESEARCH

SEMINARY

TARKINGTON

TOWPATH

UNIVERSITY

VARSITY

YALE

```
M R A F R O O P O E G Q E U
A S O M I M C C O M M O N S
G H R Q H F N Y N G G I G P
N A H E G H O Y M Y V N L R
O R C D P W T R R E B O I U
L V T H G I G A R A D B S K
I A I C S Q N S P E R A H D
A R F R U I I U U W S B C N
L D A A M T K G J P O T I A
V V K E Y C R L O R M T A L
W E S S K E A N A S S A U L
R F F E P Y T L U C A F C J
E A B R C N A T I R U P Y V
H A W T H O R N E L A Y C B
```

CHINESE CHECKERS

Despite its name, Chinese Checkers is not from China. This game was invented in Germany under the name Stern-Halma in 1892. In 1928, American company J. Pressman & Co. created "Hop Ching Checkers." Brothers Bill and Jack Pressman made up the name "Chinese Checkers" around that same time to keep with the current interest in all things Oriental (the discovery of King Tut's tomb in 1922 and the introduction of the game mah-jongg in 1923). The passage below explains how to play this popular and fun game.

Chinese checkers is a board game that can be played by two to six people. The object is to move colored marbles to the corner opposite their own starting position. This is done by jumping over other pieces.

```
R C D E H M O E M U X B R N
G S C O L O R E D K K I S O
U N S M N V S L O I E R O I
B S I S R E K C E H C W L T
R V S P N T B J T L N V N I
U E I I M T H Y J S P T H S
J H H D V U G E T E X O O O
C C T T K J J A O L U S E P
M X G C O D R A O B A I N P
R E V O W T Y B W R J X I O
R M B R I D S P L A Y E D S
A E Y N U L P I B M C U C I
U Y G E A T G A M E T A H T
V X L R O C U L S X W Y C E
```

STORY TIME

Where are the following 29 entries hidden? RUMOR has it that they're camouflaged in the grid below. PLOT out your strategy for solving this MYSTERY about words associated with works of FICTION.

ACCOUNT

ALLEGORY

ANECDOTE

DESCRIPTION

EPIC

EPISODE

FABLE

FANTASY

FICTION

HOAX

INTRIGUE

LEGEND

MYSTERY

MYTH

NARRATION

NEWS

NOVEL

PARABLE

PLOT

RECORD

REPORT

ROMANCE

RUMOR

SAGA

SCENARIO

SEQUEL

TALE

WHODUNIT

YARN

```
P Y R L H T P D H T Y M C U
D H Y O D A F Y A R N T C E
E N A R R A T I O N H I C O
C X E A E R D G C Q E N L H
W Y B G O T E L A T A U E B
S L M P E L S T Q M I D V X
E C E C L L C Y O N D O O Y
Q R E A Y I R R M D E H N F
U T H N P S I H R R C W V A
E D G E A E P I S O D E S N
L E U G I R T N I C M B N T
B E A P U V I Q M E C U O A
A U H R G S O O O R C L R S
F A C C O U N T C G P L I Y
```

The arrival of SANTA and his REINDEER marks the beginning of the holiday season in the annual Thanksgiving Day parade held in New York City. Join the fun as you search the diagram for a variety of terms related to this festive EVENT.

ANNOUNCERS

APPLAUSE

BALLOONS

BANDS

BANNERS

BELLS

CADENCE

CANDY

CHARACTERS

CHEERY

CHILDREN

CHILLY

CLOWNS

COLD

COSTUMES

DELAY

DESIGNS

DREAMS

ELVES

EVENT

FLOATS

LIGHTS

MAGIC

MARCHERS

MUSIC

RAIN

REINDEER

RIDE

SANTA

SLEIGH

SMILES

SNOWMAN

WAVING

```
G D A P P L A U S E V L E W
R E I N D E E R M C O L D C
S S B D N W A V I N G C H I
N I A R S O B U L E S A C S
F G N E M N U M E D R N S U
B N N A M W O N S A E D D M
P S E M U T S O C C H Y N T
M G R S S T R T L E C E A A
E Y S L H Y E S V L R E B T
P D L G A R L T N D A S G N
I E I L S E N W L W M B A A
B L E R I E U I F L O A T S
W D W G V H H D V E U L S E
P O H E F C C I G A M Y C A
```

FEELING BLUE?

Sure, we all get the blues now and then, but can you guess what we recommend to chase them away? That's right . . . solving puzzles!

BITTER

BLUE

DEJECTED

DEPRESSED

DESPAIRING

DESPONDENT

DISMAL

DISTRESSED

DOLEFUL

DOWN

FORLORN

GLOOMY

GLUM

GRIEVED

HEARTSICK

HURTING

MELANCHOLY

MOROSE

MOURNFUL

PENSIVE

SOMBER

SORROWFUL

SORRY

TROUBLED

UNHAPPY

WISTFUL

WOEBEGONE

```
O H U R T I N G D D V D W Y
N T N E D N O P S E D G F M
R C H S D E P R E S S E D O
O N A O Y R S D L P O I F O
L E P R W L E S D A B R C L
R V P O O J O T E I M K R G
O I Y M E M L H T R C S E Y
F S U C B U U G C I T J I T
K N T E E V F L S N B S R D
T E R C G C N T U G A O I N
D P J S O R R O W F U L I D
G D O W N A U F C B T B E E
G L U F E L O D L L W S E M
G S U H E O M E V U M K I S
D T N M W U D E V E I R G W
```

If you're having a hard time locating all 30 of the words in this list that begin with the letter "U" and you're UNCERTAIN you'll find them all, don't give in and cry "UNCLE!" Stick with it UNTIL each one has been circled!

UKULELE	UNBUTTON	UNDERLINE
UMBRELLA	UNCANNY	UNDERSTUDY
UMPIRE	UNCERTAIN	UNDRESS
UNAWARE	UNCLE	UNEARTH
UNBROKEN	UNDERFOOT	UNEASY
		UNICORN
		UNION
		UNISON
		UNITE
		UNKEMPT
		UNLOCK
		UNPACK
		UNTIL
		UNTOLD
		UNUSUAL
		UNWIND
		URBAN
		USHER
		UTENSIL
		UTTER

```
K U D S B U N E A S Y P T K
P S N L R M N T D U D L O U
F S I D K T P P U N O I N U
Y E W C E M O N A I A I C M
C R N O E R B O U C S A L P
R D U K H R S T F O K I K I
H N N L O N E T N R T E C R
Y U D K A N A U U N E U O E
N R E H S U M B U D P D L T
N N R I O S S N R D Y E N T
A L L E R B M U A U L D U U
C N I A T R E C N U N I T E
N U N A W A R E K U N C L E
U N E A R T H U N T O L D E
```

"ORE" WORDS

There's no gold or silver here, but if you EXPLORE the word list, you're guaranteed to hit paydirt. There's "ORE" GALORE — every word contains it! So, now that you know what's in store, don't waste any more time . . . just dig in!

ADORE

AFORESAID

AMORETTO
(infant cupid)

ARBOREAL

ARBORETUM

ASHORE

BEFORE

CHORE

DEPLORE

EXPLORE

FLORET

GALORE

HOREHOUND
(herb of the mint family)

IMPLORE

MOREEN
(fabric)

MOREL
(mushroom)

MORELLO
(cherry)

OREAD
(mountain nymph)

OREGANO

OREGON

RESTORE

SCORE

SHORE

SNORE

SOREHEAD

SPORE

TOREADOR

YORE

```
M F U F G S L R N U Y A P D
S O L F N P P E M O R E E N
C E R O L P M I R N R H S U
O D R E R R H E D O L T D O
R E L O L E E U H P M F R H
E L C P D L T S Y U F E O E
B X S S X A O N T O G R B R
D E P L O R E E T O Y B O O
A R O L E B R T N E R D B H
Y O R H O O E A U E A E X S
X L E I B R G O I E F D G A
D A E R O E E E R O H C X Y
D G A M R A F O R E S A I D
G P A O H L T E U E A P R S
```

It takes time to grow the garden of your dreams, and a variety of **TOOLS** and materials are needed. But before you start digging in the **DIRT** and begin planting **SEEDS**, why not see what's blooming in the garden below.

ARBOR

BEES

BENCH

BIRDS

BUGS

CLIPPERS

COMPOST

CROPS

DIRT

FENCE

FERTILIZER

FLOWERS

HOE

HOSE

LEAVES

MULCH

PLANTS

RAKE

ROCKS

SEEDS

SHEARS

SOIL

SPADE

STAKES

TOOLS

TRELLIS

TROWEL

WAGON

WATER

WEEDS

WORMS

```
B F S D S F P O A C Z A A M
H S E K A T S T H B A Z O D
G T F R H C N E B E H G O S
K N E E T W A V D O O D H
G P A L N I F F L A S E E B
S V A B I C L I P P E R S A
R R U T P O E I P S R L A E
F G A R W M S Z Z L G B K R
S D E E W P H K S E E A F I
A D R L H O C B C W R D Z N
I S R L T S L T O O L S O V
H I D I R T U R B R R G E U
P A E S B A M R E T A W N G
E C R O P S A T T W W Z U U
```

Born in Cummington, Massachusetts, William Cullen Bryant (1794-1878) was the first great American poet and one of the most influential newspaper editors of his time. Below is the text from one of his poems, entitled "Oh Fairest of the Rural Maids."

Oh fairest of the rural maids! Thy birth was in the forest shades; Green boughs, and glimpses of the sky, Were all that met thine infant eye. Thy sports, thy wanderings, when a child, Were ever in the sylvan wild; And all the beauty of the place Is in thy heart and on thy face.

```
S E D A H S R T S V N V L Y
U T H Y F A C E H A U L H D
E N I T V O I D V I A T T N
H S O C L N S L L E N H R A
T P W D F L Y E R I E E I D
F O U A N S A E S A H R B L
O R N L N A W I R P W C E I
Y T M A I D S T H Y M R C W
T S E R O F E H T N I I A A
U T Y U V M W R G K Y S L K
A H E R T C D E I U I N P G
E Y T A D G R E E N O U E N
B T H E S K Y T V A G B H H
C T Y F O H F A I R E S T R
```

STREETS OF PHOENIX

Phoenix is the capital and the largest city in the STATE of Arizona; it is also one of the fastest growing cities in the United States. By the time you get to Phoenix, see if you can locate the 38 streets found in this southwestern city.

ADAMS
AMELIA
ASHLAND
BERYL
BRILL
CAROL

CENTRAL
CULVER
DUNLAP
ENCAN-TO
GRAND

GRANT
HADLEY
JACKSON
JONES
LAMAR
LANE
LEWIS
MADISON
MONROE
OREGON
PIERCE
PIMA
POLK
PORTLAND
PUGET
ROMA
ROOSEVELT
SAN JUAN
SHEA
STATE
THOMAS
VAN BUREN
VERNON
VILLA
VISTA
YUCCA
YUMA

```
D K G T L E V E S O O R P A
N L R R O M A A A T P I M A
T O A R E B S E N O J E N P
H P N O S K C A J B L L N L
O O T R E R C L U I U Y O V
M N K C E N T R A L U R G V
A O D I E V A L N D A E E D
S Y P N I H L L N C A B R N
D U N L A P Y U C C A M O A
R M L D E L U R C E V S S L
P A L J R W H G H K I T G T
A E I L U N I S E D S A J R
Y G R A N D L S A T T T S O
E L B E K R A M A L A E I P
```

NATIVE AMERICAN DAY

When explorers and settlers first arrived from Europe, Native Americans already populated the entire North American continent. The passage below explains a special day that occurs every fourth Friday of September.

Native American Day celebrates and honors the first Americans who lived in the United States. The term "Native Americans" has been used in recent years as a sign of respect and recognition that they were truly the first people to populate this nation.

```
A A Y M A M E R I C A N S N
C N P Y E H T Y L U R T I I
E D D P L N A H N S H H V D
T H E R A D L P F A S E W E
F O T T E S U O T H T F V S
L N I N C C P A P S A I U U
D O N N I E O I S N T R V T
N R U A O L P G N A E S P E
I S S P C L O S N C S T C O
H L L R W I T M E I S I H T
N E E B A V R N W R T W G R
F O M A Y E T E I E F I L N
S Y V A T D Y F M M R O O H
V S R C E L E B R A T E S N
```

FLOWERS FOR MOM

Can't find something to get mom for Mother's Day? Brighten her special day with some flowers! You could get her a ROSE bouquet, or you might get her an ORCHID she can wear as a corsage. Go ahead, say it with flowers!

ALYSSUM

AMARYLLIS

ASTER

CANNA

CARNATION

CROCUS

DAFFODIL

DAHLIA

DAISY

GLAD

HYACINTH

IRIS

JONQUIL

LILY

LUPINE

MARIGOLD

NARCISSUS

NASTURTIUM

ORCHID

PEONY

PETUNIA

PHLOX

POPPY

ROSE

SNAP-
DRAGON

SNOWDROP

STOCK

SWEET PEA

TULIP

VIOLET

ZINNIA

```
S N O W D R O P H L O X J I
Y U O H Z A L T E L O I V X
D N C I T N U O S T O C K U
L A O O T N P V L D U K P A
O I F E R A I L H A D N M U
G N Z F P C N C X L O A I J
I N Y R O S E R A G R R J A
R I L Y P D O L A Y C C L L
A Z I I P O I R L C H I K Y
M G L Z Y U D L A N I S M S
U U E S Q P I S O R D S Z S
T R I N A S T U R T I U M U
W A O N A E P T E E W S U M
D J S I R I G A S N M X W E
```

SOFA TALK

One of life's simple pleasures is lazing around on the ol' reliable COUCH. Kick off your shoes, stretch out, turn on the television, and before you know it you'll be dozing off. At least that is until someone enters the room and turns off the TV, prompting you to wake up and say, "Hey, I was watching that!"

ARMS

BRACKET

BUDGET

COILS

COLOR

COMFORT

COUCH

CUSHION

FABRIC

FASHION

FLUFF

FOAM

FRAME

LEATHER

LEGS

MAPLE

MATERIAL

MODEL

OAKS

PADDING

PILLOWS

PINE

RELAXED

SCREWS

SIT ON IT

SPRINGS

SPRUCE

STURDY

STYLE

UPHOLSTERY

```
G A N T F R A M E Y R U F C
E N R E L A X E D S K A O E
S C I G D A S R Y C B C A N
H I C D X R U H K R O S M T
K C L U D T D C I M W W T E
L L U B S A S C F O K E B K
L E D O M O P O L W N R B C
S A K F C X R L L I O C U A
L T I N O T I S P L N S W R
I H Y R X P N O O F H P D B
O E A L E C G C I I F R M H
C R Y R E T S L O H P U C D
W G M I M G A N O E U C L I
L C X X K S S M A P L E S F
```

It's a good idea to carry insurance because, as they say, better safe than sorry. When it's time to renew or purchase your next insurance POLICY, expect to hear and see many of the terms listed below.

AGENT

ANNUITY

AUTOMOBILE

BENEFICIARY

BENEFITS

CARRIER

CASH VALUE

CLAIM

CLAUSE

CONDITIONS

COVERAGE

EXCLUSIONS

FILE

FIRE

FLOOD

GROUP

HEALTH

HOME-OWNER'S

HOSPITAL

INSURER

LIFE

LOSS

OPTION

PACKAGE

PLAN

POLICY

PREMIUM

RATES

RENEWAL

RIDER

TERM

```
R E I R R A C F H N P F B O
E X C L U S I O N S B E C W
N E T N L R S M N E P L A N
E V N X E P T O N L A I N E
W R E D I R I E L I C F O A
A E G T F T H M B K E I C
L M A W I I E L D O A A T A
H L U D C E N R O M G B P S
X E N I S R E N W O E M O H
G O A U M R B K V T D O M V
C R A L U E Y T I U N N A A
Y L O S T E R M R A T E S L
C O N U H H V P O L I C Y U
M I C U P V C O V E R A G E
```

HAPPY MOTHER'S DAY!

Julia Ward Howe, author of the "Battle Hymn of the Republic," first proposed the idea of Mother's Day in the United States in 1872, and President Woodrow Wilson proclaimed it a national holiday in 1914. It was around this time that the poem below first appeared.

"M" is for the million things she gave me, "O" means only that she's growing old, "T" is for the tears she shed to save me, "H" is for her heart of purest gold; "E" is for her eyes, with love-light shining, "R" means right, and right she'll always be, Put them all together, they spell "MOTHER," A word that means the world to me.

```
S F I A Y V Y R S T I F V P
D N S E Y E R E H B E P U T
T E A R S S H E E V I R F E
H L L E P S M T A H E I E V
A O E I M I I G R S V G H A
T L R F L R E H T O M H P S
G G W L M H T D O Y F T V I
N T I A S N N H F T O S G H
I O A H Y A O G E G D H I E
N M E H T S N A E M O E M M
I E U H T I W T S D A L H T
H P G L W Y H W W O R L D S
S I L O V E L I G H T O L T
R O R U R S G N I H T B W A
T G M F E I S F O R H E R A
```

There will always be someone who dares to challenge the power of nature, sometimes in the oddest ways. On July 4, 1928, Jean Lussier successfully claimed the title of the first person to go over Niagara FALLS in a 750-pound rubber ball. Find the ways that we are continually reminded of nature's awesome power.

AVALANCHE

BLAST

BLIZZARD

DROUGHT

EARTHQUAKE

EDDY

FALLS

GALE

GEYSER

HAIL

HURRICANE

LANDSLIDE

LIGHTNING

MONSOON

MUDSLIDE

RAIN

RIPTIDE

SLEET

STORM

SURF

TEMBLOR

TEMPEST

THUNDER

TIDAL WAVE

TORNADO

TWISTER

TYPHOON

UNDERTOW

VOLCANO

```
V T Y P H O O N A C L O V U
M O N S O O N V K H R T V T
U R E G E K A U Q H T R A E
D O A N L L T E M P E S T M
S E U I A T T C O D K I R B
L G A N N C S U R F D O B L
I H C T D Y I A G A T G T O
D H Q H S E Z R L S H H D R
E F R G L Z R W R B G A R W
Q S A I I L A T H U N D E R
D L D L D V E Y O R H W S W
E L B V E E D R O W O C Y C
B A V L L D D T W I S T E R
H F C S E D I T P I R A G L
```

Born in Hanover County, Virginia, Patrick Henry (1736-1799) was one of the most celebrated orators and political leaders of the American Revolution. Below is an excerpt from his famous speech given on March 23, 1775.

What is it that gentlemen wish? What would they have? Is life so dear, or peace so sweet, as to be purchased at the price of chains and slavery? Forbid it, Almighty God! I know not what course others may take; but as for me, give me liberty or give me death!

```
E V I G R O S W O U L D B N
E M I P T I L I B E R T Y D
F O E C I R P S I T A H W N
I T B V D Y E H T T E N H A
L H H L I E P W T R D F A S
S E L H B G S H M T O O V N
I R Y O R P E A C E S R E I
E S H D O G Y T H G I M L A
H A O T F T A R O C E E I H
K T F S A H A S E L R K M C
L U C K W E E H T V N U E L
Y B E T C E D N T O A E P M
C C O U R S E E W T B L W L
T N T E O G P T M R I E S P
```

If you don't do anything **FOOLISH** you should have no problem solving this puzzle. Hidden in the diagram below are 35 words that contain the letters "OO." So **LOOSEN** up, find your **GROOVE**, and use your **NOODLE** to find them all.

BABOON

BAMBOO

BEDROOM

BOOKEND

BOOKLET

BOOTIE

CABOOSE

CARTOON

CHOOSE

COCOON

COOKIE

COOKOUT

COOLER

DOODLE

FOOLISH

GROOVE

LAGOON

LOOSEN

MAROON

MOONLIT

NOODLE

OUTLOOK

POODLE

RACCOON

ROOFTOP

ROOKIE

ROOSTER

SCHOOL

SHAMPOO

SMOOTH

SNOOZE

SOOTHE

TYCOON

WOODEN

ZOOLOGY

```
S A S M O O T H A A O R B S E
W I O K Y E A U R N E S O O L
C O Z D L L P N O E L O C I D
C O O K I E B O Z K T E N Y O
F L O D Z N D O M H O S O N O
M O L L E L O B E D R O O M D
B O O K E N D A N O O O C O U
R H G L S R B B O P T B Y O R
A C Y V I Y W F M R L A T N W
G S M L P S T A A O N C M L E
R T E S O O H C R O O F K I N
O A M D P S C I O K O B T T L
O U T L O O K O O I C O M N I
V E L D O O P V N E O K V A K
E T W N O O G A L B C B O K B
```

WHALE'S WORLD

In the Bible, Jonah was swallowed by a whale and was in its belly for three days and nights. In literature, Herman Melville's sea classic centered around Moby-Dick, the indomitable WHITE whale that plagued Captain Ahab and his crew. And ORCA the KILLER whale terrified moviegoers as he sought revenge against the men who killed his pregnant mate. Find below the 31 terms related to whales and WHALING.

BALEEN

BEACHED

BEAK

BELUGA*

BLOWHOLE

BLUBBER

BLUE*

BOWHEAD*

BRYDE'S*

CETACEAN

FIN*

GRAY*

HARPOON

HUMPBACK*

HUNT

KILLER*

MELON-
   HEADED*

MIGRATION

MINKE*

NARWHAL*

OIL

ORCA*

PILOT*

RIGHT*

SEI*

SONG

SPERM*

STRANDING

TEETH

WHALING

WHITE*

*type of whale

```
R D P E W A G U L E B K M E
G G U Y T H U N T T O L I P
B L D M E K W H I T E G N B
B A L E E N C R E L L I K M
T I W M T L N A E C A T E C
O E L O H W O L B B G H U K
S T R A N D I N G P B K W T
E L R I Y D T H H H M U S N
D A F C B E A C H E D U L G
Y H B Y S R R E W W A R H B
R W A S P I G Y H T C D G B
B R C O E G I T L W R N E K
G A O S R H M U G B O A P D
F N C T M T S E C S K B K W
```

THEY RHYME WITH "OOHS"

Have you heard the NEWS? Human responses involving pleasure, surprise, and admiration often result in exclamatory sounds known as "oohs" and "ahs." These words have no meaning other than the emotions they denote. The words in this list all rhyme with "oohs." As you CRUISE through the maze of letters, note the variety of spellings that can produce the same sound in English.

ABUSE
ACCUSE
AMUSE
BEMUSE
BLUES

BRUISE
CHEWS
CHOOSE
CLUES
CONFUSE

CREWS
CRUISE
DUES
EXCUSE
FUSE
LOSE
MOOS
MUSE
NEWS
PERUSE
REFUSE
RUES
SCHMOOZE
SHOES
SHOOS
SKEWS
SNOOZE
STEWS
TABOOS
TATTOOS
TRANSFUSE
VIEWS
WHOSE

```
E Z M C C C L U E S U F E R
S Z O V U H K T D S B S K E
U K O N V K L A C C U S E Z
F T S O O B A T B F V M X A
S W L K M T N T N U N S E P
N M A U C H O O S E S V H B
A M S W E R C O W W W E A R
R E T E X C U S E R E R M K
T V D N S L N I K E H T U F
X E D L X O V B S O C H S P
L I P B O B H I F E H O E K
L I U Z I S U W A U O U U T
R U E S U R E P R H N H D N
K L Z K B L U E S U F S S C
```

FABRICS

In 1969, a writer for *American Fabrics* magazine declared, "DENIM is one of the world's oldest fabrics yet it remains eternally young." See if you can find that popular bluejeans material and 29 of its peers in the grid below.

ACETATE

BAIZE

BROCADE

CALICO

CANVAS

CASHMERE

CHAMBRAY

CHENILLE

CHIFFON

COTTON

DAMASK

DENIM

FELT

FLANNEL

FLEECE

GABARDINE

JERSEY

LEATHER

LINEN

MOHAIR

NANKEEN

ORGANZA

POLYESTER

POPLIN

RAYON

SAMITE

SHANTUNG

TAFFETA

TARTAN

VELVET

```
N I L P O P O L Y E S T E R
T E J D C O E A I V C L T R
N A T R A T R F L N H O N V
N E F I R B E F L E E C E T
O T T F M D M F L A N N E L
T C C A E A H I S L I V K U
T C H N T T S H O D L V N D
O C I G L E A G R E L M A A
C M F E P N C A V I E M N R
I A F K T V B A S R A Y O N
L O O U C A N V A S T H Y S
A Z N A G R O N K L H G O J
C G Z F A L Y E S R E J Z M
P B A I Z E D A C O R B C T
```

If you think there's something wrong with this puzzle title, you're wrong — but you're also right! We decided to spell it with two "R"s because all of the people in our puzzle are entertainers with double "R"s in their surnames.

BARRIS (Chuck)

BARRYMORE (Drew)

BERRY (Chuck)

BURR (Raymond)

CARRADINE (David, Keith)

CARROLL (Diahann)

DARREN (James)

FARRELL (Mike)

FERRER (Jose, Mel)

FERRIGNO (Lou)

FORREST (Steve)

GARR (Teri)

HARRINGTON (Pat)

HARRISON (George)

HARRY (Deborah)

JARREAU (Al)

KARRAS (Alex)

KERR (Deborah)

LAMARR (Hedy)

LORRE (Peter)

MERRILL (Robert)

MORRISON (Van)

MORRISSEY

MURRAY (Bill)

NORRIS (Chuck)

PERRINE (Valerie)

PERRY (Matthew)

SARRAZIN (Michael)

STARR (Ringo)

WARREN (Lesley Ann)

```
N E R R A W M C N Y N I E B
N O R R I S M H R M R E N R
R A T A U U L R O J N O I H
C R S G R B A R R I S I R E
I K A R N H R B D I L Z R J
E O A T N I Z A R R A S E H
O Y E S S I R R O M M J P W
J N G O B R A R C Y A N C M
S A N U A H Z Y A E R E E L
B A R C Y S T M R H R R D B
F E R R I G N O R E R R E F
F O R R E S T R O I Z A O P
E E Y A A A A E E L M C D M L
B P E J H K U L L E R R A F
```

TASTY TOMATOES

The record for the heaviest tomato ever belongs to a seven pound, 12 ounce, tomato of the DELICIOUS variety that was cultivated in Edmond, Oklahoma, in 1986. Have a FANTASTIC time picking the tomato varieties we've planted in the garden of letters below.

BETTER (Boy)

BIG BEEF

BRAGGER

BRANDYWINE

BURGESS (Early Salad)

CELEBRITY

DELICIOUS

EASY (Peel)

FANTASTIC

GARDENERS (Delight)

GOLDIE (Hybrid)

HUSKY (Gold Hybrid)

LONG-KEEPER

MARGLOBE

NEW YORKER

PATIO (Hybrid)

PONDEROSA (pink)

PRINCE (Borghese)

RED CHERRY

RUTGERS (California Supreme)

SAN MARZANO

SUPER (Sweet 100 Hybrid)

TINY TIM

TROPIC

TUMBLER

WINTER (Red Hybrid)

```
E M A R G L O B E T T E R S
A Z S M P S D C D R E A A L
S L O I R E P E E K G N O L
Y R R T I N L N A I M K D O
F E E Y N I E H A A D R S W
A L D N C W C W R T E L S C
N B N I E Y I Z Y D K K O B
T M O T K D A N C O B A I G
A U P S R N R H T U R G P C
S T U E O A E A R E B K I T
T H A I B R A G G E R P E T
I Y T I R B E L E C O T T R
C A Y Y A S F F H R E P U S
P R K U S R E G T U R F A W
```

You're bound to find more than a **LETTER** in your mailbox these days. There's likely to be **BILLS** and lots of **JUNK MAIL**. See if you can deliver all 30 mailbox items below!

ADVERTISEMENT

ANNOUNCEMENT

BILLS

BOOK

CARDS

CENSUS

CHECK

CONTEST

CORRESPONDENCE

FLYER

FORM

GIFT

INQUIRY

INVITATION

INVOICE

JUNK MAIL

LETTER

MAGAZINE

MESSAGE

NEWSPAPER

NOTE

NOTICE

OFFER

PACKAGE

PARCEL

STAMPS

STATEMENT

SUMMONS

SURVEY

SWEEPSTAKE

```
T B I L L S U R V E Y L S S
T E R T K S T K G H S I U T
B N L C S D R A C W T A S N
P R E P A P S W E N A M N E
A H Y M T S K E Y I T K E M
C O R R E S P O N D E N C E
K M L M I S N V O C M U I C
A F C E T U I O I B E J O N
G L O A C T Q T M W N N V U
E Y K R A R O N R M T K N O
D E G T M N A K I E U P I N
F R I S T A M P S B V S N N
G O F F E R E T T E L D F A
N O T E B M E N I Z A G A M
```

LOST IN SPACE

More than 10,000 asteroids have orbits sufficiently well known to have been catalogued and named, and thousands more exist. CERES, the largest asteroid, has a diameter of about 630 miles. The three next largest are HYGEIA, PALLAS, and VESTA. Launch yourself into the diagram below and find these minor planets.

AMPHITRITE

ARETHUSA

AURORA

BAMBERGA

CAMILLA

CERES

CYBELE

DAPHNE

DAVIDA

DORIS

EGERIA

EUGENIA

EUNOMIA

EUPHROSYNE

EUROPA

FORTUNA

HYGEIA

INTERAMNIA

IRIS

JUNO

MINERVA

PALLAS

PATIENTIA

PROCNE

PSYCHE

SIEGENA

THEMIS

THISBE

UNDINA

VESTA

```
A D S A A M P H I T R I T E
P R O C N E T H E M I S U O
A P O R U E N Y D N C G N J
I S I R I N G G T E E S D S
J E T E U S L E U N O M I A
D A V I D A R I I Y A O N L
A D V I I A R A T S E V A L
P T I R M V A E E O P Y G A
H G E N E N L E T R N R R P
N G I B U N L H R H E U C J
E A I T N E I T A P U E J D
N A R V B S M M E U R S I M
C O H Y B V A G R E B M A B
F F C E E H C Y S P D E M U
```

Here is a list of some of the memorable movies from the 1930s and 1940s. They have all come to be recognized as classics. When you have circled all the entries, the leftover letters will spell out the titles of four other famous movies from this era.

ALGIERS

BAD GIRL

BAMBI

BOYS TOWN

CAMILLE

CHAMPION

CIMARRON

DEAD END

DETOUR

DUMBO

FANTASIA

FURY

GASLIGHT

GILDA

GUNGA DIN

HAMLET

HENRY V

JEZEBEL

KING KONG

LAURA

LIFEBOAT

REBECCA

RED DUST

SKIPPY

TABU

THE CHAMP

THE WOMEN

TOPPER

WILSON

```
C T H G I L S A G A S A Y W
B C E L N R T O P P E R I A
D A N L E O F C M A U L G J
N M O I M I K A N F S A G E
E I G M O A H G N O Y U B Z
D L W A W C H U N T C R A E
A L Y U E C S N P I A A M B
E E B H H E H G M E K S B E
D A T L T B T A O B E F I L
T S U D D E R D M L B O U A
B A D G I R L I Y P P I K S
N D S T O A G N E G I L D A
V Y R N E H C O D E T O U R
A C D U M B O Y S T O W N H
```

PROFILE: DANIEL WEBSTER

New Hampshire native Daniel Webster served as a LAWYER, CONGRESSMAN, senator, and Secretary of State. His impassioned SPEECHES, especially those supporting the unity of the States, earned him the nickname "BLACK DAN with the silver tongue."

BLACK DAN

BOSTON (residence)

BUNKER HILL (oration)

CHARISMA

CONGRESS-MAN

DARTMOUTH (college)

DEBATES

DIPLOMAT

ELMS FARM (childhood home)

FEDERALIST

HISTORY

LAWYER

LETTERS

ORATOR

PUNCH BROOK (fishing spot)

SALISBURY (N.H.; birthplace)

SENATE

SPEECHES

SPENDTHRIFT

STATUE

UNION (supporter)

WHIG (party)

```
N A D K C A L B E T A N E S
T O M H I T S E H C E E P S
S I R S N O I N U S T E P O
I S O M I W H A E S N L D P
L E T T E R S T B D L O A U
A L A A J E A N T I S M R N
R M R I T B O H H P N H T C
E S O D E U R R C L Y I M H
D F O D A I E S N O T S O B
E A X C F K E N S M O T U R
F R R T N R E Y W A L O T O
S M A U G H I H O T E R H O
B I B S A L I S B U R Y A K
O S C O N G R E S S M A N R
```

HERBAL TEAS

Many blends of herbs, seeds, leaves, flowers, and roots can be combined to make herbal teas. You'll find several varieties of this delicious beverage hidden throughout the diagram below.

ALFALFA

BLUEBERRY

BURDOCK

CHAMOMILE

CINNAMON

CRANBERRY

DANDELION

ELDER

EUCALYPTUS

FLAX

GINSENG

GOLDENSEAL

HOPS

KAVA KAVA

LEMON

LICORICE

MINT

NETTLE

PARSLEY

RASPBERRY

RED CLOVER

ROSE HIPS

SAGES

SARSAPARILLA

SENNA

VANILLA

WILD CHERRY

```
L C C X Y C S P I H E S O R
X R O I N R A V A K A V A K
F S E N N A R H T D O S F C
G O L D E N S E A L P L L O
S S C V L B A A H B I D A D
B E U L Y E P M E C A G F R
P V G T M R A R O N D L L U
A A N A P R R R D N A L A B
R N E T S Y I E F X S B I O
S I S N S C L X B P V N W W
L L N I E I L A O E O L N I
E L I M O M A H C M U L W E
Y A G N E T T L E U U L H F
O F U R E V O L C D E R B C
```

MOSTLY VOWELS

Some folks pay $250 for a vowel (at least on "Wheel of Fortune," that is!), but you can have all these for free! The words listed here have more vowels than consonants. Can U find them all?

ADIEU

AERATE

AIDE

ALIBI

AMOEBA

APOGEE

AUTOMAT

AVOCADO

AXIOM

AZALEA

CEASE

EAGLE

EERIE

EMCEE

EQUINE

EYESORE

GENIE

IDEA

IDIOM

IGLOO

IODINE

IOTA

MEDIA

MOVIE

OASIS

OBOE

OLEO

ONION

OOZE

OPERA

ORIOLE

OUNCE

OZONE

PIQUE

PIXIE

PUREE

QUEUE

QUIET

UNION

VAGUE

```
N O U B B Y A T O I V Y I N
E E R I E U G A V S B E O D
L P I X I E B X S A I I O S
G C O C N S G I M M N S L V
A A P I T A M O T U A X A A
E Y E S O R E M P N O I N O
U S R L A B Z A I A D I T O
Q O A M A I O M E E A G E Y
I U S E A Z O R M Q C L I M
P N E D C I A D G U O O U C
D C I U D T D O I I V O Q T
A E V I E Z B E R N A E D I
U M O D E O Z O N E E R U P
P E M C E E X T Z M Q P Y E
```

214

CARVED IN STONE

An artist who greatly influenced 20th-century sculpture was France's Auguste Rodin (1840-1917). Working with both BRONZE and MARBLE, he confronted distress and moral weakness, as well as passion and beauty. He refused to ignore the negative aspects of humanity. In the diagram below, find 33 terms relating to sculpture.

ABSTRACT

ARMATURE

BOUCHARDE

BRONZE

BUST

CAMEO

CARVE

CAST

CHISEL

CLAY

FIGURE

FORM

GENRE

GRAIN

INTAGLIO

MALLET

MAQUETTE

MARBLE

MOBILE

MODEL

PATINA

PITCHER

PLASTER

POINT

RELIEF

RIFFLER

SCULPTOR

SHAPE

SPATULA

STABILE

STATUE

STONE

TERRA COTTA

```
V C A M E O E G S P G A S E
M B A V C A S T O N E T T L
B M R B M O B I L E A T F B
F A U O S A N M E B E O N R
C S F A N T L D I U R C R A
T G O I A Z R L Q M S A E M
H R T G G A E A E C C R L O
Y A L C H U M A C T U R F D
P I T C H E R A L T L E F E
O N U H R I Y E A U P T I L
N O O N E C S M R A T S R Y
B F E I L E R E H O O A M M
O G E U T A T S L A R L P Z
V F H E P G N A I L C P I S
```

A BUNCH OF BATS

The bat is a flying mammal that relies on echolocation, a sonarlike system used to detect an object, to navigate its flight path. With echolocation, a bat can emit high-pitched sounds that reflect off the object and return to the bat's ears. Swoop down to the diagram below and find 26 species of bats.

BROWN

CUBAN
(flower)

EGYPTIAN
(free-tailed)

FISHERMAN

FRUIT

GREATER
(horseshoe)

HARPY (fruit)

HOARY

HOG-NOSED

HORSESHOE

LESSER
(horseshoe)

LITTLE (brown)

LONG-
TONGUED
(fruit)

MASTIFF

MEXICAN
(free-tailed)

PAINTED

PROBOSCIS

SILVER-HAIRED

SMOKY

SPEAR-NOSED

TOMB

TUBE-NOSED (fruit)

TWO-LINED

VAMPIRE

VELVETY
(free-tailed)

WHITE

```
M F N E B H H C O O B P Y S
E T I H W N A H F V W G M I
X G R E A T E R F B M O T L
I E Y S S G U F P I K U O V
C B O P E I I D R Y B N K E
A U R H T T C E O G V D R
N Y B O S I W S N T D A E H
R R O A W E A O O A E M T A
L E M R N N S N L B S P N I
A I S Y P E G R S I O I I R
P L T S D U N A O F N R A E
P B Y T E V L E V H G E P D
R S L D L L N P E L O A D R
L N A M R E H S I F H B K U
```

FRAGRANT SOAPS

You had better be careful in the shower on those mornings when you're extra tired. With fragrances like GRAPEFRUIT, ORANGE, PEACH, and STRAWBERRY, you just might take a bite out of your bar of soap! At least if that happens, you won't be using any bad language for a while!

AVOCADO

CARNATION

CARROT

CHAMOMILE

CINNAMON

CLOVER

EUCALYPTUS

FREESIA

GARDENIA

GERANIUM

GRAPEFRUIT

JASMINE

LAVENDER

LEMON

LILAC

MANGO

MARIGOLD

ORANGE

ORCHID

PATCHOULI

PEACH

PEPPERMINT

PINE

PRIMROSE

SANDAL-WOOD

STRAWBERRY

VANILLA

VERBENA

VETIVER

```
T M V E S O R M I R P I N E U
A R A W Y A M A R I G O L D Y
C V N G M A N G O S I M D Y V
L D I H C R O D U T O R R A C
O I L U O H C T A P Q L M O A
V F L G L G P N P L E H R J I
E R A E M Y R R E B W A R T S
R O V R L A M A P N N O C Y E
E D O A C I V R P G I J O H E
D J C N L N M E E R M D D R
N U A I I E A O R V F I S C F
E V D U C D M F M B I R M A I
V V O M B R P O I A E T U I J
A C I N N A M O N J H N E I O
L I L A C G E O T B U C A V T
```

GRAPHIC DETAILS

A GRAPH can make complex information understandable. Although once exclusively used in mathematics and STATISTICS, these useful charts have now penetrated many other fields, such as advertising, marketing, and public relations.

AREA

BAR CHART

CENTRAL

CIRCLE

COLUMN

CURVE

DATA

GRAPH

GROUP

INDEX

LIMIT

LINE

MEAN

MEDIAN

MODE

ORDINATE

ORIGIN

PIE CHART

PLOT

POINT

POLYGON

QUANTITY

RANGE

SAMPLE

SCALE

SHADED

STATISTICS

STEP

TENDENCY

TIME

VALUE

```
G C H S B Q P M T C E Q M E
P I P S C A L E E M G D I L
Y R A U U I T N O G Y L O P
G C R S O A T C P H N A E M
C L G B N R O S O P S A A A
M E D I A N G R I L Q T R S
R V D L U R Y E N T U D E H
U R N Q A Q C I T X A M A P
O U X L M H N P T N T N R
C C S H A D E D A L T T S L
X T Y R E M D U O R I G I N
Q E T X I E N I L M T O Y L
P L O T B U E V I A Y G U E
U M L X U B T L A G V A S T
```

MUSICAL BROTHERS

There are no Doobies in the **DOOBIE** Brothers, and the **RIGHTEOUS** Brothers weren't even related. However, most of these other musical brothers feature at least a pair of male siblings.

ALLMAN

BAILES

BALFA

BELLAMY

BLUES

BRECKER

CANDOLI

CHAMBERS

CLANCY

CORNELIUS

DELMORE

DOOBIE

DORSEY

EVERLY

GATLIN

GLASER

GOOD

HEATH

ISLEY

JOHNSON

LOUVIN

MAINES

MILLS

NEVILLE

OSMOND

RIGHTEOUS

STANLEY

STATLER

SUTHERLAND

WALKER

WILBURN

```
Y H U D O O B I E M E G L R
C R E K L A W L B L C G D W
N E M A I N E S O K A D N E
A L R L T N D U N J N S O V
L A E E I H V T O M D Y M E
C S L L R I G H T E O U S R
I H T L N O N E A W L U O L
D A A U M S M R L F I M R Y
G G T M O A T L U L L D M E
U L S N B J N A E B I A D L
V A B L U E S N N D L V B S
K S L L I M R D A L O I E I
Y E E G D O R S E Y E O W N
N R E K C E R B U F C Y G U
```

RESOLUTION, AGAIN

Some say a New Year's resolution is something that goes in one year and out the other! Here's a list of subjects that are commonly part of New Year's resolutions. When you've circled all the entries, the leftover letters will finish this comment: "If you had kept every resolution you made last year . . ."

CHURCH

DIET

EDUCATION

EXERCISE

FRIENDS

GRADES

HABITS

HEALTH

HOBBY

LAZINESS

LEISURE

LETTERS
   (writing more)

LOVE

MOOD

ORGANIZA-
   TION

PATIENCE

PERFORMANCE

PRACTICE

READING

RELATIONSHIP

REPAIRS

SAVING

SPENDING

TARDINESS

TEMPER

TIDINESS

TIME

TV VIEWING
(reduce)

WORK

```
S N O I T A Z I N A G R O H
Y S S P E N D I N G E O E O
U W E S E D A R G P O A U B
P L L N D D O O M T L B E B
I S E K I I L E T T E R S Y
H N I S S D T N H I Y I P S
S N S M S A R S R E M A D G
N O U D E E A A T C T E C N
O I R H N V N S T I B A H I
I T E E I E G I E T E A U W
T A L N D N I N Z C V T R E
A C G H I Y C R R A O W C I
L U I D T E C H F R L O H V
E D A A N S R I A P E R D V
R E X E R C I S E B O K R T
R E E C N A M R O F R E P D
```

Can you GRASP all the "GR" words hidden in the GRID? We're sure you'll be GREAT at it once you get into the GROOVE!

GRAB

GRACE

GRACIOUS

GRADE ·

GRADUATE

GRAFT

GRAIN

GRAM

GRAND

GRANT

GRAPH

GRASP

GRATE

GRATUITY

GRAVEL

GRAVITATE

GRAVITY

GRAVY

GRAY

GRAZE

GREASE

GREAT

GREEN

GREET

GRID

GRILL

GRIN

GRIP

GROCER

GROOM

GROOVE

GROTTO

GROUND

GROUP

GROVE

GROW

```
H C G G G R A V I T A T E
F M C R R L A E A L U T C P
Y D A I O E S O N H B A R G
Y I L P O V E V Y I R G D E
N L E I M A E T T G R A D E
H V D N A R G R I D R G T V
S P V W E G R O U N D A P Y
B U G C G R E A T W R S N Y
G O O H P A R G A G A C T T
D R M I H D D G R R M I F R
G G O O C U R O G E V A A T
G R S O T A T N B A E V R O
W O A U V T R F R S T N G G
E W F Y O E H G C E Z A R G
```

Henry George (1839-1897) was an American social reformer who proposed the idea of a single tax. He believed that the land of the nation is a gift of nature, and therefore it is unfair that a few should become wealthy through rising property values. This text comes from his book *Progress and Poverty*.

So long as all the increased wealth which modern progress brings goes but to build up great fortunes, to increase luxury, and make sharper the contrast between the House of Have and the House of Want, progress is not real and cannot be permanent.

```
L H B U I L D E H T L L A R
A T N S U C U P G R E A T I
P U L X A W B L P U N E B C
S R U T S D N M O D E R N H
P R O G R E S S M F I T Y C
Y B B G E S N A K N E O O I
E O U W R A K U G B O N T H
V H T L A E W S T N T F H W
M E T G V R S O I R O H E F
B E O A G C N S A C O L H I
M E H T D N A S I U V F O C
S F H N A I T E S S W O U S
O B A C B O R E P R A H S R
O F W A N T N E N A M R E P
```

Besides being a major producer of COTTON, POULTRY, and RICE, Arkansas is also the United States' leading producer of BAUXITE, a source of ALUMINUM which is used to make recyclable items.

ALUMINUM

APPLES

BARITE

BAUXITE

BERRIES

BROMINE

CATTLE

COAL

CORN

COTTON

EGGS

GRAPES

GYPSUM

HOGS

HONEY

IRON

LEAD

LIMESTONE

LUMBER

MELONS

NATURAL GAS

OATS

PAPER

PEACHES

PECANS

POULTRY

RICE

SEEDS

SILVER

SOYBEANS

SPINACH

TALC

TOMATOES

WHEAT

ZINC

```
R C B S E P A R G C D N R I
M P O U L T R Y D Y S P I P
R H C A N I P S A N E G S T
M E L O N S M Y A C O N G A
C L B G U H M E A O T N O E
P T H M Z Y B N S T A O H H
T T B I U Y S B M T M R G W
U A N A O L U E U O O I S G
N C L S R S T R N N T N E S
R R I C E I A R I I N O E X
L E Z O X L T I M A M L D R
A E P U G V V E U T P O S B
O D A A P E X S L P C O R N
C B S D P R P E A C H E S B
```

WASHINGTON RIVERS

DUCKABUSH? TWISP? Washington State certainly has more than its share of creatively named rivers. Take a look below and you'll see what we mean.

BOGACHIEL

CARBON

CHEHALIS

CHIWAWA

CISPUS

DOSEWALLIPS

DUCKABUSH

ELWHA

ENTIAT

KETTLE

METHOW

NACHES

NISQUALLY

NOOKSACK

PALOUSE

PUYALLUP

QUEETS

QUINAULT

SATSOP

SAUK

SKYKOMISH

SNOQUALMIE

SOLEDUCK

TOUTLE

TWISP

WASHOUGAL

WENATCHEE

WYNOOCHEE

```
E A T T H B K C A S K O O N T
S C H A W W E N T I A T U S P
N T H W C T O U T L E B D N Y
O I E I L E I H C A G O B A T
N E S E W E G P T H S W Q C K
S N O Q U A L M I E B D L H E
K O L C U Q W A W H M H R E E
Y B E S T A G A G C S K H S H
K R D P U L L A Y U P C U O C
O A U H C L U L B E O O P L T
M C C T I P R A Y O L H O T A
I H K P S C K D N A S T S S N
S N S I P C L Y P I I A T A E
H M W R U C W Q H D U T A E W
P T K D S Q Q M P K W Q S K K
```

224   SECONDARY WORDS

Here's a list of words all secondary in importance. That is, the word "second" can be placed before each term below to form another word or phrase. So, circle away without a second THOUGHT, and, before you know it, solving this puzzle will become second NATURE to you!

BANANA

BASE

BEST

CHANCE

CHILDHOOD

CLASS

COMING

COUSIN

DEGREE

EMPIRE

ESTATE

FIDDLE

FLOOR

GROWTH

HAND

LIEUTENANT

LINE

MATE

MORTGAGE

NATURE

PAPERS

PERSON

RATE

REPUBLIC

SELF

SIGHT

SOURCE

STORY

STRING

THOUGHT

WIND

```
M G C D C S Y E U T Y H W G
I W L O B E S T C O M I N G
H T W O R G R A I N N A Y D
P D D H T O A T L D A N T E
I E R D O N N S B C A H G E
M G R L L D A E U W F A C U
M R F I T B N N P L G U Y T
H E N H P O A H E T C R H O
S E C C S M B S R T O O E F
G R U R A T E O E T U B O I
R C E U U M M Y S G S E F D
M P N P L O B T H G I S I D
R A D N A H S T R I N G C L
I R I P G P R T N A T U R E
```

PLAYING BRIDGE

BRIDGE, the popular CARD GAME, is thought to be of Levantine or Indian origin. In 1903, AUCTION bridge, in which the highest bidder names TRUMP, was invented. The CONTRACT principle became a worldwide craze in 1930 after a challenge match was won by Ely Culbertson. In the list below are 35 terms associated with this fun game.

AUCTION
BIDDING
BRIDGE
CALL
CARD
CLUBS
CONTRACT
DEALER
DECLARE
DIAMONDS
DUMMY
EAST
GAME
GRAND SLAM
HEARTS
HONORS
JACK
KING
LEAD
NORTH
PARTNERS
PENALTY
PLAY
QUEEN
REDOUBLE

RUBBER
SCORE
SOUTH
SPADES
SUITS

THIRTEEN
TRICK
TRUMP
WEST
WHIST

```
B D L H O N O R S Q N S K A
I N E P A L C G E K R C C M
W J A C K A O C M L A O I J
T W Y T L A N E P T A R R R
D A E L C A T G D E R E T E
H H N S H M R I W L B U D Y
T D T S T R A E H B E I M S
S P B R U M C L U U N M P P
I U R E O G T R S O U A A A
H P I N S N G B I D D I N G
W S D T H I R T E E N E Y U
R S G R S K C B S R E A S T
Q P E A A U H S B U L C R K
B Q L P A C C S Q P B H A G
```

We wish you luck on your quest to ACQUIRE these 31 terms hidden below that contain the letter "Q."

ACQUIRE

ANTIQUE

BANQUET

BOUQUET

EQUATE

EQUINOX

LIQUID

PLAQUE

QUAIL

QUAINT

QUALITY

QUANTITY

QUARREL

QUARTER

QUARTZ

QUEEN

QUILL

QUIP

QUITE

QUIVER

QUIZ

QUOTE

SEQUEL

SQUAD

SQUARE

SQUASH

SQUEAL

SQUEEZE

SQUID

SQUIRE

UNIQUE

```
B D I U Q S P D A C L P D H
D Z E Q Q Y L L E T Y A D E
L I T U T A B L A T U I T Q
U B A R B X Y P I Q U I L L
O R U E A Q O T S Q U A S H
E U Q I N U N N I Q A E I Z
Q O E H Q A Q L I L Q S E B
B P P R U I I A L U A Q Z N
A S R Q E N N T E U Q U O B
O Q Q A T T Q L R D N E Q N
E U Q U I P R U R X T E N I
Z I U Q E Q T A A O R Z V T
T R U Y Z A C Q U I R E H O
R E V I U Q L Q Q Q L P O E
```

STREETS OF CANTON

How do you get to the Pro Football Hall of Fame at 2121 GEORGE HALAS Drive in CANTON, OHIO? Practice! But first tackle this puzzle which contains the names of 31 streets found throughout Canton, Ohio's ninth largest city.

BARR

BLAKE

CANTON

CLARENDON

CLARK

CLEVELAND

COURT

CROMER

DRESSLER

DUEBER

EASTON

EVERHARD

FAIRCREST

FULTON

GEORGE HALAS

HARMON

LESH

LINCOLN

MAHONING

MARKET

MCGREGOR

MONUMENT

NASSAU

NAVARRE

OHIO

PORTAGE

PROMLER

STARK

STRIP

WERTZ

WHIPPLE

```
V E C R R D R A H R E V E F
U L L E R W R E M O R C N U
T E A L T A E E L C I O C E
P S R M R N B R S P T R K G
P H E O U A E K T S P A N C
O M N R O V U N A Z L I L M
R A D P C A D E L B N E H U
T R O G E R G C M O V N R W
A K N S T R I P H E C V F N
G E O R G E H A L A S N O O
E T T F N M M A F T E M I T
M O N U M E N T A V R Z L L
C L A R K D N R N A S S A U
Z A C N T Z K O H I O B H F
```

Pinochle, which developed in the United States in the mid-19th century, has similarities to the older French card GAME bezique. Pinochle can be played by two, three, or four people who use a unique DECK of 48 CARDS. Though it contains four SUITS, just like a regular 52-card deck, there are only 12 cards per suit, with two each of the NINES, TENS, JACKS, QUEENS, KINGS, and ACES.

ACES

BIDDER

CARDS

CLUBS

DEALER

DECK

DIAMONDS

DISCARD

GAME

HAND

HEARTS

JACKS

KINGS

LEAD

MINIMUM BID

NINES

OBJECT

OPPONENT

PLAY

POINTS

QUEENS

RANK

SCORE

SPADES

STRATEGY

SUITS

TENS

TRICK

TRUMP

VARIATIONS

WINNER

```
H O R E L A E D Q I D S L S
S O M D T V K I W I N N E R
B K P S C Q Q B A E K N A R
U E C P I G A M E C I S D H
L E L A O O O U L N P H J V
C A O D J N Q M P C A B A Q
Y U B E D B E I V O H R G S
N G J S I I N N E K I Y G T
G T E N S D I I T A C N I I
T C C T C D P M T O I E T U
A S T R A E H I R K R I D S
V H S U R R O O I O V R T E
L O Q M D N T V C T R B Y O
V W G P S I D S K L G I B P
```

RIDDLE SEARCH

This old rhyme describes something that almost everyone wears every day. That's the only clue we'll give you; it's up to you to figure out what it is.

Good
fellows
we are,
who
can't be
saved;
From
first
to last,
we are
enslaved.
Our
office is
hardest,
And
food
is the
worst,
Being
crammed
with raw
flesh,
Till
we're
ready
to burst,
Though

low in
our
state,
Even
kings we
support;
And at

balls
have
The main
share
of the
sport.

```
F L E S H A V E T H O U G H
Z O G S U P P O R T Q S O G
T W E R E T O B U R S T O N
S I E C I F F O T R T A D I
E N Z L D S X Z A I S T H E
D I L N H F W R D R A E B B
R A A A S I T E N W L M A W
A M R P W R N A A Z O Z L A
H E R U O S Q D W R T R L R
S H Z P L T J Y F H E Q S H
A T S A L V C R A M M E D T
V X V W E B T N A C V M X I
E E H O F T H E W E A R E W
D O O F Z Q K I N G S W E W
```

WASHINGTON COUNTIES

It's impressive if you were President of the United States and a county in Washington was named in your honor, as in the case of Presidents **ADAMS, GARFIELD, GRANT, JEFFERSON,** and **LINCOLN.** But that kind of pales in comparison to being a former Prez and having a *whole state* named after you!

ADAMS

ASOTIN

BENTON

CHELAN

CLALLAM

CLARK

COLUMBIA

COWLITZ

DOUGLAS

FRANKLIN

GARFIELD

GRANT

ISLAND

JEFFERSON

KING

KITSAP

KLICKITAT

LEWIS

LINCOLN

MASON

OKANOGAN

PACIFIC

PIERCE

SAN JUAN

SKAGIT

SKAMANIA

SNOHOMISH

SPOKANE

STEVENS

THURSTON

WHATCOM

WHITMAN

YAKIMA

```
S K A M A N I A B O E A T S C
S N O S A M P F T S K A G I T
P N O S R E F F E J T D F W G
U I E H Z M B K Z I N I C E R
Y L J V O G N I K I C W N L A
H K W S E M O C T A H W V D N
P N Y A N T I O P I A P L A T
D A A L A L S S T C M E U C Y
G R I G K A V M H H I J O L P
Y F B U O G A E U F N W I A I
A F M O P N L K R A L C S L E
K K U D S A A A S I D T G L R
I S L A N D G K T T I A V A C
M N O T N E B Z O K U E M M E
A O C R D B L I N C O L N S W
```

BUILDING BLOCKS

A mixture of clay, straw, and water, **ADOBE** is an unburnt, sun-dried **BRICK** used for building walls, particularly in Latin America and the southwestern United States. It is included in the list below, along with 27 other building and construction materials.

ADOBE

ASPHALT

BRICK

CABLE

CERAMIC

CHROME

CINDER
    BLOCK

COPPER

GLUE

GRAVEL

GROUT

INSULATION

LINOLEUM

MARBLE

MOLDING

MORTAR

PANELING

PASTE

PIPING

PLYWOOD

SCREENING

SEALANT

SHINGLE

SLATE

STUCCO

TAPE

WIRE

WROUGHT (iron)

```
I L G C I W I N N A H M D A
N N L I V A B R S M O V O S
S T U C C O P P E R G K C P
U U E N M C W A T S C R G H
L O E T S A P A H I E N D A
A R M N M G R I R E I G D L
T G V A P W N B N D Y O D T
I A R L C G R I L K B U O M
O E P A L I N O L E U M O T
N M L E V G M I U E D S W M
C O W S A E Y A P G N L Y M
L R R C A B L E R I H A L C
T H R G C R W I R E P T P M
K C O L B R E D N I C E E C
```

THE RECORDING STUDIO

Many musicians are investing in home studio equipment to record their songs in a comfortable, familiar environment. In the list below, you will find 30 words associated with a recording studio.

ALBUM

AMPLIFIER

BAND

CABLE

CASSETTE

CLARINET

COMPACT DISC

DRUMS

FLUTE

GUITAR

HEADSET

KEYBOARD

LIGHT

MICROPHONE

MIXER

MUSICIAN

ORCHESTRA

OUTLET

PIANO

SAXOPHONE

SHEET (music)

SPEAKER

STOOL

SWITCH

TAPE

TROMBONE

TRUMPET

VIOLIN

VOCALIST

WIRE

```
S F L U T E T E N I R A L C
A Y G E D K R S H I K F S V
R T E S D A E H I E L I W H
T H Y E T T I Y I L D O C U
S Y C I E C F L B T A T I S
E A U O N A I P C O I C P V
H G X F O G L A A W A E O K
C T D O H O P W S L A R M V
R E R T P M M T S K B T D D
O P U E O H A W E T E U N I
A M M C R D O R T L O A M R
M U S I C I A N T A B O U A
U R E X I M W U E P P A L S
E T R O M B O N E C W E C U
```

NOT JUST FIDO

These days, **BUDDY**, **JAKE**, and **ROCKY** are among the favored names for male dogs, while fashionable female dogs have the monikers **LADY**, **MAGGIE**, and **MOLLY**. Here are some of the most popular names given to man's best friend.

BABY

BANDIT

BEAR

BRANDY

BUDDY

BUSTER

CHARLIE

GINGER

JAKE

KITTY

LADY

LUCKY

MABEL

MAGGIE

MAXIE

MICKEY

MISSY

MISTY

MOLLY

MUFFIN

NICOLE

PATCHES

PEPPER

PRINCESS

ROCKY

RUSTY

SAMMIE

SHADOW

SHEBA

SMOKEY

SNUGGLES

TIGER

TIGGER

```
O N N M I S T Y M A B E L X
L I I B R A N D Y Y D A L E
U T F E I E B U U X T E B I
I I F M I Y R E G G I T O Y
B D U M D L L S H G K I I E
B N M D M B R H G S L G Y K
U A U A A Y P A T C H E S A
S B X U L G M D H U K R S J
T I L L U I R O Y C O M E O
E L O C I N O W I T O N C U
R M U D R G O M M K S D N J
L A X C R E P P E P J U I A
E M E I K R M Y S S I M R C
B Y B B L Y K C O R P Y P C
```

Samuel Johnson was the leading literary scholar and critic of his day (1709-1784). He helped to define the great period of literature known as the Augustan Age. Below you'll find a quote from this celebrated author.

The difference between a well-bred and ill-bred man is this: One immediately attracts your liking, and the other your aversion. You love the one till you find reason to hate him; you hate the other till you find reason to love him.

```
D F O T N O S A E R H T L Y
I M M E D I A T E L Y M R O
F T I A H Z A U Q H L R D U
F J H T N H G A O T H E R F
E A E E O I T N M Y N A W I
R N V T O T S D T I Q S N N
E E O E R T E T A H U O Y D
N E L A R R H H A O E N M P
C W C H B S L E Y L K O D R
E T G N I K I L R U O Y N T
S E H Q C M L O B Z O M I E
N B D E P I U V N U Y L F F
L U D X T M D E R B L L I Y
```

FOUND IN WORKS OF VAN GOGH

Vincent van Gogh (1853-90) lived and painted in poverty, and sold only one drawing in his short, tragic lifetime. Now his works sell for millions of dollars and are prized by museums and collectors all over the world. Below is a list of things found in some of van Gogh's paintings.

BED

BOATS

BOOKS

BRIDGE

CAFE

CANDLE

CHAIR

CHURCH

CROWS

CYPRESSES

FIELD

FOUNTAIN

GARDEN

HAYSTACKS

HILLS

HOUSE

LARK

LOOM

MILL

MOTH

ONIONS

ORCHARD

PARK

PIPE

PLOUGH

SELF

SHOES

SUNFLOWERS

THUNDER-CLOUDS

TRAIN

VASE

VINEYARD

WHEATFIELD

```
I F H A Y S T A C K S P W F
B L H C R U H C A N D L E V
O E G O E U U W A R D F M Y
S S D F R G N I A T N U O F
W U R I B S D Y A C I M T H
O O A E D L E I F T A E H W
R H H L W N R S R F R F O Y
C B C D I O C O S B T B E L
S M R V H B L N N E D R A G
H I O I T G O F L K R R E U
O L L P V I U A N D K P A F
E L E O N A D O T U S R Y M
S K B O O K S U L S S I A C
P Y I L K M S E U P I P E P
```

MEXICAN HOLIDAY

Salma Hayek was born in Veracruz, Mexico in 1968. Her breakthrough Hollywood feature role was in *Desperado* (1995), costarring Antonio Banderas. Since then, she has starred opposite leading men such as George Clooney and Will Smith. Locate the 27 terms below associated with Salma's Mexico.

ACAPULCO

BAJA

BEACHES

CANCUN

CANTINA

CINCO DE MAYO

CLIFF DIVING

DIEZ Y SEIS (Independence Day)

ENCHILADA

FIESTA

MARACAS

MARGARITA

MARIACHI (band)

MARKETPLACE

MEXICO CITY

PESO

PIÑATA

RESORT

RUINS

SALSA

SERAPE

SIESTA

SOMBRERO

TAMPICO

TEQUILA

TIJUANA

TORTILLA

```
T R D D I E Z Y S E I S C T
R X X C Y S N A N I T N A C
O S Y T I C O C I X E M N E
S E F G N N B M H R P D C P
E H I U N A C P B I H A U A
R C E V J I D O C R L M N R
Q A S A O H V O D P E A X E
M E T T J C D I T E U R D S
A B A S N A L E D J M G O A
R O S E P I K U I F L A F Z
A L L I T R O T P U F R Y L
C D A S A A R A T A N I P O
A T S M P M E N Y Z C T L P
S N I U R T E Q U I L A U C
```

QUOTESEARCH

American humorist and entertainer Will Rogers (1879-1935) was born in Indian Territory (he was part Cherokee) in what would later become the state of Oklahoma. In June, 1930, he attended a church service at the Tremont Temple Baptist Church in Boston, and, after the sermon, the minister asked Will if he wouldn't mind saying a few words. Below is what he said that morning, and in these words you will find one of his most famous remarks.

When I die, my epitaph, or whatever you call those signs on gravestones, is going to read, "I joked about every prominent man of my time, but I never met a man I didn't like." I am so proud of that I can hardly wait to die so it can be carved.

And when you come to my grave you will find me sitting there, proudly reading it.

```
R S Y M O T J Y L D U O R P
G E A R W Y O U C A L L C F
Y N A A E U V G T R H A D L
I O I D C V D N O S N G I S
M T U O I V E I R B J B E H
E S M W G N A T E M U S K A
P E T K I S G T A M O T N R
I V U M N L I I D H Y D I D
T A O P N C L S T R W I S L
A R B V A M E D P H E D E Y
P G A N E V E R E M D N I F
H P U K A K O N I V P T D O
O E I R O U I T H E R E O N
R L G J D A Y O F T H A T A
H T I O S M A I D W G R C M
```

STATISTICALLY SPEAKING

In a group of fifty people, the probability of two of them having the same birthday is about 97%! Take a look at the diagram below to find terms related to compiling and analyzing statistics.

AVERAGE

BIMODAL

CENSUS

CORRELATION

DATA

DEVIATION

EVENT

HINGE

HISTOGRAM

MEAN

MEDIAN

MIDRANGE

MODE

NOMINAL

ORDINAL

PARAMETER

PERCENTILE

PIE CHART

QUARTILE

RANDOM

RANGE

RANK

RATIO

SAMPLE

STATISTIC

TEST

VARIATION

```
I E T M C S T L R M E S G D
S G Q S U S N E C G A E E L
R A N G E Q T T N P L V L T
P R C T L E R A C P I E I V
L E O Q M A R H M A B N T V
D V R A H D N A T P K T R P
T A R C I T S I T A T S A O
N A E M E G O D D I V L U H
P I L R B N A A A R O A Q I
P M A R G O T S I H O D M N
A N T M V A R I A T I O N O
K H I N G E K K L T D M I L
L M O D N A R E M E D I A N
T I N O M I N A L K S B H B
```

GOOD DOG!

With a little bit of training and a lot of love and attention, any **PUPPY** can learn to be obedient. If you and your pup attend a **CLASS** at an obedience school, likely it will be the beginning of a wonderful relationship.

ARENA

BARRICADE

BOOKS

CHAIN

CLASS

COLLAR

COMMANDS

CONTROL

DISTRAC-
TIONS

DOGS

GYMNASIUM

HANDLER

HEEL WORK

INSTRUCTOR

KENNEL

LEAD

LEASH

LESSON

MIRRORS

POSTS

PRACTICE

PUPPY

SIGNALS

STUDENT

TEACHER

TRAINER

TREAT

TRICKS

```
T R E A T R I C K S R R S B
H W K R O T C U R T S N I C
C C R T G H I O H U D O G S
K O E G L Y R R Y D A S N K
C C L C T R M C E E D O A O
H O D L I M E N D N I L L O
A O N M A T H H A T I E S B
I T A T A R C M C S S A L C
N L H R R P M A I A I D R K
H E E L W O R K R Y E U T T
S N C S C T L Y R P D T M T
A N S T S O P A A P W U C K
E E I I K O M L B U Y U T R
L K D P Y T N C I P P Y T K
```

The list of terms below is special in that we don't reveal the particular category into which all the terms fall. So, while searching for all 30 terms, see if you can guess which category they fall into: Birds, Fish, Flowering Plants, Insects, Mosses, or Trees. The answer is with the solution diagram.

APTERYX

BARBUL

CHOUGH

DUNLIN

FULMAR

GALLINULE

GODWIT

GUACHARO

HOATZIN

HOOPOE

JACANA

JAEGER

JUNCO

KAKAPO

KNOT

LAMMERGEIR

MEGAPODE

MURRE

NOTORNIS

PEWIT

PHOEBE

PRATINCOLE

SERIN

SISKIN

SORA

TOURACO

TROGON

TURBIT

VIREO

WEKA

```
S Y F U L M A R A L T A P K
V H O O P O E R I V E E A R
L R T I W D O G U I W K P H
S E R I N S H N A I A R H J
G G U W X Y R E T P A K O R
A E S R S I N R O T O N E E
L A M M E R G E I R I D B W
L J N L M V E N A Z Z H E S
I G I A T O C H T L G R R R
N J L O C O C A R U O T R O
U J N N L A O V O B R Z U L
L K U E U H J H G R H B M V
E J D G E J C W O A S J I Y
I A A S I S K I N B G Z C T
```

INITIALED NAMES

The names in this puzzle belong to well-known personalities in such fields as business, entertainment, politics, sports, and writing, who decided to use their initials instead of their given names.

BALLARD (J. G.)
BARNUM (P. T.)
BARRIE (J. M.)
BEAN (L. L.)
CALE (J. J.)
CUMMINGS (e. e.)
DE KLERK (F. W.)
DOCTOROW (E. L.)
ELIOT (T. S.)
ESCHER (M. C.)
FIELDS (W. C.)
FORSTER (E. M.)
FOYT (A. J.)
GILBERT (W. S.)
GRIFFITH (D. W.)
HANDY (W. C.)
HARVEY (P. J.)
HINTON (S. E.)
HUTTON (E. F.)
KING (B. B.)
LANG (K. D.)
LAWRENCE (D. H.)

LEWIS (C. S)
MARSHALL (E. G.)
MILNE (A. A.)
MORGAN (J. P.)
O'ROURKE (P. J.)
ROWLING (J. K.)
SALINGER (J. D.)

STINE (R. L.)
THOMAS (B. J.)
WALSH (J. T.)
WELLS (H. G.)
WHITE (E. B.)
WODEHOUSE (P. G.)

```
W I Y E V R A H Y H L C E R
H K K N N W O D E H O U S E
E I R R A B N W T S M M C T
T N N B E A N I L M M M H S
I G N T H L F W S I U I E R
H M T Y O F K T V L N N R O
W S A L I N G E R N R G E F
E W O R O T C O D E A S O C
L R G T S N T R L K B D A T
L G T T E H A W O R F L K N
S U I R O L A N G U E E I M
H N W M L L E L I O T I M G
E A A A S I W E L R N F L E
L S B H C N A G R O M L H B
```

If you're ever in South Philadelphia, be sure to pay a visit to its renowned Italian market, a five-block area combining an open market and specialty food stores. Whether you're seeking FRESH PRODUCE, MEATS, or you just want to pop in for a MEAL, you're sure to find what you're looking for at the oldest and largest working OUTDOOR market in the United States.

CHEESE

CHICKEN

DINNER

DISPLAY

FAMILY

FLAVORS

FRESH

FRUITS

GARLIC

HARVEST

IMPORTED

INGREDIENTS

LOCATION

MEAL

MEATS

MENU

OUTDOOR

PLACES

POULTRY

PRICES

PRODUCE

RECIPE

SCALE

SELECTION

SIDE DISH

SPICES

STREET

TASTE

TOMATOES

VEGETABLES

VENDORS

```
S E L B A T E G E V S S S H
T T V S F S Y P G S E C E F
I E N D P U I L E C U A C U
U E C E L O A D I S P L A Y
R R I T I E U P E M E E L E
F T L R M D S L R D A E P P
O S R O D N E V T E I F H I
T T A P C C H R O R N S C C
A A G M T A N U G Y Y N H E
S E C I R P T H P N R U I R
T M O V A D B I S M I F C D
E N E T O M A T O E S Y K M
H S R O V A L F Y N R Y E S
T P R O D U C E D U E F N N
```

SUPPORT SYSTEM

A COLUMN is used to support the main part of a building, and a RAFTER supports a roof. Builders and painters often use a SCAFFOLD to reach high places. Can you locate some of the many things that can be used as a support?

BANISTER

BENCH

CANE

CHAIR

COLUMN

COUNTER

CRADLE

CRUTCH

DESK

GIRDER

JAMB

LEGS

MANTEL

PALLET

PERCH

POLE

POST

PROP

RACK

RAFTER

REST

SCAFFOLD

SEAT

SHAFT

SHELF

SPLINT

STAFF

STILTS

STOOL

TRIPOD

```
H R N L I B D S T K S T R M
G D E S K M C I T M G S T G
R K K T F A H S G I R D E R
I M S A F J A N K L L N E E
F G K F I A I D D A T E S
P P O F F N R P P C S S T
K L E T N A M C L I H J P S
D S A B P C P U N E P D T O
I E L D A R C A L O P O R P
S D J E K U B F L O O P A H
S P L I N T H E N L C I C U
P G B C R C O U N T E R K I
U T E B F H S B J C E T G M
G A L L F C D N D P H C F D
```

There are 28 different skilled workers hidden in the diagram below; so ply your solver's craft, and find them with your usual flair.

ARCHITECT

BARBER

BEAUTICIAN

BRAZIER (works in brass)

BRICKLAYER

BUILDER

CARVER

COOPER (makes barrels)

ERECTOR

FARMHAND

FITTER

FULLER (shrinks and thickens cloth)

GLAZER

MASON

MECHANIC

MILLER

PLUMBER

POTTER

RIGGER

ROOFER

SADDLER

SPINNER

STONECUTTER

TANNER

TINNER (tin miner)

WEAVER

WELDER

WRECKER (works in demolition)

```
W E L D E R E K C E R W P R
S P I N N E R M K T D L C T
P T F H Y T E E C C U B U C
O D O B I C C E L M R W A G
T T N N H R T A B D E A N C
T R N A E I O E R A D O A R
E E N I H C R O V V S A E E
R I O C B M U E F A E T S Z
C Z R I U N R T M E T R R A
O A G T I I A A T I R C I L
O R M U Z N L P F E L O G G
P B Z A N F U L L E R L G G
E A R E D L I U B A R B E R
R U R B R I C K L A Y E R R
```

PAUL'S TRAVELS

Throughout his travels, Saint Paul the Apostle did much to advance the development of Christianity. Here are many of the places he visited to help spread the word.

ACHAIA

ANTIOCH

APOLLONIA

ATHENS

BEREA

CAESAREA

CILCIA

CORINTH

CYPRUS

DAMASCUS

DERBE

EPHESUS

GALATIA

JERUSALEM

MACEDONIA

MILETUS

PAPHOS

PHILIPPI

PHRYGIA

PISIDIA

RHEGIUM

RHODES

ROME

SALAMIS

SAMOS

SELEUCIA

SYRACUSE

TARSUS

TYRE

```
A S B A E A O A I G Y R H P
U M T E I A N L R H O D E S
R B A C G T I P R S D S P U
E M L C I R A D A D U H H S
D I E O E P R L I C R R E R
C P C L H D A M A S C U S A
Y H R O A M O R U G I S U T
P I S A I S Y N E I O P S H
R L R S C S U D I M G D N T
U I L B U H N R A A O E E N
S P C A E R A S E A C R H I
A P O L L O N I A J Y B T R
O I E B E R E A A T I E A O
I O M U S U T E L I M Y E C
```

SCHOOL SPIRIT

You'll earn your **VARSITY** letter by locating all of the words associated with high-school sports hidden in the the playing field below.

ATHLETES

AWARD

BAND

BASKETBALL

BLEACHERS

CAPTAIN

CHEER

COACH

COMPETE

EXCITEMENT

FAMILY

FANS

FOOTBALL

GAME

HOME-
    COMING

PEP RALLY

PLAY

PRACTICE

RIVALRY

SKILL

SOCCER

SOFTBALL

STADIUM

TEAM

FIELD

TRYOUT

UNIFORM

VARSITY

WRESTLING

```
K C G D G F T R C O P N E X
F N T G N I M O C E M O H S
W P M E F A M I L Y Y F K E
C L M A I P B I B R C I R T
B A S K E T B A L L L I I E
G Y P T L T H A E L M A X L
Y N E T D R V E A A U C V H
L T I H A I C B C B I Y M T
L C R L R I T Y H T D T R A
A H H Y T F N R E O A I O W
R E C C O S S M R O T S F A
P E A S I U E N S F S R I R
E R O M T N T R A C K A N D
P W C U T P F T W F B V U Y
```

LET'S HAVE BRUNCH!

If your first meal of the day falls between breakfast and lunch, then you're about to enjoy brunch! Here are some of the scrumptious items you may want to sample from the brunch menu.

BACON

BAGEL

BIALY

BISCUIT

CEREAL

CHEESE

COCOA

COFFEE

CREPE

CRULLER

DOUGHNUT

EGGS

FRUIT

HASH
    BROWNS

JUICE

MELON

MILK

MUFFIN

OATMEAL

OMELET

PANCAKES

QUICHE

ROLL

STEAK

TART

TOAST

WAFFLE

YOGURT

```
B A O C O C E L R E W D N U
C B T S E C I U J A A I T H
J H W P R R T I C O F F E E
S T E A K U E I B F F D L G
G R Y E E L Y A U M L A E G
C K M H S L G M L R E S M S
T T L C A E L F D M F L O N
S C A I L R K O T R U G O Y
B J B U M A U A R C Q O H N
R H W Q T G O N C G T L Y T
O H A S H B R O W N S T S O
T G G N L W G C J N A Y A Y
N D U N D O G A S R O P O T
Q T I U C S I B T N T U A F
```

LET US "ENT"ERTAIN YOU!

Get ready to circle the following 31 words that all end with the letters "ENT." This could be your big MOMENT, when you begin your ASCENT to the throne. We know you've got the TALENT to solve the puzzle. Good luck!

ABSENT	CEMENT	EVENT
ACCENT	CLIENT	EXTENT
ADVENT	COMMENT	FLUENT
AGENT	CONVENT	INDENT
ASCENT	DECENT	INTENT
		INVENT
		LAMENT
		LUCENT
		MOMENT
		PARENT
		PATENT
		POTENT
		RECENT
		RELENT
		REPENT
		RESENT
		SILENT
		SPENT
		STUDENT
		TALENT
		URGENT

```
A B T R E L E N T N E L A T
T N E G A G A L X M R M B N
E D F A D M O M E N T N S P
S V D L V P A R E N T L E L
T I E T E T X R T N E D N I
N U L N N A C C E N T N T S
E T N E T X E D C C E B F L
T C T C N C U O T E E U T C
A O O S E T M C T N R N L N
P N M A S M G N V G E I T F
T V T N E C E D E C E P N O
A E S N R V I N U N I V E G
I N T E N T T L T R O T P R
F T G I S B P C C I L C S V
```

VAUDEVILLE'S WORST

Vaudeville, a stage show of unrelated songs, sketches, dances, and magic acts, sparked the careers of entertainers such as Harry Houdini and W. C. Fields. Although far less talented, the Cherry Sisters made a name in vaudeville, too. Read about their ironic claim to fame in this passage.

Most

entertainers

promote

their

talent,

but the

Cherry

Sisters knew

they

weren't

very

good.

Taking

the direct

approach,

the sisters

advertised

themselves

as "America's

Worst Act,"

hung a

net for

protection,

and performed

in spite

of the

flying

vegetables.

```
R O F T E N C N C M S S L A
G S H C A O R P P A R T N B
R N I P I I C C C E C D E U
T E I S C T S I N A P H T T
H C T K T C R I T E T N T T
E H H O A E A S R F E H H H
M U M E M T R F O L E E E E
S N O A R O O S A Y S U I D
E G S E W R R T K I R V R I
L A T L M P Y P S N Y E M R
V N S E L B A T E G E V V E
E O D P T N E R E W O W V C
S A D V E R T I S E D O U T
O F I N S P I T E C I S D C
```

A TRIP TO TAIWAN

Taiwan is located in the China Seas. The eastern half of the island is steep and craggy, while the western half is flat, fertile, and well-cultivated. **TAIPEI** is the bustling capital city, with a population of nearly 2.7 million people. **KAOHSIUNG** is a large industrial city, and **ALISHAN** is a beautiful resort town in the mountains. Search for these and 31 other Taiwanese place names.

ALISHAN
ANTUNG
CHIAYI
ERSGUI
HAITUAN

HSINCHU
HSITOU
HUALIEN
KAOHSIUNG
KEELUNG

KUANSHAN
KUKUAN
LANYU
LISHAN
MAKUNG
MEISHAN
OLUANPI
PULI
SUAO
TAICHUNG
TAIHO
TAINAN
TAIPEI
TAITUNG
TANSHUI
TIENMU
TOULIU
TUNGPU
TZUHU
WULU
WUSHE
YAKOU
YEHLIU
YUSHAN

```
G W U L U M N E I T C L Z K
T M C K T G N U L E E K N H
A U O L U A N P I U P K S M
I O G S H A I U K Y U I A A
H K N S H H N T H K N K A Y
O A U S E H E S U C U A M T
Y Y I K T I A A H N I H T U
C E S T O U N U G A G A H N
M H H K U O T I S H N U T G
U S O L L A U E R S G U I P
H U A L I E N C H I A Y I U
U W K N U U G U U L T N W L
Z I A G N L I S H A N A H I
T N P G W W S W I K T L E H
```

A NEW CAR!

When the time comes to trade in the old clunker for a new set of wheels, what kind of VEHICLE will you opt for? Do you go with a practical family SEDAN or a daring sports car? Or how about a handy pickup TRUCK? And what OPTIONS do you want? Whatever you choose, make sure you take a TEST DRIVE through the diagram and find the terms associated with buying a new car.

AIR BAGS
CD PLAYER
COLORS
CONVERTIBLE
COUPE
DEALER
ENGINE
FEATURES
HORSE-POWER
INSURANCE
LEASE
LOAN
MILEAGE
NEGOTIA-TION
OPTIONS
PAYMENT
PRICE
PURCHASE
REBATE
SAFETY
SALE
SEDAN

STEREO
SUNROOF
TEST DRIVE
TRADE-IN

TRUCK
TRUNK
VEHICLE
WARRANTY

```
P T I W F A O K C U R T I V
C O U P E L C I H E V F N H
Y E V G T N E M Y A P O S P
S N V M I L E A G E I O U L
E T I I S A L E C T L R R P
D A E E R P B O A W C N A Y
A D S R D D I I A H O U N S
N S A C E A T R A N L S C E
K A E A H O R S E P O W E R
N F L H G A E T E S R M N U
U E P E N C V V A T S V G T
R T N T I P N S G A B R I A
T Y Y R S N O I T P O B N E
Y F P H W K C R E B A T E F
```

Daffodil bulbs live underground through the bitter winter and then emerge as beautiful blooms in many different colors. Here are 29 types of this popular spring flower.

ACCENT

AEOLUS

AEROLITE

ALBATROSS

ARMADA

BLARNEY

CARLTON

CHUNGKING

DAMSON

EMPEROR

FESTIVITY

FORTUNE

HAWERA

HEBRON

MAGNET

MERMAID

NOBILITY

OLYMPIA

PIGEON

RED SEA

SNOWFLAKE

ST. EGWIN

ST. OLAF

TAIN

TEXAS

THELMA

TORCH

VANILLA

VICTORIA

```
A E O L U S K H C R O T N W
S M N O R B E H V A E O U O
F P Y U K H U C L T T F O A
A E T T T N O B I L I T Y D
L R I D G R A L R T R B T A
O O V K A T O A D B E E T M
T R I G R R C F A L X A H R
S N T O E M E R M A I D E A
G T S A W M U N S R D D L D
T S E K A L F W O N S Y M D
D I F G H W N T N E C C A X
T D N I W I C A A Y G I P N
U E A I A I P M Y L O I V K
T R N T V A N I L L A C P S
```

ON THE HOUSE

Prior to President Theodore Roosevelt officially giving the WHITE House its current name in 1901, the building was known variously as the "President's Palace," the "President's House," and the "Executive Mansion." This "Capital" color and other words that precede "house" have made their home in the diagram here.

BIRD
BOARD
BOAT
BUNK
CARRIAGE
CLEARING
CLUB
COFFEE
COUNTRY
COURT
DOLL
DREAM
FARM
FIRE
FRATERNITY
GATE
GREEN
GUARD
LIGHT
MANOR
MEETING
MOVIE
OPERA
PACKING
PLAY
PORTER
POWER

RANCH
ROAD
ROOMING
ROUND
SCHOOL
SORORITY

STATE
STATION
TOLL
TOWN
WHITE
WORK

```
R G E L F L T O L L D S F F
D W T L G A T E K B C G R I
U R L H O W R I G H C N A R
Y O A B G H C V O R H A T E
D N U O R I C O F F E E E T
P L A Y B T L M U O P E R A
C G N I T E E M P N T H N T
K N D I G I A O Y W T H I S
Y I S R C N R C R M O R T U
A K S T A T I O N D E R Y T
D C O Y E U N M R W U G K L
C A R R I A G E O O O M N R
Y P O R M H A P C O S T U F
L F A R M M G N I D R I B G
```

TEA PARTY

The British custom of afternoon tea was first introduced around 1840 by the Duchess of Bedford. Circle the 29 things you might find at a tea party that are listed below.

BREAD

BUTTER

CAKES

CHINA

COOKIES

CRACKERS

CREAMER

CUPS

DOLLIES

FORKS

HONEY

JELLIES

KNIVES

LEMON

MILK

NAPKINS

PASTRY

PLATES

SANDWICHES

SAUCERS

SCONES

SILVER

SPOONS

SUGAR

TABLECLOTH

TARTS

TEA CART

TEAPOT

WASTE BOWL
(for tea leaves or bags)

```
S D S N O O P S R J J H A T
S A N D W I C H E S E L B A
N E O E G Y L N S I L V E R
I R P N C H B J O Y L T O T
K B L H C U P S E M I L W S
P P A S T R Y N R Y E A O V
A W T T C O O K I E S L K D
N N E E N H L R G T C L T B
I R S K A S P C E S I U E C
H T E G K P R B E M E C A Y
C V N R Y A O V I L A K C S
P S O L G W I T R J B E A T
M F C U L N S R E K C A R C
S G S O K L D I A G E R T C
```

JEWELERS' SETTINGS

Gems can be cut into various shapes that bring out each stone's individual beauty. The list below consists of many shapes as well as types of settings jewels are commonly set in.

BAGUETTE

BEZEL

BIZANTINE

CLUSTER

CROSS

CUSHION

DIAMOND

EMERALD

FILAGREE

HEART

INITIALS

LOCKET

MARQUISE

NUMBERS

OCTAGON

OVAL

PEAR

PEARL CUP

PINS

PRINCESS

RADIANT CUT

ROUND

SCALLOP

SQUARE

STAR

TEARDROP

TRIANGLE

TRILLION

```
S A K Q S D N O M A I D C Q
R B Q N Q E T O L I P D L E
E G I S U R N P I O U S U Z
B P Z S A U C I E L C N S U
M I O E R F N S T A L K T T
U B H C E I I A L N R I E B
N P M N T U E L G N A I R T
O K O I Q A O F A M E Z Q T
I V A R M P G H L G P T I O
H L A P D N U O R R R L C B
S M L L V R O F N D A E U E
U T G E I B A G U E T T E Z
C R O S S E M E R A L D S E
O R R A D I A N T C U T H L
```

CACTUS CRITTERS

The cactus thrives in the desert areas of the United States, and it plays an important part in the lives of the creatures that exist alongside it.

Many desert animals depend on the cactus to survive. For example, elf owls may use a hole carved by woodpeckers to raise their babies inside. A ringtail might use it as a perch to search for enemies or its next meal, while tortoises often munch on prickly pear fruit.

```
P E R C H T O S U R V I V E
Y O T S A E S U T H G I M N
M N S S R L I T H C N U M E
M T A E A E I C E G F H S M
D T R M A U K A I O O I E I
I E I E R R E C R L A A S E
N N N F S S C E E R L Y I S
A E G O U E X H O P B C O E
N X T Y D A D T F D D D T L
B T A F M N V E E O E O R F
W M I P O V E V O L R D O O
I Y L K C I R P N O I I T W
P E A R B A B I E S W H T L
I N B V C I N S I D E R W S
```

HOCKEY TERMS

For more than a century, the **STANLEY CUP** has remained unchallenged as the symbol of supremacy in the sport of ice hockey. It is the oldest trophy competed for by professional athletes in North America, pre-dating tennis's Davis Cup by seven years. Here are some terms that are associated with this sport.

ASSIST

BLADES

BLUE LINE

BOARDS

CENTER

CHECK

CREASE

DEFENSE

FACE-OFF

FORWARD

GOALIE

HAT TRICK

HOOKING

ICING

LEFT WING

LINESMAN

NET

OFFSIDE

PASS

PENALTY

PERIOD

POWER PLAY

PUCK

RIGHT WING

RINK

ROUGHING

SLAP SHOT

SLASHING

SPEARING

STANLEY CUP

```
P F O R W A R D R B W C T E
M Y T L A N E P O N L E S I
P A P M F F N A M S E N I L
B L A D E S R G T L S T S A
O P S N C D C A H A A E S O
W R S L S H N U G P E R A G
D E G S G L E F K S R Y N R
O W D N E D A C T H C I N O
I O E Y I C I S K O W I G U
R P C S E R I G H T W I N G
E U F O T A A P F I B K I H
P F F T B L U E L I N E C I
O F A P Y C L H P I U G I N
R H O O K I N G R S C Y U G
```

NEW BRUNSWICK LOCALES

Located on Canada's east coast, New Brunswick is the country's only officially bilingual (French and English) province. Head on up to the Great White North and visit these cities and towns of New Brunswick — or, as French New Brunswickers would say, Nouveau-Brunswick.

ALMA

ANAGANCE

ARGYLE

BATH

BAYFIELD

BOCABEC

BRISTOL

CHATHAM

CLAIR

CLIFTON

CONNELL

DEBEC

DOAKTOWN

FAIRISLE

GRAFTON

HARCOURT

HOWARD

JUNIPER

KARS

KILBURN

LEPREAU

LINDSAY

MARTINON

MINTO

NORTON

RENOUS

REXTON

SHEILA

SURREY

UPHAM

```
Y N L Y I C E B A C O B S W
A K O E D P E L B C K H N O
S E A R P O N J S L E O R D
D U R R T R N G W I T B R W
N A G U S O E M L F R A E I
I J Y S T J N A A T W I M D
L H L X O E T R U O C R A H
B L E R R P G T H N H N H F
A R E J E E X I M N A R P I
T U I N B P N N C G T U U P
H T Y S N P I O A L H B W W
D O A K T O W N U L A L M A
W M I N T O C B U S M I H Y
B A Y F I E L D A J J K R U
```

QUOTESEARCH

Charles Haddon Spurgeon (1834-1892), an English Baptist preacher, joined the Baptist communion in 1850. He was so popular that the Metropolitan Tabernacle was built and opened in 1861 to accommodate his large audiences which topped more than 10,000 people. The following passage is a quote from England's best-known preacher for most of the second half of the 19th century.

The greatest works are done by the ones. The hundreds do not often do much — the companies never; it is the units — the single individuals, that are the power and the might. Individual effort is, after all, the grand thing.

```
G R A N D A T W P L I I E N
B H L Y N F O A A I N N L E
Y G L D T R H U N D R E D S
T T T O K R D S I T I V O T
H H H S E I E V E S C E U I
E O E E V N I T L E H R P N
K A D I S D O T F T S P L U
A B D N U I H D H A Y G V E
E N E A E G N C E E S N P H
I F L P I T U G I R H I N T
I S F M S M F N L G A H C S
T R M O R E W O P E H T H E
Y D U C R C U O U H E V W N
V D O N O T E R A T A H T O
```

"X" MARKS THE SPOT

There's an INFLUX of words containing an "X" that have made their way into the diagram. Sit back and RELAX as you search for them all.

AFFIX

ANNEX

APEX

APPENDIX

BEESWAX

CHATTERBOX

CLIMAX

COAX

COMPLEX

CONVEX

DUPLEX

EQUINOX

FLAX

FLEX

HOAX

INDEX

INFLUX

JINX

KLEENEX

LATEX

ONYX

PERPLEX

RELAX

SPHINX

SYNTAX

TELEX

VORTEX

XEROX

```
D C P J Y T D I U F R M S X
R F P I J E S I N D E X Y V
T Y A F F I X A L F E R N J
X P S A A S N O I N L S T P
U X E L P U D X N C H U A A
K I A H M K C A O I X O X P
O D I M X J B M O S U E A E
D N O O I E P B V X L Q L X
X E N E E L K M O P V N E F
O P A S E P C T R K K T R K
R P W X O B R E T T A H C M
E A W V Y F P L E L A P F L
X A O C O N V E X A P M J S
L F S H W L O X B A C X U D
```

THE CONGO RIVER

In Africa, the CONGO River's length (2,900 miles) is second only to that of the Nile. Its river basin is the second largest in the world, after the Amazon, with a drainage area of 1,335,000 square miles. The river and its main tributaries, most of which are navigable, are listed below.

ALIMA
ARUWIMI
BOMOKANDI
BOMU
BUSIRA
CHAMBESHI
CONGO
FIMI
GIRI
ITURI
KASAI
KOTTO
KWANGO
KWILU
LINDI
LOMAMI
LOMELA
LOPORI
LUALABA
LUAMA
LUAPULA
LUBILASH
LUFIRA
LUKUGA

LULONGA
LUSHIKO
LUVUA
MARINGA
MONGALA
SANGA

SANKURU
TSHUAPA
UBANGI
UELE
WAMBA

```
R I R O P O L E B M W D I O
L H K I T U R I O A O K D G
S I V R K N R M M R M W N V
A U V U L I N B O I K I I G
G N G O G N A W K N W L L I
N A G N O L U L A G G U M A
A B O R U R U K N A S A R I
S P O P P W P B D H M L L A
C H A M B E S H I O C A U A
I U R U G C K K L L E B M R
L A I P H L O M E L A A O I
B K S M G S T N E N U S B F
L O U A I L T U G L E W H U
G E B W K F O I S O E D B L
```

DRAWING THE LINE

This is definitely not a puzzle for the FAINT of heart! ZIGZAG your way through the diagram and loop the following ways a line can appear.

ANGULAR

ARCHED

BENT

BROAD

BROKEN

CROOKED

CURVED

DARK

DASHED

DOTTED

DOUBLE

FAINT

HEAVY

HORIZONTAL

JAGGED

LIGHT

LONG

NARROW

PARALLEL

PERPENDI-
CULAR

ROUGH

SHORT

SLANTED

STRAIGHT

VERTICAL

WAVY

WIDE

ZIGZAG

```
F P E R P E N D I C U L A R
P O L B I A L E L L A R A P
D V B U R L L T K T C L F V
Y P U R K O L T N O U A I G
G L O E B P A O O G R O E A
J W D L V F Z D N N V B P T
G I L H E I J A G G E D T A
W W I C R O O K E D D R T N
N L G O T Z R O E E O G N D
E T H G I A R T S H Z E E A
W N T G C I N Y S C G H B R
R I Z U A A B G V R S U Y K
G A L T L R U H E A V Y O T
G F R S O U I D D B W P T R
```

AFRICAN PARKS

We're off on a puzzle safari! Adventure and beauty await as you explore the diagram below and come across the names of 28 African National Parks.

AMBOSELI

AWASH

BANHINE

ETOSHA

GORON-GOSA

HLUHLUWE

KASUNGU

KRUGER

LEFINI

LENGWE

MASAI MARA

MATAPOS

MERU

MIKUMI

MKOMAZI

MKUZI

MLILWANE

NAIROBI

NGORONGORO

NYIKA

RUAHA

SABIE SAND

SAMBURU

SELOUS

SHIMBA HILLS

TARANGIRE

TSAVO

UMFOLOZI

```
A G Y A W A S H M E R U I O
N U O S N E M L N D W A M V
L A O R L K I I E N Y I K A
E I N O O L H R R A M S U S
F V U M W N I E H S A M Z T
I S A A A G G H K E S I I M
N Z N B N U I O A I A K E A
I E F A R L L W S B I U W T
P R R K I A E Y U A M M U A
O A H A U R S N N S A I L P
T N N G O R O N G O R O H O
A Y P R U F B B U W A D U S
I Z O L O F M U I U E A L Y
W U R U B M A S E T O S H A
```

STATES OF CONFUSION

If you find yourself in **DALLAS**, South Dakota, and you ask, "How 'bout them Cowboys?," chances are the residents might not know you were inquiring about a certain professional football team. Below are cities whose names are the same as cities that are better known for being located in other states.

AKRON (Ala.)

ALBANY (Ga.)

ANNAPOLIS (Mo.)

ATLANTA (Ida.)

AUSTIN (Colo.)

BOSTON (Ind.)

BUFFALO (N. Dak.)

CLEVELAND (Okla.)

DALLAS (S. Dak.)

DAYTON (Ore.)

DENVER (Iowa)

DES MOINES (Wash.)

HARTFORD (Iowa)

HOLLYWOOD (Ga.)

HOUSTON (Pa.)

LAS VEGAS (N. Mex.)

MEMPHIS (Fla.)

MIAMI (Ind.)

MINNEAPOLIS (Kans.)

NASHVILLE (Ill.)

NEWARK (Del.)

OAKLAND (Iowa)

PHILADELPHIA (Tenn.)

PHOENIX (Ore.)

PORTLAND (Colo.)

SAN DIEGO (Tex.)

SCRANTON (S.C.)

SYRACUSE (Neb.)

TOLEDO (Ill.)

TRENTON (Mich.)

```
O A K L A N D A Y T O N Y R B
N U O L A F F U B O P F S N O
H S V D T S Y R A C U S E O N
A T Y V E M V D L B X A N T D
R I M M I N N E A P O L I S H
T N H A M A V A G S T L O O D
F K M P L E S E S A O A M B K
O I R T L Y N I R H S D S G S
R H R A N E L O H C V X E O A
D O N A W O D U R P U I D D N
P D B E P E T A R K M N L E D
R L R A P F N S L O A E B L I
A T N A L T A A U I U O M O E
M N D O O W Y L L O H H E T G
A P R N O T N E R T H P R T O
```

Nathaniel Hawthorne (1804-64), novelist and short-story writer, was one of the great masters of American fiction. His novels and tales are penetrating explorations of moral and spiritual conflicts. Below is a quote from this great writer.

Happiness in this world, when it comes, comes incidentally. Make it the object of pursuit, and it leads us on a wild-goose chase, and is never attained. Follow some other object, and very possibly we may find that we have caught happiness without dreaming of it.

```
W W O L L O F I T A N D I S
V I R E H T O B J E C T F I
I T M B T R D L R O W H I N
N H A P P I N E S S H G N C
T O E M O S U Y N V E U D I
H U E O C S R S A I N A T D
I T C O M E S D R M A C H E
S S M J V N L I C U E T A N
E E U D P I E J B J P W T T
S V N S W P W V B L J F I A
A A L A D P L O E D Y E O L
H G N I M A E R D R K F U L
C O E V A H E W L A D P J Y
A N D I T M R L M E S O O G
```

During World War II, when so many men were fighting in Europe and the Pacific, there were not enough players to fill the rosters of all of the National Football League teams. In 1943, the Philadelphia Eagles and the Pittsburgh Steelers combined their players and became the Phil-Pitt Steagles. Here is the roster of the 1943 Steagles.

BOVA (Tony)

BUTLER (John)

CABRELLI (Larry)

CANALE (Rocco)

CONTI (Enio)

DOLLY (Dick)

DOYLE (Ted)

FRANK (Joe)

GAUER (Charles)

GRAVES (Ray)

HEWITT (Bill)

HINKLE (John)

KILROY (Frank)

KISH (Ben)

LAUX (Ted)

MASTERS (Bob)

MICHAELS (Ed)

MILLER (Tom)

PASCHKA (Gordon)

SADER (Steve)

SCHULTZ (Eberle)

SEARS (Vic)

SHERMAN (Alex)

STEELE (Ernie)

STEWARD (Dean)

THURBON (Bob)

TOMASIC (Andy)

WUKITS (Al)

ZIMMERMAN (Leroy)

```
S G G M F B X R E D A S C M
P Y A R L U U L C O N T I W
Z I U R A M A T N S T L U S
A Y E L K N I H L R L K E O
N Y R S A I N U X E I A S V
P A S C H K A R R T R D M E
T O M A S I C B S S Y V I V
T S L R T C A O A A O U C L
I K E N E C H N A M R E H S
W O N V W M X U F G L L A U
E A F A A S M M L E I Y E V
H X Z V R R U I E T K O L S
Y L L O D F G T Z M Z D S F
W V T B K I S H R V O U S T
```

The following passage is an observation made by American humorist Robert Benchley (1889-1945), who was also drama critic for *Life* and *The New Yorker*.

There is something about saying "O.K." and hanging up the receiver with a bang that kids a man into feeling that he has just pulled off a big deal, even if he has only called up central to find out the correct time.

```
N G G G R T S H A S O N L Y
P G D U G N A B U A M A N O
N S A R V N Y H P N B F T Y
F U D B G N I H T E M O S S
R D S I Y K N L H E K T U N
J V N G K M G F E A R F J T
B G U D C E I R N E V E S C
F B U E S E T D V O F F A H
E E R A I D N I F O T L H F
B H E L E C E T M L L N T R
Y T T L R C O R R E C T I I
V T L A E O M F D A F W W J
T U M R H B B U L R L N B B
P O L U T T P Y O U H S C T
```

Much of our knowledge of the **PAST** comes from the work of archaeologists. These scientific detectives are the people who **EXCAVATE** a historical **SITE** and meticulously sift through **LAYERS** of dirt and dust in search of clues. Sometimes they find **TREASURE**, and other times they find **POTTERY** or ancient **RECORDS**. Do a little excavating of your own as you uncover 27 words pertaining to archaeology in the diagram below.

ARTIFACTS

ARTWORK

BEADS

BONES

EVIDENCE

EXCAVATE

FEATURES

GOLD

LAYERS

METHODS

OBJECTS

PAST

POTTERY

RADIO-
CARBON
(dating)

RECORDS

RELATIVE
(dating)

RESEARCH

RUINS

SITE

SONAR
(scanning)

STRATA

TABLETS

TEMPLE

TOMB

TOOLS

TREASURE

TYPOLOGY

```
S D R O C E R S E B A F A W
E S R E Y A L X T T O O L S
N L T A L H C R A E S E R O
O V P R D A J R B R L H B N
B S O M V I T M C U E B E A
Y I T A E S O I K S O C A R
X T T C D T K C V A N Y D T
Y E E S E R U T A E F G S I
K B R C O J E X D R H O R F
K D Y W F F B I M T B L U A
S U T T R U V O X G A O I C
X R S S M E T H O D S P N T
A B O O A O G L V Y N Y S S
P W A L U P D I S S P T V I
```

"W" MAMMALS

WAPITI is another name for the North American elk, and a WOMBAT is an Australian marsupial that looks like a bear but is about the size of a badger. They join the 25 other "W" mammals in the list below.

WALLABY

WALLAROO

WALRUS

WANDEROO (monkey)

WAPITI

WARINE (monkey)

WARRAGAL (wild dog)

WART HOG

WASH BEAR (raccoon)

WATERBUCK

WATER BUFFALO

WATER CAVY

WATER DEER

WATER OPOSSUM

WEASEL

WEEPER (monkey)

WHALE

WIDOW MONKEY

WILDCAT

WILDEBEEST

WOLF

WOLVERINE

WOMBAT

WOOD BABOON

WOODCHUCK

WOOLY (monkey)

WOW-WOW (gibbon)

```
C W B O M N O O B A B D O O W
O V I L E S A E W O W W O W I
S Y T A B M O W F W E R K A D
K Y I W W U W O L F E C P L O
C B P B O I V K R D P R O L W
U A A Y L O A T N B E B A A M
B L W D V T D A G R R F U R O
R L C A E A W C E O F M A O N
E A H T R M C E H U H E S O K
T W K A I I D R B U B T U W E
A H W M N R N R E H C R H Y
W I L D E B E E S T F K L A K
L M U T C T W A R R A G A L W
W W A R A B W O O L Y W W E M
T W P W A T E R O P O S S U M
```

NONSENSE!

Let's have no foolishness, now! This is a puzzle to take seriously, even though it consists of words for various kinds of silliness. Most of them originated in informal conversation and writing in English and other languages.

ABSURD

BALDERDASH

BALONEY

BLAH

BOSH

BUNK

CLAPTRAP

DRIVEL

FIDDLE-FADDLE

FLIMFLAM

FLUBDUB

FOLDERAL

GUFF

HOGWASH

HOKUM

HOOEY

HORSE-FEATHERS

HUMBUG

MALARKEY

MUMBO JUMBO

NONSENSE

PIFFLE

RUBBISH

TOMMYROT

TRASH

TRIPE

TRUMPERY

TWADDLE

```
V K N U B U D B U L F O I H
M G T R U M P E R Y I W K O
H M S E D R I V E L D T B O
J U A K B M U K O H D A N E
G M P L P A R T P A L C L Y
R B A W F A L T B O E F N F
U O H B L M O D N L F G O H
B J V A S R I E E I A L N S
B U M N Y U Y L P R D H S A
I M U M P O R D F E D S E W
S B M H I F F D R V L A N G
H O R S E F E A T H E R S O
T N K O U U L W W F H T E H
H U M B U G N T R I P E L I
```

BOYS NAMES

Here's a bevy of names that may "B" useful if you're expecting a new baby boy in your life. There are 39 in all; we hope you'll "B" entertained by this boffo puzzle!

BARNEY
BARRY
BART
BASIL
BAXTER
BEAU
BENEDICT
BENJAMIN
BENNY
BERNARD
BERT
BILLY
BJORN
BLAINE
BLAIR
BLAKE
BOBBY
BOONE
BOOTH
BORIS
BOYD
BRAD
BRAM
BRANDON
BRENDON
BRENT
BRET

BRIAN
BROCK
BRODERICK
BROOK
BRUCE
BRUNO

BRYAN
BUCK
BUDDY
BURKE
BURT
BYRON

```
C X M I S E R I A L B T B O
B D E E U D B J O R N R L T
O A C O B A R R Y E I T A R
J K R H X Y E A R A B Y K B
M C C T T E N B N L T N E R
A O E K N O D N A R B N T O
R R M O B D O I U R E E R D
B B O O A R N B U D N B K E
S B U R K E U N I B J E N R
U I B B S D O C A H A L Y I
C L H X D R T R E B M S K C
U L K Y Y B B O B U I E I K
X Y A B O R I S R C N N H L
O R S O B O L O O K O I N H
```

NORTH AMERICAN BIRDS

John James Audubon, who came to the United States from Haiti in 1803, gained world renown for his magnificent paintings of North American birds. You can check his *Birds of America* for a SWIFT look at such creatures as the CARDINAL or the WOODPECKER. Of course if you don't want to wait TEAL you can get a copy, we suggest you just take a look out your window!

BLACKBIRD
BLUEBIRD
CARDINAL
CATBIRD
CROW

CUCKOO
DOVE
DUCK
GOLDFINCH
GOOSE

GREBE
GULL
HERON
LARK
LOON
MAGPIE
MALLARD
MEADOWLARK
MOCKING-BIRD
ORIOLE
PELICAN
PHOEBE
PIGEON
PIPIT
QUAIL
RAVEN
ROBIN
SNIPE
SPARROW
SWALLOW
SWAN
SWIFT
TANAGER
TEAL
TERN
WOODPECKER
WREN

```
P Q P I G E O N F S S I A G
G E U N R O C R W E V O D K
L S L A R K L A N I D R A C
O T V I I B L D T E I D O U
O E E F C L T L F B R K S D
N A S R O A H L E I I W G R
S L O W N C N U B I N R K A
P W O A U K L G E F P C D L
A L G C H B N O R E H G H L
R E K S N I P E G L N H A A
R O I I K R A L W O D A E M
O N B C R D F S W I F T W R
W O O D P E C K E R L C R S
R M M T I P I P H O E B E I
```

COUNTRY CROONERS

At the age of 19, Faith HILL moved to Nashville, Tennessee, to pursue a career in country music. In January 1994, Hill made history when her debut single "Wild One," from *Take Me As I Am*, held the No. 1 position for four consecutive weeks on Billboard's Country Singles Chart. It was during the 1996 "Spontaneous Combustion" tour that Hill met her future husband, fellow singer Tim MCGRAW. Hum along as you find the names of the following 30 country singers.

BROOKS (Garth)
CHESNEY (Kenny)
CLARK (Terri)
DIXIE CHICKS (The)
EDWARDS (Kathleen)
GILL (Vince)
GRACIN (Josh)
HAGGARD (Merle)
HILL (Faith)
JACKSON (Alan)
KEITH (Toby)
LYNN (Loretta)
MCBRIDE (Martina)
MCENTIRE (Reba)
MCGRAW (Tim)
MESSINA (Jo Dee)
NELSON (Willie)
PAISLEY (Brad)
PARTON (Dolly)
PRIDE (Charley)
RIMES (LeAnn)
ROGERS (Kenny)
STRAIT (George)
TRAVIS (Randy)
TRITT (Travis)
URBAN (Keith)
WILLIAMS (Hank, Jr.)
WILSON (Gretchen)
WOMACK (Lee Ann)
YOAKAM (Dwight)

```
L L I G C K A T V P G A H N
C V L R E Y U N U K A P I C
T P R I D E R E X H A C A E
Y N T M H N B S D R A W D E
R H O E O S A I T R U I L Y
L N O S L E N O G R R L E O
Y T L S K H N R P B A L M C
D I X I E C H I C K S I L R
W S W N E A A M R I W A T O
X I R A G B T J A O R M J G
W V M G R R H P M K V S L E
P A A V I G Y A G W A V K R
E R I T N E C M B R O O K S
D T T V R K W M L Y N N Y W
```

The Little 500 is a bicycle RACE held annually in Bloomington, Indiana, on the main campus of the Indiana UNIVERSITY system. The race, which was founded in 1951, is modeled after the Indianapolis 500, and forms the centerpiece of the plot of the Academy Award-winning film *Breaking Away* (1979).

BALLANTINE

BLAIR

BUCKNER

COLLEGE

DODDS

DRISCOLL

DUNN

FAIRVIEW

FESS

GENTRY

GIFFORD

GRANT

HOWE

HUNTER

KIRBY

KIRKWOOD

MADISON

MOODY

MORTON

OLIVER

ORRIS

PALMER

RACE

ROGERS

UNIVERSITY

VERMILYA

WALDRON

WALKER

WALNUT

WOODLAWN

WYLIE

```
W A W Y P M O O D Y Y W F H
L Y A A A Y L I M R E V L T
P T L R L R I L T W F U Y Y
U H N I M K V N O N E S T Y
B M U A E U E H O C S I D B
W A T L R G R R A F S N K W
R D L B E G D R D R P I I O
E I V L S L G R E S I R R O
N S L F A I R V I E W O K D
K O W W F N I N O P G V W L
C N T F F N T G D E F O O A
U D O R U U K I R B Y R O W
B R B D O D D S N I H B D N
D N N V Y M L F R E T N U H
```

QUOTESEARCH

Born in Richmond, Virginia, author Tom Wolfe began his professional career as a newspaper reporter. *The Right Stuff*, his account of the early space program, was published in 1979 and won the American Book Award for nonfiction. The following passage comes from this bestseller.

If a man has a talent and cannot use it, he has failed. If he has a talent and uses only half of it, he has partly failed. If he has a talent and learns somehow to use the whole of it, he has gloriously succeeded, and won a satisfaction and a triumph few men ever know.

```
N I K N D W L K W U S E I T
Y O T A L E N T A N D F E E
L S I T T O L T A S A H E H
T O A T W O A I H M T N H T
R S G H C L N E A E R M W I
A N D L E A R N S F I I G F
P A R N O H F U A F U F S O
S N T W P R O S A C M H S N
A O A F E T I I I H P E O N
H W L V A H L O D T H H M E
E D E D E E C C U S A A E M
H N N I D A N D U S E S H W
T A T I F F L A H Y L N O E
I R F O E L O H W V H Y W F
```

PICARD AND COMPANY

The years 1993-94 marked the final season for "Star Trek: The Next Generation." However, that was not the last we saw of Captain Jean-Luc PICARD. To date, there have been three movies featuring the "Next Gen" crew. If you're a fan still waiting for a fourth installment, you can at least recall the TV journeys of the *Enterprise* with this puzzle featuring members of the crew and some of the characters they met in their travels.

ARDRA
ARIEL
BARCLAY
BATEMAN
BEATE

BOOTHBY
COREY
CRUSHER
DATA
DURKEN

GEORDI
GUINAN
HAYES
HUGH
JARTH
KAZAGO
KELL
KRITE
KURN
LANEL
LEACH
LORE
LURSA
LWAXANA
MARTA
MAVEK
MIRASTA
MORAG
NAYROK
N'VEK
O'BRIEN
PICARD
RIKER
SAREK
SELA
SHELBY
TASHA YAR
TROI
WESLEY
WORF
ZAYNER

```
H T R A J K P L G K P A G G
U K E T U E W A E T I R K S
G T A R S A R E K I D D E E
H Y N A O O U R S R R R L E
H B A M M L A N E L O A L M
I L Y L I Z C K Y W E W H W
U E R U C R I B A A G Y Z O
P H O R U R A D H X M A G R
I S K S N T A S H A Y A R F
C O H A E E B T N Z K O Y
A E R M Z L I B E A T E Y L
R L A T A D U R K E N V E K
D N A N I U G E B L E A C H
C O R E Y B H T O O B M W W
```

With an area of 495,755 square miles, the Republic of Chad is the fifth largest country in Africa. Despite its size, however, the country has a population density of only about 10 persons per square mile. We've hidden 36 of Chad's prominent cities, towns, and villages below, including the capital, N'DJAMENA.

ABECHE
ABOU DEIA
ADRE
AM DAM
AM TIMAN
AOZOU
ARADA
BAIBOKOUM
BARDAI
BILTINE
BOKORO
BONGOR
BOUSSO
DJEDDA
DOBA
FADA
FIANGA
GEZENTI
GOURO
GOZ BEIDA
KELO
KYABE
LARGEAU
LERE
MASSAKORY
MOISSALA

MONGO
MOUNDOU
MOUSSORO
N'DJAMENA
NOKOU

OURI
PALA
YEBBI BOU
ZIGEY
ZOUAR

```
M N K Y A B E C H E K B F P
L A R G E A U C B R F I A O
G M D K A I A O Y E I L D S
O I I M U B K R D L A T A P
S T G L A O O I A S N I T G
S M Y A R K B U S D G N M Y
U A M O A O P I D N A E E G
O R O S S U O M B E D G E O
B G S H I M O O A B I Z R U
Z A N E M A J D N Z E A D R
M O Z O O K D U N N B Y A O
C R U Z M E G R T U Z Y B G
H R O A J L P I A N O K O U
I U G D R O G N O B G M D A
```

Long before winning a Best Actor Academy Award for *Wall Street*, Michael Douglas spent his time on streets found on the opposite side of the country. He, along with Karl Malden, starred in the police drama "The Streets of San Francisco." Below are some of the streets where they may have worked their beat.

BATTERY

BEALE

BRANNAN

BRYANT

BUSH

CHESTNUT

ELLIS

FOLSOM

FRANKLIN

FREMONT

GEARY

GOUGH

HARRISON

HOWARD

HYDE

JACKSON

JONES

KING

LARKIN

MAIN

MARKET

MASON

MISSION

PACIFIC

POLK

POWELL

SPEAR

STEUART

STOCKTON

TAYLOR

TOWNSEND

UNION

VALLEJO

VAN NESS

```
F T V A L L E J O E L A E B
O Y H Y D E M W A R L R D R
L I S A Y A S B O C J N R A
S N U P R S U L I F K O A N
O T B K E R Y F R R G S W N
M H E N T A I C O E J A O A
V T N U T C R S F M D M H N
M A I N A S U R O O N C O A
V Y K P B R A H M N E I S O
K B R Y A N T U N T S E H C
F K A A K L O P L S N A Y W
S I L L E W O P I O W F L G
N O I N U G K M J G O U G H
G N I K W S T O C K T O N O
```

STREETS OF LINCOLN

Lincoln, NEBRASKA, was originally named Lancaster, but was renamed in 1867 soon after the assassination of President Abraham Lincoln. The capital of the CORNHUSKER State, Lincoln is the home of the University of Nebraska and birthplace of current Vice President Dick Cheney.

ARLENE

BANCROFT

BROWER

BURNHAM

CALVERT

CONNIE

CORNHUSKER

COTNER

CUSTER

DUNN

FOLSOM

HOLLY

KEARNEY

KESSLER

LOGAN

MORRILL

MORTON

NEBRASKA

NEMAHA

OLD CHENEY

PIONEERS

PLATTE

RANCHO

THAYER

VAN DORN

VILLAGE

WEBSTER

WOODS

```
N D G P I O N E E R S D H F
M O R R I L L I P A C T A S
G W T F E A N D C N A F G K
W H M R H N U F C C L O C E
N E A A O L T V R H V R U A
E N M C H M A O M O E C S R
P E U F M N F F C K R N T N
N L U D D U R M S R T A E E
A R A O F E V U F B P B R Y
G A R T T O H D B Y R U C F
O N E S T N L E G A L L I V
L V B T R E L S S E K L H V
R E W O R B T K O S D O O W
W Y C R E Y A H T M O P R H
```

POETRY SEARCH: STEVENSON

Robert Louis Stevenson (1850-94), the Scottish novelist, poet, and essayist, is probably best known for his novels *Treasure Island*, *Kidnapped* (set in his native Scotland), and *The Strange Case of Dr. Jekyll and Mr. Hyde*. The poetic piece below is taken from his *A Child's Garden of Verses*; it is the first verse of "My Shadow."

I have   goes in   can be

a little   and out   the use

shadow   with me,   of him

that   and what   is more

than I

can see.

He is

very, very

like me

from the

heels

up to

the head;

And I

see him

jump

before

me, when

I jump

into

my bed.

```
O P L L O K D O B A J D E K
B R P P I T F R D I E I D C
M M M W N K W B E B N A C M
T N U S A V E R Y V E R Y H
A W J P H L O M B H U M I Y
H L I F T M I H E E S N A C
W G M T S O V H F W T I G R
D L I I H J T D O O H S E T
N L H J W M A H R U E E H H
A R F B O N E T E R E O N A
P T O R D V B S C U L G I T
W M F O A N D I J U S T I F
U S U H H D I U V P Y E C M
U T I J S E E I M K L D L R
```

WINNING JOCKEYS

Giddyap, horsey! Hmm, it's probably a safe bet that's not the command jockey Bill HARTACK used to spur Northern Dancer on to victory at the 1964 Queen's Plate. You can find him and 39 other jockeys who have won this prestigious race riding throughout the diagram below.

ALCOTT (Ben)
ARCARO (Eddie)
ATTARD (Larry)
BAILEY (Howard)
BIRLEY (Denny)
BRAMMER (Danny)
BURNS (Guy)
CLARK (David)
DUGAN (Eddie)
FELL (Jeff)
FOLEY (Jimmy)
GATES (Allie)
GOMEZ (Avelino)
HARRIS (Wayne)
HARTACK (Bill)
HAWLEY (Sandy)
HAZARD (John)
HORN (Frank)
INOUYE (Tak)
LANDRY (Robert)
LANG (Chick)
LEWIS (Harry)
LITTLE (Henry)
LYKE (Larry)
MANN (Frank)
MASON (R. J.)

MINK (Lee)
NASH (Ronnie)
PARSONS (Bill)
PHAIR (Charles)
PICHON (Leslie)
PLATTS (Robin)
REGAN (Frank)

ROGERS (Chris)
SOUTER (John Paul)
WALLS (George)
WALSH (Jimmy)
WATSON (Bobby)
WATTS (Harry)
WISE (Charles)

```
P N S W A L L S I N O U Y E
H S E I R K I N S E L L E F
S T T A W E T Y R D N A L R
A L A T W E T G E O E S I W
N Y G P A B L U G E H N A U
Z K B I R L E Y O A O R B H
B E T C B O P A R S O N S D
Y M M H W R H T T O C L A P
B E I O S A A A A T A H N H
D B L N G C W M Z W A A A A
W U R O K R L I M A G R G I
K U G S F A E A H E R N D R
B I C A I Z Y L R I R D A Y
Z I D M N N A M S K E A E L
```

BATTLE HYMN

Julia Ward Howe was born in 1819 and lived until 1910, long enough to see the "Battle Hymn of the Republic" she wrote in 1861 become one of the most famous and loved American songs.

Mine

eyes

have

seen

the

glory

of the

coming

of the

Lord;

He is

trampling

out the

vintage

where

the

grapes

of wrath

are

stored;

He hath

loosed

the

fateful

lightning

of His

terrible,

swift

sword;

His

Truth is

marching on.

```
S I H F O Z E L Y G L O R Y
T R E N K N Z Y C S B F L Z
E R H M I F F L E E H T F O
R Z A M A R E P G S R H S K
R T T M X R A H A U Q E W C
I C H I P R C Z T V G U O J
B O Z E G L C H N N F M R Q
L O U Q H E I S I H I V D G
E F G T Z S K N V N V Z U L
S W I F T W T H G E G H O Y
G R H E C H I O Z N L O R D
Z A H A G E E V R E S C N D
S T U I V R L U F E T A F U
U H L K I E Z Y D S D Y C H
```

FRIENDS FOREVER

Real friends tell you your faults and foibles and assist you with their hands and hearts in times of trouble. Qualities that we all admire in our friends are listed below.

AFFABLE

AMIABLE

AMUSING

ATTENTIVE

CARING

CHEERY

CORDIAL

FLEXIBLE

GENIAL

GENUINE

GIVING

HELPFUL

HONEST

KIND

LOYAL

NATURAL

NICE

OPEN

POLITE

REAL

RELIABLE

RESPONSIVE

SINCERE

SOCIABLE

STEADY

SUPPORTIVE

TOLERANT

TRUE

TRUSTWORTHY

WARM

```
E R E C N I S O C I A B L E
F A R V E E L B I X E L F V
D I F C I O E G E N I A L I
R N I F Y T A M I A B L E T
E N I A A Y N U R V N D R R
S S L K D B N E L A I U S O
P T N A R E L O T E S N T P
O W E H G I A E E T C H G P
N T P U A Y I H W I A E N U
S N O B R T D O A L R L I S
I R L E H T R N R O I P S E
V E E Y A T O E M P N F U R
E H E A H N C S O T G U M U
C S E Y L N A T U R A L A D
```

GERANIUM GARDEN

Geraniums are popular garden or greenhouse shrubs grown for their colorful flowers, their ornamental foliage, and often for the aromatic oils extracted from both. Their long, beak-shaped fruits give them the name stork's-bill. Look for the 33 varieties planted in the grid.

ALPHA

ALTAIR

APRICOT

AURORA

BIMBO

CONGO

FANTASIA

FERN LEAF

FLIRT

GINGER

HAPPY

HAWKEYE

JUBILEE

KRISTA

LADY MARY

LA FRANCE

LIME

LITTLE GEM

MABEL

MEDLEY

MRS. COX

NUTMEG

ORANGE

RADIO RED

REDONDO

ROGUE

ROSEBUD

ROSETTE

SNOWFLAKE

SWISS MISS

TRUE ROSE

VENUS

VOODOO

```
O C F N H E C N A R F A L T
G I N G E R K F R H E B R S
N W K R I S T A H E S I U E
O Y R A M Y D A L W L N R G
C H T R B I P I I F E L E N
I L R O O P B S F V W Y D A
A O U R Y U S A E H E O O R
N O E U J M E T H K T A N O
Y D R A I L T N W P P R D S
E O O S N E U A L R L M O E
L O S R S T H F I I P A B B
D V E O M R S C O X M B M U
E F R E U G O R L C B E I D
M E G E L T T I L X F L B F
```

CAT BREEDS

Traditionally presumed to have come from the Isle of Man, the MANX is a breed of tailless domestic cat. The Manx may be born with a tail but ideally should be totally tailless with a hollow at the end of the backbone where the root of the tail should be. It is also distinguished by its characteristic hopping gait. Find this fascinating feline and 26 of his friends in the puzzle below.

ABYSSINIAN

BALINESE

BIRMAN

BRITISH
(Shorthair)

BURMESE

CORNISH
(Rex)

DEVON (Rex)

EGYPTIAN
(Mau)

EXOTIC

HAVANA
(Brown)

JAPANESE
(Bobtail)

KORAT

MAINE
COON

MANX

NORWEGIAN
(Forest Cat)

OCICAT

ORIENTAL

PERSIAN

RAGDOLL

SCOTTISH (Fold)

SELKIRK (Rex)

SIAMESE

SINGAPURA

SOMALI

SPHYNX

TONKINESE

TURKISH (Angora)

```
X P T L B M X K O R A T I S
B H A V A N A H R N X L N B
R H A B Y S S I N I A N T U
I V S H X I E A N M K S A R
T S P I T N I B O E I L L M
I S I T K G I S E N C T E E
S T O A E R J L G X E O X S
H C V W M T U A Y B H N O E
S D R A A E P T P A D K T N
I O N C O U S N T A P I I I
N A I S R E P E I O N N C L
R C U A I Y Y I A I Y E G A
O L L O D G A R N Y G S S B
C D X J A Y A O N O V E D E
```

SHARP AS A TACK

Here's a puzzle for **OBSERVANT** solvers. Use your **DEXTEROUS** puzzle skills to locate the 31 terms that can be used to describe **SHARP** people.

ALERT

ASTUTE

AWARE

BEST

BRAINY

CAPABLE

CEREBRAL

CLEVER

CREDITABLE

DEEP

DEFT

DEXTEROUS

ESTIMABLE

GIFTED

GREAT

INGENIOUS

INTELLIGENT

KEEN

KNOWING

LAUDABLE

OBSERVANT

QUICK

SAGE

SAPIENT

SHARP

SKILLFUL

STERLING

SUBTLE

TALENTED

WISE

WITTY

```
T Q T L F V S H A R P A E N
P E G A S T U T E A C K V R
Q E S U L A R B E R E C T D
K T K D D E X T E R O U S E
Y N I A R B N D N B L U N T
E E L B A M I T S E O I S F
W G L L Y T E E E I I E N I
B I F E A T R L N D B P O G
Q L U B L V T E W G Q T A O
U L L S A B G I V R F X W S
I E E N U N A S W E P V A R
C T T S I X E P D A L E R T
K N O W I N G E A T U C E N
K I N E M W I H K C P K L D
```

BAYS OF AUSTRALIA

Have you ever wanted to explore Australia, but didn't know exactly how to begin? Well, get your feet wet by finding the 30 Australian bays we've hidden.

ABBOT

ANXIOUS

APOLLO

ARCHER

BEAGLE

BLUE MUD

BREMER

BYRON

CARNOT

COLLIER

CONE

GORDON

GUICHEN

HERVEY

JERVIS

JURIEN

KEPPEL

LAGRANGE

MARGARET

MELVILLE

NAPIER

NICHOL

REPULSE

ROEBUCK

ROLLING

SHARK

TEMPLE

TIN CAN

TRIAL

UPSTART

```
G T M R N T R K M L K E R I
B O A S I V R E J A L C C T
Y B R N C A K I S G O U Y I
R B C D H T C A A L Y D D C
O A H S O A U E L L U O U B
N C E N L N B I S L L P M M
M U R L E Y E U E L P M E T
N A P I E R O H O A M L U R
C D R V N I R P C R V R L E
P U R G X B A T I I G X B M
J E G N A R G A L G U L P E
H N A G M R O L L I N G U R
A O D C C K E P P E L E O B
U C H D A X C T R A T S P U
```

FLY AWAY

The aviation industry was born on December 17, 1903, when the Wright brothers made the first successful flight. Today, airplanes are an indispensable part of our lives. CRUISE through the diagram below to find 34 terms associated with aviation.

AIRCRAFT

AIRWAY

ALTITUDE

ANTENNA

APPROACH

BANK

CABIN

CLIMB

CONTROLS

CRUISE

FIELD

FUEL

FUSELAGE

LANDING

LIFT

LOOP

MANEUVER

MOTOR

PILOT

PITCH

PROPELLER

RADAR

RADIO

RANGE

ROLL

RUDDER

RUNWAY

SPIN

TAKEOFF

THROTTLE

THRUST

VELOCITY

WHEELS

ZOOM

```
W E G T K R E V U E N A M L
R V B N H S R A D L L O R S
B Y A Z I R F M O T O R P L
E B U U K D O I I Z L I R R
G G R G P A N T E N N A E S
N C A B I N U A T L C D L C
A H G L V D C K L L D E L O
R U C Y E T L E F U E L E N
D P B A L S S O R H B H P T
T R M W O U U F W A C A O R
G A I R C R A F T T D L R O
H D L I I H P F I W I A P L
V I C A T T I P C P F B R S
P O O L Y L F Y A W N U R E
```

STREETS OF MOSCOW

Moscow, an urban hub with over 11,000,000 inhabitants, is the political, educational, and cultural heart of Russia. Within the great walls of the Kremlin lie RED Square and the tomb of LENIN. Several street names such as CHEKHOV, DOSTOEVSKY, GORKY, PUSHKIN, and TCHAIKOVSKY, honor Russians who have made great contributions to the arts.

BAUMAN
BOTANIC
CHEKHOV
DIMITROV
DOSTOEVSKY
DUROV
FADEEV
GORKY
HERZEN
KACHALOV
KALININ
KIEV
KIROV
KOMSOMOL
KROPOTKIN
KUTUZOV
LENIN
MANEZH
MARX
OBUKH
PEACE
PETROVKA
PUSHKIN

RADIO
RAZIN
RED (Square)
SEROV
SHVERNIK

TCHAIKOVSKY
TVER
VOLGIN
VOROVSKY
ZHDANOV

```
H Z H D A N O V X H Y A P B
E Y E I R V O R I K K M K S
R R K A C H A L O V S U H E
Z R Z S K M K M O P V V B R
E I R E V T S R Y N E V V O
N R H K V O T Y I R O A M V
I C M R M E K N N R T G C V
G P Y O P S E I U K S V R E
L X L P V L K D A E O O A I
O B I O X P A L A H D Z D K
V O R T I M I D T F C U I G
G O R K Y N X C I N A T O B
V C F I I H Z E N A M U A B
Z H Z N I K H S U P C K N C
```

A member of one of America's great acting families, Lionel Barrymore (1878-1954) first appeared in minor roles. A much admired character actor, he is best remembered for his work in the films *Dinner at Eight*, *You Can't Take It With You*, and 15 *Dr. Kildare* movies. Barrymore received an Academy Award for his performance in *A Free Soul*. This passage is a quote from Barrymore.

The great actor always must act. He must make a ceremony of waking up in the morning. He must sit in his room and act so that his whole body vibrates to the thrill of it. Forever he must be a poseur. Every last second of his life must be pose and posture.

```
A P E B T S U M E H H W P R
E O L L H H C E R E M O N Y
K F O R E V E R Y A S A C O
A H I M G E E C R T C L F S
M I U L R L D M U T L W D U
H S S W E O E R O T A A N D
T M I H A H E R U K S Y O T
I K T H T W G D I E L S C M
S O Y N N S T N T K S A E U
T L I D B I G A I I D O S S
S P A M O H R E H N F H P T
U M U S T B E S A T R O W A
M T H R I L L O N M O O R C
W U O V Y C M P D A R S M T
```

HOBBY LOBBY

A hobby is something that is of interest to you and can provide hours of enjoyment and satisfaction. If you're reading this, chances are one of your hobbies is puzzle solving. Perhaps one or more of the 25 hobbies below might also pique your interest.

BASKETRY

BICYCLING

BIRDWATCH-
ING

CAKE
(decorating)

CAMPING

COIN
(collecting)

CROCHETING

DRAWING

FISHING

GARDENING

GOLFING

HUNTING

KAYAKING

KNITTING

MACRAME

METALWORK-
ING

MOUNTAIN
(climbing)

ORIGAMI

PAINTING

PHOTOGRAPHY

POTTERY

STAMP (collecting)

TENNIS

WHITTLING

WRITING

```
C B I R D W A T C H I N G K
S T Y D W U H C Y P N N A K
G G G H R G N I H S I F R A
N N E P M D P T L M G D Y
I I I K A M R C T O G E A
T P K T T A R Y A L L N N K
I M R O T E C G F W D I I I
R A O S K I H I O K I T N N
W C W U B S N C M T F N G G
K W L H N G I K O A O U G B
E P A I N T I N G R G H N M
Y R T E K S A B N K C I P T
Y R E T T O P I M E O P R L
W E M A R C A M N C T D Y O
```

The word "sabotage" means to undermine something, to bring about its destruction or defeat. Its origin dates back to the inception of automation into factories and the reaction of the displaced workers.

The word "sabotage" comes from "sabot," a French word for shoe. In the Industrial Revolution, when automated mills were first introduced, French workers who lost their factory jobs would throw a shoe — sabot — into the machines to wreck the engines, and thus "sabotage" the business.

```
K K W S A B O T A G E V W D J
O S M A E D H E L E M I L L S
A E B B A N D T H U S U A S D
U E U O N O I T U L O V E R N
T O R T J H N G W W C S O E Y
O H I I W I G K N O T W H K R
M S E N I H C A M E H T E R O
A R H T D S K E K C E R W O T
T O T O W U S T N G W H T W C
E F G S J O S E A E O H T H A
D E C U D O R T N I R W E C F
F E G F L F O H R I D E T N I
J D R O U B N H T I S I W E R
E O H S A Y B J H I A U L R S
M W E S A B O T A J M L B F T
```

NEED HELP?

Sometimes we just can't make it on our own. Here is a list of folks who are there to lend a hand if and when we should need it.

ASSOCIATE

ATTENDANT

BEST MAN

BRIDESMAID

CHAMBERLAIN

COMPANION

COURIER

ESCORT

GROOMS-
MAN

GUIDE

HELPER

INTERN

LADY-IN-
WAITING

MAID

NURSE

ORDERLY

PAGEBOY

PORTER

SERVER

SQUIRE

STAFF

TECHNICIAN

USHER

VALET

WAITER

```
N U R S E R V E R E H S U U
G U I D E M H E N U M F Y W
H N H T B A I D A A P D R S
A N I A L R E B M A H C Y F
Y A A T U T I N T E R N C F
W M C O I H S D S L N C N A
W S C O P A T T E N D A N T
I M B R M S W R B S I I M S
E O T D E P N N O C M F A I
S O E E O P A W I C V A B M
Q R B R L Y L N U Y S Y I N
U G T L G A H E I F D E F D
I E N Y W C V I H O V A U L
R P A G E B O Y V E N M L U
E N E T A I C O S S A E S N
```

Known as "The Biggest Little City in the World," RENO is famous for its gambling casinos, and is home to the UNIVERSITY of NEVADA. Although the city is the setting for Comedy Central's hit series "Reno 911!" (a parody of the long-running television show "COPS"), the show is not filmed in Reno, but the characters do mention actual street names, some of which are listed here.

ARLINGTON

BEECH

DESERT

DOUBLE R

EVANS

GEAR

KEYSTONE

KIETZKE

KINGS ROW

KIRMAN

KUENZLI

LOCUST

MILL

NEVADA

NUGGET

ODDIE

PLUMAS

QUINCY

RALSTON

RENO

SIERRA

SULLIVAN

SUTRO

TACCHINO

UNIVERSITY

VALLEY

VASSAR

VIRGINIA

WELLS

WHEELER

WINSTON

```
G R E I H N V K I R M A N Y
W M U A C T A A Q U I N C Y
O D D I E A S V D N N S N P
R A E G E C S B I A O O I L
S O G U B C A G W L V I U U
G U S P N H R V A L L E Y M
N O T S N I W W D Z K U N A
I R N Z V N V H N Z O S S S
K E Y S T O N E T L N D I U
S L L E W Q U E R A E E H T
L B Q Z B K I L V S R R G R
O U Q Y P K L E E R I N B O
N O T G N I L R A L S T O N
U D A Z M V T S U C O L Y C
```

FIREFIGHTER TRAINING

New York City's police officers are referred to as "New York's finest," and the city's firemen are deemed "New York's bravest." The 36 terms below are all related to the intensive training PROGRAM fledgling firefighters face. The HEAT is on to see if you've got what it takes to find them all.

AIR TANK

ALARM

BRAVE

CHIEF

CLASS

COMPANY

CREW

DRILL

ENROLL

FIRE

FIRST AID

GEAR

GLOVES

GROUP

HEAT

HELP

HOSE

INSTRUCTOR

LADDER

LEARN

MASK

PREVENTION

PROGRAM

PUMP

READY

RESCUE

RISKY

SAFETY

SMOKE

STAMINA

STUDY

TEACH

TECHNIQUE

TOOLS

TRUCK

WORK

```
A H P U O R G C R E W S T C
P O S D P R E V E N T I O N
R S K A I V A D A U Q M O Q
O E R I F A R H D G P Y L U
G V S R N E T Y Y A A M S L
R O T C U R T S N I L A O E
A L P M U P H Y R L N S U U
M G E C E E C T R I S K Y Q
L P K A A L A R M S F S P I
O L L O R N E A A E M K C N
G L I E K N T L I V I O T H
C R G R H S C H E A T D K C
B B O T D L C I D R V H H E
D W M T C D T P E B V N B T
```

YUMMY CHOCOLATE!

Chocolate is an ingredient found in many delicious desserts ranging from a BOMBE, a frozen dessert consisting of a round mold of ICE CREAM or sherbet with a custard or MOUSSE center, to CHEESECAKE!

BOMBE

BONBON

BROWNIE

CANDY BAR

CHEESECAKE

CHIPS

COOKIE

CREAM PIE

CUPCAKE

DOUGHNUT

ÉCLAIR

FONDUE

FROSTING

FUDGE

GANACHE

ICE CREAM

MADELEINE

MALT

MILK

MINT

MOUSSE

PUDDING

SAUCE

SHAKE

SOUFFLÉ

SPRINKLES

SUNDAE

SYRUP

TORTE

TRUFFLE

```
P C U P C A K E L F F U R T
U O H H C K T R I A L C E F
R S I E B M O B W N E Y U L
Y P I C E C R E A M W D D S
S E T F I S T A A S G O O U
M U K R P P E D B E L U R O
I D W O M U E C I Y F G E B
N N E S A L D K A F D H E L
T O M T E C O D L K C N E S
E F B I R O M E I A E U A U
S C N N C F K I N N D T D C
U E U G O A M A L T G R N D
S F F A H B G P T K E S U K
M O U S S E L K N I R P S A
```

MR. & MRS. RASCAL?

While compiling the data for the first United States census in 1790, researchers recorded an unusual assortment of surnames, some of which are listed here. Take a trip back in time by circling these colorful surnames which today are almost nonexistent.

BEADS

BEANS

CAME

COMBS

CORNS

COUGH

COWHORN

CRYSICK

CUSHION

FITS

FLYBAKER

FOWL

GOUGE

GUMP

HERO

LADDER

LATCH

LIPS

LIVERS

MEASLEY

MENDINGALL

MILK

MINTS

MUSH

NUTHAMMER

PETTYFOOL

PHYSIC

RASCAL

SHELF

SHORTDAY

SIMMERS

SMALLCORN

STRUT

```
E G U O G K K S S T R T S G
T U R T S U R I M T C P R C
E E D H P E F V E I I K E I
H M E N D I N G A L L F V S
T L A D G C R Y S I C K I Y
F G A C B B S A L R S M L H
O L O O F Y T T E P M U G P
W N Y S L V A M Y E A U E B
L K R B D L M D R S L O S S
D L K O A A B S T N L G B H
L A T C H K E F B R C M E G
W V S T B W E B M O O C A U
L A U B P E O R L C R H N O
R N O I H S U C M I N T S C
```

In helping with the war effort, the DESOTO division of Chrysler suspended production in early 1942 so it could produce military aircraft parts. It wasn't until March of 1946 that automotive production resumed. The DeSoto went on to become a classic like the other 30 antique autos listed below.

ARGO

AUBURN

BELL

BUSH

CASE

COLE

CRANE

DESOTO

DORT

EDSEL

FIAT

HUDSON

KAISER

KISSEL

LA SALLE

LOZIER

METZ

NASH

NATIONAL

PEERLESS

PILOT

PREMIER

RAMBLER

REO

RITZ

STANLEY

STUDEBAKER

STUTZ

WAHL

WELCH

WINTON

```
U W G F S F D Z I Y T H K E
B I A G M T R N Z R P A Z A
S U Z H W I U W O W I W G I
T R T C L E S D E S O T O K
A L U W K C O L E C D P Z I
N O T N I W C R D B R U L S
L B S I C H R Y G E A E H S
E A Z U F I A T M W M K E E
Y B N P T L N I S F B L E L
W S L O Z I E R B T L D H R
D R L L I R F H U A E B D E
Y I M M E T Z S S B R S P E
P W S O D B A A H B U G A P
M S O L U Z L N U K B A O C
```

WORDS FOLLOWING "WATER"

Make your MARK as an expert solver by circling the 42 words hidden in the diagram. Each one can be preceded by the word "water" to form a new word or phrase.

BALLET
BARREL
BOTTLE
BUFFALO
CLOSET
COLOR
COOLER
CRAFT
CRESS
CURE
DEER
DRAIN
FALL
FLEA
FLOW
FOWL
FRONT
GAUGE
GLASS
HEATER
HOLE
LEVEL
LILY
LINE
MAIN
MARK
MELON
METER

MILL
PIPE
POLO
RESISTANT
SHED
SPOUT
SUPPLY

TABLE
TANK
TOWER
VAPOR
WHEEL
WINGS
WORKS

```
M A R K V E L L A F N G C P
P E B U F F A L O L R I O I
E T T W R C E T C O H L A A
B G D E E R Y N L W O F H M
N P U W R E L O O C L W P Y
C M A A L S C R S E E N Y E
H S B E G S K F E T O W E R
K H V A E S I H T L I C Y O
K E Y L L A W E E N R L B P
L D L B B L P M G A I I E A
E I P T A G E S F L T A U V
M R P I T N A T S I S E R D
R Y U S P O U T A N K L R D
K R S C E E B A H E P F D N
```

MYTHICAL CREATURES FROM A TO J

Every culture seems to have its own creatures of folklore. Some are helpful, like the FAIRY, while others, like the GORGON, are feared. Tread carefully through this list of 33 legendary creatures and see how many you can capture in the diagram.

ABIKU

AHUIZOTL

AIGAMUCHAB

ANKOU

ARWE

BABA YAGA

BANSHEE

BASILISK

BODACH

BROWNIE

BUNYIP

CLURICAN

CYCLOPS

DOGAI

DRAGON

ELVES

FAFNIR

FAIRY

FAY

FENRIS

FOMORIANS

GHOUL

GIANT

GIGANTES

GNOME

GOBLIN

GOLEM

GOO-TEEKHL

GORGON

HARPY

HYDRA

JINNI

JOTUNN

```
V L S I R N E F I A V V B N
A S N A I R O M O F D A A B
G G T G N F V G Z F N C A I
A O H O F R F V A S I S R M
Y B O D A C H I H R I E W E
A A A T F P R E U L D V E L
B W F H E Y E L I O B L R O
A C L Y C E C S Z N K E T G
B W T D J U K E O R W N H N
I U H R I O M H T B A O A I
K K N A N O T A L I U G R L
U J V Y N F N U G L I R P B
H W H G I V A P N I T O Y O
C Y C L O P S E T N A G I G
```

SO ANNOYING

Put your pet peeves aside and have fun solving this puzzle. Even though it's filled with annoying words, we hope it won't RUFFLE your feathers!

AGGRAVATE

AGITATE

ANNOY

BADGER

BAIT

BEDEVIL

BESET

BOTHER

CHAFE

EXASPERATE

FLUSTER

GALL

GOAD

GRATE

HECKLE

HOUND

INSULT

IRRITATE

MIFF

MOCK

NEEDLE

NETTLE

PESTER

PLAGUE

RANKLE

RIDE

RILE

RUFFLE

TAUNT

TEASE

TROUBLE

WORRY

```
Y E T A T I R R I F U Y E I
R X L I T M D E A B O N L G
R E H T O B R E E N O E K D
O E K O T X P S N L M O C K
W T G F F E E A P B E H E W
K A A D S T N E F L A T H P
R V L T A U N T N F A I K L
X A E T T B D R E R I G T S
N R I R U F F L E L E M U P
M G A O B G I P D T K D H E
A G P U E R S T L U S N I D
B A K B W A F B E V X U A R
W L X L X T N E A B R O L R
M L B E D E V I L T G H I F
```

302 THE PONY EXPRESS

The Pony Express mail service was started in 1860 by freight magnate William H. Russell with a trail of 157 relay stations across Kansas, Nebraska, Wyoming, Nevada, and California. It reduced coast-to-coast mail time from six months to ten days, but it was a venture that lasted only eighteen months. Some facts about the Pony Express riders are noted below.

The Pony Express had about eighty riders, and each man rode about seventy-five miles. Horses were changed every ten to twelve miles, and only two minutes were allowed to change mounts. Since the rider's trail was fraught with danger, the recruitment posters read "Orphans preferred."

```
E C D M I L E S S E R P X E
W V W E R E I S E T W O S T
A N L E N N O A E V E R Y I
P N A E C R N P R L E A A E
R D D E W O L L A T I N C O
E E T A S T Y M S H D M T H
F H C A T E I O E I G H T Y
E E W R N N P M C U S I H N
R F R A U G H T H N W T O O
R E H T O I S D A N G E R P
E H E W M R T H N A A N S E
D S A V E I P M G R B T E H
S R E D I R Y A E T O O S T
E D I R O F E N D N U D U H
O R G E G N A H C O T X E T
```

IN A WORD — MOTHER

In honor of moms everywhere, here's a puzzle with terms that can either be preceded or followed by the word "mother" to form new words or phrases.

BOARD

CAREY'S CHICKEN

COUNTRY

COURAGE

DEN

EARTH

FIGURE

GOD

GOOSE

GRAND

GREAT-GRAND

HEN

HOOD

HOUSE

HUBBARD

IMAGE

IN-LAW

LODE

LOVE

NATURE

OF GOD

OF INVENTION

OF PEARL

SHIP

STEP

SUPERIOR

TERESA

TONGUE

WELL

WIT

```
I R S S K H D U P P V C H M
H M C D R W A L N I Y T C V
U W A I E C R R O I R F T S
B C A G I A W P E A T D E N
B Y Y P E T S S E S N R N O
A F N P F D O E L A U A S I
R T F K I O C O R D O O H T
D O O F G O D G F E C B H N
Y N I F U E T O N A T U R E
L M A R R A D C E A T B W V
O C A R E Y S C H I C K E N
V G Y R G P U H W E Y T L I
E U G N O T U H I S P H L F
E I T H D T F S L P I K E O
```

In the game of baseball, stealing is an art form — stealing *bases*, that is. Stealing is a skill that is advantageous in two ways: it advances the runner one or more bases, and also distracts the pitcher. Listed in order below are the top 30 stolen base leaders in major league history as of the end of the 2005 season.

HENDERSON (Rickey)

BROCK (Lou)

HAMILTON (Billy)

COBB (Ty)

RAINES (Tim)

COLEMAN (Vince)

COLLINS (Eddie)

LATHAM (Arlie)

CAREY (Max)

WAGNER (Honus)

MORGAN (Joe)

WILSON (Willie)

BROWN (Tom)

CAMPANERIS (Bert)

NIXON (Otis)

DAVIS (George)

HOY (Dummy)

WILLS (Maury)

VAN HALTREN (George)

SMITH (Ozzie)

DUFFY (Hugh)

MCPHEE (Bid)

LOFTON (Kenny)

BUTLER (Brett)

LOPES (Davey)

CEDEÑO (César)

DAHLEN (Bill)

WARD (John)

LONG (Herman)

DONOVAN (Patsy)

```
G W D R H B B P N B O U I T
S F A K P S B Y R E R R X I
I N V R O M F O X Y L O E U
R R I E D L C P C O L H W N
E W S L A K O V M O R G A N
N E R T L A H N A V O N O D
A O H U G O C A G B M S I U
P A S B Y W C M M S L E N F
M C C R A I N E S I E L N F
A A E G E O T L W H L P I Y
C R N N T D L O P E S T X S
G E M F M I N C E D E N O G
R Y O F W R M E I G B H N N
C L K C G S D T H T I M S M
```

IT'S KARAOKE NIGHT!

It's karaoke night, so take the STAGE, grab the MICROPHONE and belt out one of your favorite SONGS as you sing along with the prerecorded MUSIC that is being rendered by the karaoke machine. And if you don't know the words, don't worry. There should be a TV MONITOR in front of you which will scroll the LYRICS across the screen for you. Now get out there and release that inner Frank Sinatra or Céline Dion that only comes out when you're in the shower!

AMATEURS
APPLAUSE
BEST
COMPETE
CONTEST
DUETS
ENTERTAINING
EXCITING
FAVORITES
HARMONY
HOST
LYRICS
MELODY
MICROPHONE
MONITOR
MUSIC
PARTY
PERFORM
POPULAR
PRIZES
RENDITIONS
RHYTHM
SINGERS
SOLO

SONGS
STAGE
STYLE
TALENT

TEMPO
VOCALS
WINNER
WORDS

```
R R A L U P O P E G A T S S
H S P M T S E T N O C E E Y
Y L P W A G N I O L B T W Y
T A L E N T T P H Y I E O E
H C A N U I E A P R L P R Y
M O U W C R R U O I C M D T
L V S X F M T V R C U O S R
H N E O O S A S C S L C H A
O H R N L F I N I E G R G P
S M Y L N O N C M N I N O Y
T T X M O N I T O R G P O O
E S Y X R E N N I W M E I S
U E Y L D S G G S E Z I R P
D B U R E N D I T I O N S S
```

THE HEAT IS ON!

Is it getting hot in here? Maybe this puzzle, whose words are all associated with household heating, has something to do with it.

BLOWER

BOILER

BURNER

CIRCULATE

COIL

CONTROL

CONVECTOR

DEVICE

DUCT

ELECTRIC

ELEMENTS

ENERGY

FANS

FILTER

FLUID

FURNACE

HEATER

INDOORS

LIQUID

PIPE

POWER

PRESSURE

PUMP

RADIATOR

REPAIR

STEAM

SYSTEM

TEMPERATURE

THERMOSTAT

TUBE

UNIT

VAPOR

VENT

WATER

```
C D S T E A M C L D V E N T
V O T F L U I D D I N S I E
P S N A F R E N R U B Y H M
Y U E T T H E E Q C S A P
T F M C R S W T C I V T R E
U I E P I O O C A L L E I R
B L L T L V L M N E S M A A
E T E B A N E O R S H D P T
N E B P E L U D U E I Y E U
E R O Y I U U R F A H B R R
R R C O N V E C T O R T E E
G U C I N D O O R S Q W D T
Y L T V W S R E L I O B I A
Y C C Q C A E P I P C P U W
```

GO GET "GO"

Are you a real go-getter? Then have a go at this puzzle! Your GOAL is to locate the gobs of words containing the letters "GO." So don't GOOF off, start finding them now!

BINGO
BONGO
CARGO
DRAGON
EGOTIST
ESCARGOT
FLAMINGO
GOAL
GOAT
GOBBLE
GOBLET
GOLD
GOLF
GONDOLA
GONE
GONG
GOOBER
GOOF
GOON
GOOSE
GOPHER
GOSPEL
GOSSIP
GOTHAM
GOURMET
GOVERN

INDIGO
INGOT
JARGON
LINGO
MANGO
NEGOTIATE

PAGODA
POGO
TANGO
VERTIGO
VIGOR
WAGON

```
G L D L A O G N I B V E H A
D O T E O A R N N I S O G V
A W S P J E P O G O B L E T
P R I S B A R O O G G L O R
B T T O I I R G T N B N V C
D L O G N P I G G B H D A F
C G G G T T V G O O F R L T
V T E M R U O G V N G A P F
M O M E A A U H E O M G L O
V C V A T D C O R I G O G G
G L M J H F O S N O G N I L
E E T A I T O G E N O G A L
W A G O N D O L A B F M T M
I W N I N D I G O P H E R F
```

CHEMICAL ELEMENTS: A-M

Elements are substances that can't be divided or changed into different substances by ordinary chemical methods. There are 116 known elements. You'll receive a GOLD star if you're successful in locating 28 elements that begin with some of the letters "A" through "M."

ACTINIUM

ALUMINUM

ANTIMONY

ARGON

ASTATINE

BARIUM

BERYLLIUM

BISMUTH

BORON

CADMIUM

CALCIUM

CARBON

CERIUM

CESIUM

CHLORINE

CHROMIUM

COBALT

COPPER

GOLD

HELIUM

HYDROGEN

IRON

KRYPTON

LEAD

LITHIUM

LUTETIUM

MAGNESIUM

MERCURY

```
O B E E I R K U E H O N I C
L T M H I R E E H Y C O A D
A L U A Y U N P N D N R L O
R A I P G I R Y P R B O E U
G B T T T N M B M O G B N Y
O O E A H U E U N G C I I N
N C T G I I I S I E M S R O
B S U C A L U M I N U M O M
A H L U L H U M O U I U L I
L A E Y P I Y R O G M T H T
C S R L M U I R E C O H C N
L E A D I E N I D O R H N A
B B A R I U M I H I H S I A
K C E S I U M Y R U C R E M
```

According to Haitian legend, a ZOMBIE is generally held to be a corpse brought back to life in a state of trancelike animation by voodoo, and made to obey the commands of the person exercising the power.

KELPIE

KOBOLDS

LEPRECHAUN

MANTICORE

MEDUSA

MENAHUNE

MERMAID

MERROW

MINCH

NAGA

NISSE

NIXIE

NUCKELAVEE

NYMPH

OGOPOGO

OGRE

PIXIE

POLEVIK

POOKA

SUKUYAN

TAPIO

TARASQUE

TENGU

TORCH

TRITON

TROLL

UNICORN

VAMPIRE

VETALA

VODYANOI

WHOWIE

YETI

ZOMBIE

```
K H T M R W G W Z W B Z K Q
O P E R P O O K A O G R E I
B M N N O T I R T L M K L T
O Y G B H L T T R M A B P E
L N U C K E L A V E E T I Y
D E R I N X R P R N M W E E
S O P I H C N I M A O L I V
T M S R M O P O N H S X C K
A S U D E M G T W U I Q E I
E N Y I A C I O K N D L U V
B U X V L C H U P E T B K E
W I Q V O D Y A N O I Z D L
P M E R M A I D U A G A N O
A R E Z N R O C I N U O W P
```

CARTOGRAPHY

Up until 1989, public maps issued throughout the Soviet Union were intentionally misleading. For fifty years the security police issued the inaccurate maps for national defense reasons. During that time, however, American diplomats and correspondents in Moscow discovered that an American agency produced the best Soviet maps.

When the security police in the Soviet Union were put in charge of mapmaking, they deliberately falsified the maps. Streets, rivers, and roads were moved or left out. Americans based in Moscow found the most reliable map of the city was produced by the CIA.

```
D E L I B E R A T E L Y R S
M J C I T Y W A S L R E H T
T A N I T U P A M V J M L R
H U I R L B M J N B Y T H E
E W O C S O M N I V B C R E
S R H B V V P I N T H E Q T
E F O E G R A H C V W H M S
C J D M N R S O V I E T A N
U N I O N P L D M T Q F P A
R E L I A B L E A S F O M C
I I V M D E C U D O R P A I
T Y V D E S A B U M R L K R
Y T F E L R O N L E B D I E
J L W E R E D Y E H T V N M
D E I F I S L A F T M J G A
```

MACBETH

MACBETH has been made into a film many times and by filmmakers as diverse as D. W. Griffith, Orson Welles, and Roman Polanski. The most critically acclaimed version is an adaptation, *Throne of Blood*, by Japanese director Akira Kurosawa.

ANGUS*

BANQUO*

BATTLES

BIRNAM WOOD

CAITHNESS*

DAGGER

DONALBAIN*

DUNCAN*

DUNSINANE (Castle)

FLEANCE*

GHOST

HECATE*

KING

LADY (Macbeth)*

LENNOX*

LIGHTNING

MACBETH*

MACDUFF*

MALCOLM*

MENTEITH*

MURDER

ROSS*

SCOTLAND

SEYTON*

SIWARD

SOLDIERS

SWORDS

THUNDER

WITCHES

*character

```
G W X E B W G N D D T D R S
M D M T R I O L L M R U M R
N U R A K T R I E A O L L D
E N O C Y C G N W N O M U A
L S S E N H T I A C N N R G
T I S H T E S Q L M C O N G
O N E N I S C A D A W I X E
A A I T D M M N N C A O U R
N N H R O U Q N A B U S O E
G E O D R Y D A L E Q C K D
U W D D S Y B A T T L E S N
S Q E F K I N G O H I F R U
R R M K N O M A C D U F F H
L S O L D I E R S G H O S T
```

312

FRUIT SALAD

Anytime's the right time for a delectable fruit salad. If you're in the mood for one, we've gathered 28 tasty fruits for your picking that would make a terrific addition to any salad bowl.

APPLE

APRICOT

BLACKBERRY

BLUEBERRY

CASABA

CHERRY

CRAB (apple)

CRANBERRY

CURRANT

DEWBERRY

GOOSEBERRY

GRAPE

HUCKLEBERRY

LOGANBERRY

LOQUAT
(plumlike fruit)

MEDLAR
(applelike fruit)

MUSKMELON

NECTARINE

OREGON
(grape)

PEACH

PEAR

PLUM

POME-
GRANATE

PRUNE

QUINCE

RAISIN

RASPBERRY

STRAWBERRY

```
Y R A I S I N A A P P L E C
R R P I C E G T Y D O P H E
R A R U R C P R N G E E C N
E S I E A T R A A A R S I I
B P C T B E A N R R R T Y R
W B O A B E B U Y G M R Q A
E E T N S E L R Q U B A U T
D R A A R A R K S O T W I C
H R Y R R E B K C A L B N E
C Y Y G B Y M A G U K E C N
A Q D E M E D L A R H R E U
E P U M L I P N O G E R O R
P L G O O S E B E R R Y C P
B O N P L U M O D H I K T U
```

PRESIDENTIAL PLACES

We're taking a Presidential tour of the United States in this puzzle. All of the cities and towns in our list share their names with men who have held the highest office in our country.

ARTHUR (Tenn.)

BUCHANAN (Ga.)

CARTER (Pa.)

CLINTON (Conn.)

COOLIDGE (Ariz.)

FILLMORE (Calif.)

FORD (Va.)

GARFIELD (Ark.)

GRANT (Neb.)

HARRISON (Mont.)

HAYES (La.)

HOOVER (Ala.)

JACKSON (Miss.)

JEFFERSON (Wis.)

JOHNSON (Kans.)

KENNEDY (N.Y.)

LINCOLN (Calif.)

MADISON (Ill.)

MONROE (Ohio)

NIXON (Nev.)

PIERCE (Ida.)

POLK CITY (Fla.)

REAGAN (Tenn.)

ROOSEVELT (Okla.)

TAFT (Calif.)

TAYLOR (Ark.)

TRUMAN (Minn.)

TYLER (Ala.)

WASHINGTON (Pa.)

WILSON (N.C.)

```
R I Y N O S K C A J P N F M
M P S F M O N R O E O I W A
K E N N E D Y H B T L M I D
L I N C O L N U G L K R L I
L H A Y E S C N M E C E S S
R E V O O H I O C R I L O O
U N W N A H R R O F T Y N N
H O C N S E E L R L Y T I I
T T A A N I Y A C A I S N X
R N W N P A G L D A H D A O
A I A P T F M J T R R C G N
I L Y R H E B U W A O T A E
W C O M G N O S R E F F E J
N R O O S E V E L T Y T R R
```

IT'S ASTRONOMICAL

Proxima Centauri, our nearest STAR (not counting the sun), is a mere 25 trillion miles away! Astronomers discover these amazing facts as they look beyond the Earth to study the entire universe. You won't have to look quite so far to unearth these 32 astronomical terms in the diagram below.

BASALT
CASSEGRAIN
CHROMOSPHERE
CLUSTER
CONSTELLATION

CORE
CRUST
HALF (life)
HALO
HEAD

LIGHT-YEAR
LOBES
METEOR
NEBULA
NEUTRON
PULSAR
QUASAR
ROTATION
SIDEREAL
SOLSTICE
SPORADIC
STAR
SUBTEND
SUNSPOT
TAIL
THEORY
TIDES
TROPOSPHERE
UMBRA
ZENITH
ZODIAC
ZONES

```
T P O L A H R B D U C N M N
C O N S T E L L A T I O N T
T S E I T R A T S A D H R S
N S N S A E E D R C A E E E
F E U S E H R G A L R N S R
Z L L R T P E I F E O E E A
C U R O C S D A H Z P B B S
P M C T S O I P D N S U O A
B B R A Z M S H R E T L L U
A R C T T O P S N U S A T Q
S A F I P R A E Y T H G I L
A Y R O E H T H I R H L D L
L N R N T C Z C R O E T E M
T T S U B T E N D N P O S O
```

AIRCRAFT CARRIER

This puzzle takes you on a tour of an aircraft carrier, stem to stern, port to starboard. Used first in World War I, these ships, which store, launch, and land military planes and helicopters, distinguished themselves outstandingly in World War II. Today, nine countries maintain aircraft carriers: Brazil, France, India, Italy, Russia, Spain, Thailand, the United Kingdom, and the United States.

AMMUNITION

ANCHOR

BOILERS

BUNKS

CAPTAIN

CATAPULT (for launching planes)

CHAPEL

CHAPLAIN

COMPASS

CREW

ENGINES

ENSIGN

FIGHTER (planes)

FLAGS (signal)

FLIGHT DECK

GALLEY

GANGWAY

HANGAR (deck)

HATCHES

HAWSER (heavy rope)

HELICOPTERS

HELM

HULL

LADDER

LIFEBOATS

MESS HALL

OFFICERS

PUMPS

RADAR

RADIO

```
S L L A H S S E M N R C D Y
G A L L E Y T S H L A C R T
A B O I L E R S A P E O A H
P U B K I E G E T P H H D H
R N S T C N C A D C M U A C
A K O I O E I C N D E O R A
D S F I P N D A O G A E C F
I F H N T G H T L U W L K S
O I S R E I A A H P K A N I
S G P E R N N P T G A G Y H
G H M S S E G U W C I H U T
A T U W D S A L M S H L C W
L E P A H C R T N M L E F P
F R Y H L I F E B O A T S S
```

If breakfast is your favorite meal of the day, chances are you're familiar with Battle Creek, MICHIGAN. The Kellogg, Post, and Ralston Purina cereal plants are all located in Battle Creek, and the annual Cereal City Festival (with "the world's longest breakfast table") is held there every June. Listed here are 32 streets found throughout the city that Tony the Tiger just might describe as "Grrreat!"

ANGELL
BECKLEY
BURR
CALHOUN
CAPITAL

COLLEGE
COLUMBIA
CORNELL
EMMETT
ENWOOD

GOGUAC
GOLDEN
GROVE
HAMBLIN
HARRISON
HICKORY
JACKSON
KNAPP
LATTA
LAUREL
MARINE
MCCAMLY
MICHIGAN
NORTH
PLANTAIN
SHERMAN
VAN BUREN
WAGNER
WASHING-
TON
WEST
WILKES
WINTER

```
T N E D L O G G O G U A C P
R R U B N J K N A P P H O I
D E V O V O C A P I T A L V
O T M W H J S G N L R M L O
O N J M A L H I E A E B E V
W I L K E S A H R U N L G W
N W N O R T H C U R G I E H
E R L B N I T I B E A N S J
Y L M A C C M M N L W H M S
Y E L K C E B I A G E E B L
P P O V V O R N V R T M S A
H R R O S A I B M U L O C T
Y O R R M R J A C K S O N T
S G I C O R N E L L E G N A
```

HOME AND GARDEN SHOWS

If you're thinking about making some changes around the house (both inside and out), you may want to attend a Home and Garden Show first. You can shop, check out the latest trends and styles, and speak with friendly experts who are on hand to answer any questions you might have about home improvement.

APPLIANCES

BOOTHS

BUYER

CABINETS

CARPET

CHAIRS

DEALERS

DECK

DOORS

EVENT

EXTERIORS

FENCES

FURNISHINGS

GADGETS

GATES

GEAR

IDEAS

LANDSCAPING

LIGHTING

PLANTS

POOLS

ROOFING

ROOMS

RUGS

SALES

SECURITY

TABLES

TIPS

TOOLS

WALLPAPER

WINDOWS

```
R A E G C D L C D C T G U Y
O M V W H N A T O O L S X F
O K E S A B N T G T O S U I
F O N W I N D O W S T R S D
I K T N R S S K R N N E S E
N L E S S E C N A I L P P A
G T P L R E A L S B I A R S
S S R O D O P H A T W P E M
T E A O G N I T H G I L Y O
E T C P S N N R K U A L U O
G A G N G G G R E S T A B R
D G W S E C U R I T Y W S O
A X U G B F H R K R X T B A
G B O O T H S R E L A E D X
```

The Everglades, about 5,000 square miles of southern Florida marshland, was once the home of the Seminole Indians; it's now home to many types of wildlife. Take a trip to see how many creatures you can encounter living in Everglades National Park.

ALLIGATOR

ANHINGA (pelican-like bird)

ARMADILLO

BLACK BEAR

BUTTERFLY

CARDINAL

CORMORANT

CRANE

CROCODILE

DEER

EAGLE

EGRET

FLAMINGO

HERON

IBIS

LIMPKIN (crane-like bird)

MANATEE

OPOSSUM

OSPREY

OTTER

OWL

OYSTER

PANTHER

PELICAN

QUAIL

RABBIT

RACCOON

ROBIN

SNAKE

STORK

TARPON

VIREO (sparrow-like bird)

WILDCAT

```
O P O S S U M A G N I H N A
R G L I M P K I N L C B L Q
L E N I B O R R R R I E I Y
G P T I G U N O O C C A R S
C L N T M K T C S T S G U I
O E A Q O A O T D P S L E Q
R L C N G D L E E G R E T P
M H I I I S K F E R T E W A
O O L L I D A M R A F I Y N
R L E M V C R A N E L L M T
A W P I L V B A E D E T Y H
N O R E H B M A C S N A K E
T E H O I B L A C K B E A R
O Y S T E R T A R P O N S Y
```

WHO WON?

Always trying to keep headlines lively, sportswriters and sportscasters hardly ever tell us that teams just "win" anymore. The late broadcasting legend Harry Caray's simple shout, "Cubs win!," was a rarity. Now we hear "Mets SQUEAK BY" or "Marlins STUN Braves" or "Twins QUASH Tigers." See if you can VANQUISH this puzzle and find these 38 sports synonyms for "win."

BEAT
BLACK OUT
BLAST
BLOCK
CLIP
CLOBBER
CREAM
DECK
DEFEAT
EDGE
ELBOW
FINISH
KNOCK OVER
LAMBASTE
MASH
NUDGE
OUTSCORE
OVERCOME
OVERTAKE
PUNISH
QUASH
ROCK
ROUT
RUN BY
SKIN
SKUNK
SLAM
SNOW

SQUEAK BY
STUN
SWEEP
THRASH
THUMP

TROUNCE
UNSEAT
VANQUISH
WHIP
ZONK

```
O B A P R I H T V L R N E H
F T R O U N C E A K T Y G Y
A I C N H L R M N E B C D P
K K N M N M B O Q N F R E W
N O R I A A Z C U U D E C K
O H U E S L L R I T W G D E
C V R T B H S E S S Y D T T
K C E H S B K V H S A U Q H
O S T R Z C O O Q W O N S U
V F I A T Q O L P K Z I C M
E U N S E A T R C N N K A P
R O A H Y B K A E U Q S I I
Y L U W O B L E P K H H I L
B K C O L B R W L S W A K C
```

"STONE" PRECEDERS

The hieroglyphic inscriptions on the ROSETTA Stone have enabled archaeologists to decipher many of Egypt's ancient writings. To decipher this puzzle, circle the words that can be followed by "stone."

BIRTH	CORNER	EMERY
BLARNEY	COVER	FLAG
BRIM	CURB	GRIND
BROWN	CURLING	HAIL
COBBLE	EDGE	HEARTH
		LIME
		LODE
		MILE
		MILK
		MILL
		MOON
		PEBBLE
		PRECIOUS
		PUMICE
		RHINE
		ROSETTA
		SAND
		SOAP
		STEPPING
		TOUCH
		WHET

```
W L H B S C S I L I T Y B N
L S E F U O U Y M F E T I F
S A N D A V Y H O N H A I L
G N I P P E T S C V W M R A
S R H M W R L I D K P O D G
C U R L I N G B R E S E R U
F K O B M R E G B E D I T B
O L L I M E B B T O N G M O
N I T B C M L T L D C R E Y
G M S I H E A R T H C U O T
P K M E S R R E C N Y K R C
C U D O S Y N P E M K S L B
P K E L O R E L I M U I N C
C R Y S E N Y R A Y O M L V
```

"If at first you don't succeed, 'tis a lesson you should heed, try, try again," as the saying goes. Ponder the words below of Ralph Waldo Emerson, who maintains that failure is an essential ingredient of success — or as today's athletes succinctly put it, "No pain, no gain."

Failure
is part
of success.
A man's
success is
made
up of
failure,
because
he experiments
and
ventures
every
day.
The
power of
persistence,
of enduring
defeat,
and of

gaining
victory
by defeats
is one
of those

forces
which
never
loses
its charm.

```
N P L A R D B T S N A M A L
H E E X P E R I M E N T S E
A R D U C A V U S F S J H N
S S Z A P O W E R O F O Y E
T I U S M O P O N R N F L S
A S I C R O F S U C C E S S
E T H W C T V F I E H N G J
F E A L H E A T A S D D A Y
E N W O V I S E K X N U I R
D C S E L C C S F L E R N O
Y E R U H B Y H I E Y I I T
B Y R A N D O F A S D N N C
S E R U L I A F N N L G G I
E M Y T E C S E R U T N E V
```

322

"FIELD" TRIP

What do the following words have in common? They can all be preceded by the word "field" to form another word or phrase. Go on a field TRIP through the diagram to find all of the entries.

ARMY	CARRIAGE	FARE
ARTILLERY	COLORS	GOAL
BASIL	CORN	HOCKEY
BATTERY	CRICKET	HOSPITAL
BIRD	DRIVER	LARK
BOOK	DUCK	LENS
		MADDER
		MARSHAL
		MARTIN
		MOUSE
		MUSIC
		OFFICER
		PIECE
		PLOVER
		SALAD
		SHOW
		SPANIEL
		SPARROW
		SPORTS
		STAFF
		TRIAL
		TRIP
		WORK

```
B S Y T I B N L D M E L P I
C F E A R E D D A M U S I C
B S B G S Y M R A O U K R S
B R P U A A T I I U G I T P
W F O A R I D V Y B C N W E
Y M H S N A R E Y K M F M W
N L H P L I E R E C I F F O
H A O A I H E T A A S A C R
L I S A B L O L L C R T U R
V R P P L O V E R E O S D A
Y T I I O L K L F K L S R P
B A T T E R Y E K C O H S S
K R A L O C T N B U C O R N
A L L W G U E S C D V W B K
```

BLOCK PATTERNS

Block patterns for handmade quilts are designs cut from different fabrics with the pieces sewn together to form a square block. Some patterns such as WHIG ROSE are appliquéd to a square piece of fabric. Completed blocks are then sewn together to form the top of the quilt.

ALBUM

BEAR'S PAW

BOW TIE

COLUMBIA

COLUMNS

COMPASS

CROSS

DAY LILY

DOUBLE T

DOVE

HEXAGON

HOUSE

KING'S X

LOG CABIN

MAPLE LEAF

MOSAIC

OHIO STAR

PANSY

PEONY

PINE TREE

SALEM

SEE SAW

SHIP

SHOO FLY

SITKA

TULIPS

VERMONT

WHEELS

WHIG ROSE

WINDMILL

WRENCH

```
U U P P M R M B H S I T K A
N N A C R O S S P A W A W K
K I N G S X S I W T D I R W
M B N A L N L Y N A N O H H
U A I B M U L O C D S I V E
B C P U T I M H M H G E M E
L G L L L R L I O R E F E L
A O D Y E E L O O E S N L S
C L A V S L F S R S S O A R
Y D O U B L E T B P A G S U
S N O D Y B E A R S P A W G
N H O A X N M R F P M X M R
A Y I E I T W O B I O E S U
P F W P P C W R E N C H C R
```

MORNING, NOON, AND NIGHT

Wouldn't you agree that Rod Serling made a wise decision in naming his TV show "The TWILIGHT Zone" rather than "The GLOAMING Zone"? These and other words related to MORNING, noon, and night are hidden below. See if you can find them without burning the MIDNIGHT oil.

AFTERNOON

AURORA

CREPUSCULE
(twilight)

DARK

DAWN

DAYBREAK

DAYLIGHT

DUSK

EVENING

EVENTIDE

GLOAMING

HIGH NOON

MIDDAY

MIDNIGHT

MOONLIGHT

MORNING

NIGHTFALL

NIGHTTIME

STARLIGHT

SUNBEAMS

SUNDOWN

SUNLIGHT

SUNRISE

SUNSET

SUNSHINE

SUNUP

TWILIGHT

```
G N I M A O L G E E B B S T S
N E K E O R V N R R O V U U U
I Q F D C O I E V E N I N G N
N P H I G H N O O N B L B K D
R S U T S S D L K A I L E I O
O U G N H E T M I G D L A T W
M N U E U G K A H G U A M W N
B S N V S S I T R C H F S I E
U E W E U I H N S L B T G L B
M T A D V G R U D E I H F I C
Y A D D I M P N K I T G P G U
L E W L Y E C R U T M I H H A
D A Y B R E A K I S V N L T H
B A C C B D I M L K T O L A L
D N O O N R E T F A R O R U A
```

PINES OF NORTH AMERICA

Pines represent the largest family of conifer trees, and provide timber, paper, pulp, and resin products such as turpentine. Below you'll find 28 types of pines.

APACHE

AUSTRALIAN

BISHOP

CHIHUAHUA

COULTER

DIGGER

FOXTAIL

JACK

JEFFREY

KNOBCONE

LIMBER

LOBLOLLY

LODGEPOLE

MONTEREY

PINYON

PITCH

POND

SAND

SCOTCH

SHORTLEAF

SLASH

SPRUCE

SUGAR

TAMARACK

TORREY

VIRGINIA

WASHOE

WHITE

```
A C E H G J H S A L S S V K
P D S E C U R P S U G A R L
H O I R U T A H W M R U E V
D K N O B C O N E P E H T I
S A N D H R K C I L B A I R
Y E R E T N O M S J M U H G
E Y L L O L B O L A I H W I
R J E O A U S T R A L I A N
F A N V P H R A O I E H S I
F C O Y K E C N A R K C H A
E K Y V G K G T V S R M O M
J C N G X F X D I N N E E S
T B I S H O P G O P I R Y U
J D P F F C R E T L U O C M
```

SLUMBER PARTY

Anyone who's been to (or hosted) a slumber party knows that with all the **STORIES** told, **SODA POP** consumed, and **GAMES** of **TRUTH OR DARE** played, rarely is any "slumber" actually involved. After all, as Cyndi Lauper says, "**GIRLS** just want to **HAVE FUN**!"

BLANKETS

BOOKS

DVDS

EAT

FRIENDS

GAMES

GIGGLE

GIRLS

HAVE FUN

HOUSE SLIPPERS

JOKE

LAUGH

MUSIC

NOISE

PAJAMAS

PARENTS

PILLOWS

POPCORN

RADIO

ROBES

SECRETS

SING

SODA POP

STEREO

STORIES

TALK

TEENS

TELEPHONE

TRUTH OR DARE

VIDEOS

```
F K M A G D N A B M M O J O
A L T S P U R O B E S C O H
M A R T F R I E N D S W K S
S T N E R A P R T S C S E N
K O V K R A T E E N S M R P
S A D N J A K T L T A O C S
H G U A L M D S O G C F D P
R G M L P T S R T P G V G I
U A N B I O I S O E D I V L
S C D I I E P P C H R K G L
K W C I S U M T W L T C W O
O E E I O I A P S H A U E W
O H O U S E S L I P P E R S
B N D A K E N O H P E L E T
```

COVER UP

In this puzzle, find these 28 items which serve as covers of some sort.

APRON

BARK (tree)

BEARD

BEDSPREAD

BLACKTOP

BLANKET

BLINDFOLD

CAPE

COCOON

DOILY

ICING

JACKET

MASK

NAIL POLISH

PARKA

PEEL (orange)

ROOF

ROUGE

SHELL

SHINGLES

SNOW

TABLECLOTH

TARPAULIN

TOUPEE

UMBRELLA

VARNISH

VEIL

WRAPPER

```
S Y V V L T E K C A J G A K
C H E A T R B E A W R E I U
V Y I R U R T D P U G C K U
U A L N A M A A E U I M N A
T C I I G D B E O N O B H R
S A D S O L O R G A L T L A
P K R H L D E P E I O E I B
W R A P P E R S N L E K J A
V A E R A N C D C P L N L R
T P B A O U F E L O M A S K
H S N O W O L B S L P L F K
C J C C L B F I N I E B M V
S O M D A P R O N S H H T C
C P O T K C A L B H C O S C
```

CRUISE SHIPS

Now's your chance to become an **EXPLORER** as you set sail across the sea of letters below and locate the fleet of cruise ship names.

ADONIA

ADRIANA

AEGEAN I

ALBATROS

ARCADIA

ARION

ASTOR

ASTRA II

AURORA

AZUR

BERLIN

BOLERO

BREMEN

CALYPSO

CANBERRA

CAROUSEL

CENTURY

CLELIA II

COLUMBUS

DOLPHIN IV

ECSTASY

ELATION

EMERALD (The)

EUROPA

EXPLORER

FANTASY

FLAMENCO

GALAXY

```
T E B I I A I L E L C Y X I
L A D O N I A D R I A N A T
A S T R D O L P H I N I V Z
S T U Y S A T N A F B T M H
T O L B R N D F O R E L O B
R R R E M A Z S A U R O R A
A I M T X U P V B E R L I N
I E Z I A Y L O R Y A E Y E
I C L N L B L O R R I S Y M
G A L A X Y L N C U A U H E
R C C E T P O A M T E O N R
B U R G X I D O S N G R P B
I N Z E R I O C N E M A L F
V L D A A P E N Y C N C T G
```

"Y" NOT?

YIKES! An entire puzzle with words that begin with the letter "Y." Hopefully you won't YAWN at the idea but rather YEARN to see how many words the diagram below will YIELD.

YACHT	YOKE	YOUTHFUL
YAMMER	YOLK	YOWL
YANK	YONDER	YUCCA
YARDAGE	YORE	YULE
YARN	YOUNG	YUMMY
YAWL	YOURS	YUPPIE
YAWN		
YEAH		
YEARLING		
YEARN		
YEAST		
YELLOW		
YELP		
YEOMAN		
YESTERDAY		
YETI		
YIELD		
YIKES		
YODEL		
YOGA		
YOGURT		
YOICKS		

```
T M O F O C C H T M G D R R
A R P L E Y A P R H L M L P
Y P E Y U E E D E E C K W N
L E D O Y F D D I D M A A R
C T A U E M H Y P O C M Y F
E A S R L L M T P C O R A S
U N N S L Y U U E T Y D Y
M W F W O I G Y Y O G U R T
P A O I W K N E R O Y D E C
O Y C I A E U G E O N D T O
E K O Y T S O N G O R D S S
S U T S A E Y A R D A G E D
L P T U O N Y F E A E G Y R
L E A C N N K F Y C Y O L K
```

329

Ommegang is a Flemish word which means "to walk or march around." In medieval times, an Ommegang procession took place annually during July. The procession involved the circling of buildings or cities to invoke magical protection. Today, one historic Ommegang procession survives in Brussels. Solve the puzzle below to learn more about it.

Since nineteen-hundred, the Ommegang Pageant has emulated a famous one which took place in fifteen-forty-nine during Emperor Charles V's reign. Fantastic animals, papier-mâché giants, flag throwers, trumpeters and flute players all add to the splendor of the traditional procession.

```
O K O O T U S I N C E H T F O
N S S H O G P P L A Y E R S T
E N R S T N R A L M M G L E C
W P E T H E O M M E G A N G D
H D W N E E C T R K N I C E G
I U O A S T E N O O N D R H D
C R R I A F S E I Y R D O E E
H I H G H I S T T E N E T R T
A N T F T F I R I U C A P G E
R G N S N D O G H F L A G M R
L P O V A F N I R U S F L D E
E S S R E T E P M U R T D P I
S N T I G P N E E T E N I N P
V G D D A L L A N I M A L S A
S R F G P H L A F A M O U S P
```

STREETS OF CHARLESTON

Charleston is the second largest city in SOUTH Carolina. The Charleston was a popular type of dance in the mid-1920s characterized by outward heel kicks combined with the bending and straightening of the knees. Care to guess what the state dance of South Carolina is? It's the Shag! Who knows, maybe some of the Charleston city streets listed below lead to the local dance hall.

ASHLEY
ASHTON
ATLANTA
BARRE
BEAUFAIN
BLAKE
BOGARD
BROAD
CALHOUN
CANNON
CHAPEL
CHIME
COLONIAL
CONE
COOK
DELSEY
DUNCAN
FIFE
GEORGE
JUDITH
KING
LEGARE
LIBERTY
LINE
LOGAN
MARY
MEETING
MONTAGUE
NUNAN

QUEEN
REID
SMITH
SOCIETY
SOUTH

TRADD
TRUMBO
WARREN
WATER
WEST

```
E K A L B R O A D W N N A C
S U N F B O L A I N O L O C
R O Y R A M G N I T E E M K
E E C W R E T A H Q R P J O
I J U I R K F S R E A A Y O
D U O G E U A I E D G H D C
E D U Q A T A S F W E C H D
L I B E R T Y N H G L I N E
S T B U L H N U R L M N N E
E H M A R H C O N E E U Q N
Y B N M T E E H M R N Y A C
O T K I N G T L R A D G J P
A Q M D U N C A N N O N D K
H S O U T H W C W L L A P F
```

TRAVEL ITEMS

It's a fact: The average Italian has more than three times as many annual vacation days (42) as the average American (13). Here are some items that just might show up in the average suitcase taken along on an average vacation.

ASPIRIN

BATTERIES

BOOK

CAMERA

CASH

CD PLAYER

CLOTHES

COMB

COSMETICS

FILM

FIRST-AID KIT

HANGERS

IRON

ITINERARY

LIP BALM

MAGAZINES

NAIL FILE

PAJAMAS

PASSPORT

RAZOR

SCISSORS

SHOES

SOAP

SUNSCREEN

SWIMSUIT

THREAD

TOOTHBRUSH

TOOTHPASTE

TRAVELER'S (checks)

UMBRELLA

```
C P N C D P L A Y E R I G B
S O A E S F T R O P S S A P
E R S O E I A R E M A C E U
O W E M S R E L E V A R T M
H S P G E S C I S S O R S B
S E T N N T W S H M O L A R
N H I L I A I D N Z K T P E
A T U I Z I H C A U T F H L
I O S P A D M R S E S W T L
L L M B G K D L R R R G O A
F C I A A I O I I I B H O N
I T W L M T E O J F R M T V
L O S M H S U R B H T O O T
E P A J A M A S P I R I N C
```

MAYAN METROPOLISES

The civilization of the ancient Maya, a group of Central American Indians, flourished from around 1500 B.C. through the 17th century A.D., and is noted for its architecture and advanced system of mathematics. Listed below are 25 cities of the ancient Maya.

AKUMAL

ALTUN HA

BONAMPAK

CHICANNA

COBÁ

COMALCALCO

ETZNA

KABÁH

KOHUNLICH

LABNÁ

LA NAYA

NARANJO

PALENQUE

SAYIL

TANCAH

TIKAL

TINTAL

TULÚM

TZIBANCHE

UTATLÁN

XCARET

XPUHIL

XULTÚN

XUNÁNTUNICH

YAXCHILÁN

```
A H N U T L A L C H Q J A N
N S R B K Z I H T I N T A L
B K P Z I M I Y Q N A L H B
A S A J Z C O B A O L C B P
L B L P A O A L A S I M Y Y
K A E N M M T K C N H S I M
O J N A R A N E U H C Q X N
M A Q A T L N T O M X H B U
L S U U Y C N O X C A R E T
C I E P M A H I B K Y L A L
K O H U N L I C H A R N N U
R E L U J C C N P B C B Z X
Q U X C P O C B L A K I T Q
T J L Q I X J T H H K S E M
```

"CHECKMATE!"

In the **GAME** of chess, two people **MOVE** pieces on a **BOARD** that is divided into squares. The object of the game is for a **PLAYER** to trap or **CHECKMATE** the opponent's **KING**. Test your skills as you try to find all 30 words related to chess in the diagram below.

BISHOP

BOARD

CHECKMATE

COMPETITION

DIAGONAL

DIRECTION

DRAW

FILE

GAME

KING

KNIGHT

MOBILITY

MOVE

OPPONENT

PATH

PAWN

PIECE

PLAYER

POSITION

PROTECTION

QUEEN

RANK

ROOK

RULE

SKILL

SPACE

SQUARE

STAGE

TOURNAMENT

VALUE

```
O Y H B P C I G E V O M M D
P U O M H K N M A C A K M N
P N E M N I N W W M E N O O
O N I K K D D A A W E I O I
N O I T C E T O R P T G P T
E I B T S K I L L C H H W I
N T O U R N A M E N T T W T
T I A D O N P R C B S O A E
Q S R M O B I L I T Y V R P
G O D G K D C S A E Q A D M
S P A C E C H G L Y U O Y O
W I S L I O E I E Q E L U C
D W U D P S F H S M E R A Y
I R R P N I V C C R N P C V
```

BEJEWELED

From sapphires to rubies to diamonds, gems of all types are often used to make even the most mundane objects more extravagant, and to make already luxurious objects even more so. Below are some items which you might find decorated with jewels.

ALTAR

BELL

BELT

CANDELABRA

CHAIR

CHANDELIER

CHEST

COMB

CUMMER-
BUND

DAGGER

DIARY

DOLL

FANS

FRAME

GEM BOX

GOBLET

GOWN

LAMP

LIGHTER

MIRROR

MUSIC BOX

PAPERWEIGHT

PLATTER

PURSE

SHIELD

SPECTACLES

STEIN

SWORD

TOME

TRAY

```
X N T L E B X C P T A U D F
X B P L N S W O R D R H N C
C S R I X S R S N A F A U H
H T E L B O G U T Y S H Y A
E T G A S M B L P H N E E N
S Y G M P R A C I S H O R D
T P A P E R W E I G H T I E
X O D M C E L G R S H T I L
L L M O T D H I E O U T R I
S U M E A L Y C T M R M E E
C B T G C L R R T I B R G R
A R B A L E D N A C N O I W
F R A M E B Y H L I W E X M
W L A L S M C X P N D O L L
```

336

It's not just lip service when we tell you that listed below are 30 of today's popular lipstick shades.

AMETHYST

BLACKBERRY

BORDEAUX

BROWN SUGAR

CHESTNUT

CINNAMON

CLARET

CORAL

CRANBERRY

CURRANT

FAWN

FLAME

GARNET

GERANIUM

MAGENTA

MANGO

MAUVE

MULBERRY

PERSIMMON

PINK BLUSH

PRIMROSE

PUMPKIN

RAISIN

RASPBERRY

RUSSET

SCARLET

SUGARPLUM

TOPAZ

WATERMELON

WILD CHERRY

```
T P E N C I N N A M O N E P Y
M U I N A R E G K C H N S E D
I M U L P R A G U S N W O R B
R P C H E S T N U T A A R S O
U K B F Z N P L B T M F M I R
S I M A A Y B Y E E L Y I M D
S N P R X K R R R A R U R M E
E O R W N U M R M R Z R P O A
T U E I I E T E E A E D Y N U
C E P S L E T B L H G B V G X
O P L O N H P K H O C E L G N
R Y N R Y S F C W N G D N U I
A V A S A K R A I S I N L T M
L G T R H C C L A R E T A I A
Y V W E O Z S B F E V U A M W
```

QUOTESEARCH

The most prominent newspaperman, book reviewer, and political commentator of his day, Henry Louis Mencken (1880-1956) was a libertarian before the word came into usage. Mencken's writing is endearing because of its wit, crisp style, and the obvious delight he takes in it. And rare is the picture of him without a cigar in hand or being smoked. Here's Mencken's description of a businessman.

The only man above the hangman and the scavenger who is forever apologizing for his occupation. He is the only one who always seeks to make it appear, when he attains the object of his labors, i.e., the making of a great deal of money, that it was not the object of his labors.

```
N A M Y L N O E H T S I E H
G C O F H I S U D E A L O F
G R N E H N E H W P F F R H
U R E K I D E N O Y L N O T
N N Y A H I S L A B O R S E
S O T M T A O L S T L A W H
C T I O W G N I K A M E H T
A T B T I R H G B H H P O D
V H I Z A R E O M T L P A N
E E I S O P R V E A S A L A
N N W F I S U V E K N T W S
G W H O I S O C E R P I A Y
E T H E O B J E C T O F Y O
R G Z P A W S M J O J F S L
```

ATTENTION, CLASS!

Here's your assignment: Find the following classroom terms in the diagram below!

ASSIGNMENTS

BELL

BLACKBOARD

BOOKS

BREAK

CHAIRS

CLASSES

COUNSELOR

CREDIT

DESKS

ESSAYS

FILM

GRADES

HIGHLIGHTER

LOOSE-LEAF
(paper)

LUNCH

NOTES

PAPERS

PENS

RECESS

REPORTS

SLIDES

SPORTS

STOOLS

STUDENTS

SUBJECTS

TEACHERS

TESTS

```
G M N M F S P S J C O U E Y
D R A O B K C A L B U M S A
A L A G T I I A P O Y K S S
L H I D D E S K S E O L A T
F I L M E S S U S O R T Y N
A G R I E S T R B C F S S E
P H S S E C E R O J A N T D
T L H M E H F U O H E J S U
A I K P C D N U O P L C E T
I G D A S S I G N M E N T S
A H E E E B E L L D S R S S
S T F L R R Y P S P O R T S
K E O J H C B H M K O U O M
S R I A H C N U L A L K S B
```

Curt Simmons was only 18 years old when he broke into the big leagues in 1947, and he pitched for the St. Louis Cardinals when they won the World Series in 1964. Here's what he had to say regarding baseball's home run king.

St. Louis Cardinals pitcher Curt Simmons was a fine baseball player, so he knew what he was talking about when he made this comment about a famous slugger:

"Throwing a fastball by Henry Aaron is like trying to sneak a sunrise past a rooster."

```
A F A S T B A L L C N B M T
T O K H H N S F K O H N E H
S R A D E H A Y R N E H Y B
A N E B T M W A A B O U T A
P R N Y O H A G K S D P B S
U S S U A U R D N H D O L E
E G S T L L T O E K R A R B
F Y N T E N P W W E N R O A
R C O I E S A T H I S E O L
E P M M K S I C D E N G S L
W B M F L L T R Y I N G T O
T O I M I I A T N Y B U E C
C N S D P C R T R U C L R G
E K I L S I U O L T S S D C
```

STREETS OF JACKSON

JACKSON, the capital and largest city of Mississippi, was originally known as LeFleur's Bluff. But soon after Mississippi was admitted to the Union in 1817, it was decided to establish the state capital there. The city was renamed in honor of General Andrew Jackson (who later became the seventh U.S. President). Located about 180 miles north of New Orleans, Jackson is the hometown of two of today's hottest country music stars — Faith Hill and LeAnn Rimes. A map won't be necessary to locate these streets found throughout Jackson.

ALEXANDER	CAPITOL	CHURCH
BELLEVUE	CARLISLE	COMMERCE
BLOOM	CAROLINE	EASTWOOD
		ELLIS
		FAIRBANKS
		GEORGE
		GILLESPIE
		GREYMONT
		HAMILTON
		HENRY
		JACKSON
		LAKELAND
		OLD CANTON
		PINEHURST
		POPLAR
		QUINN
		SUMMER
		TERRY
		WESTWOOD
		WHITFIELD
		YAZOO

```
H D O O W T S E W Q U I N N
C A P I T O L H R A L P O P
R A X E L S I L R A C S V Z
U E R O L T D N A H K H D G
H U G O F F S N A C S G O E
C V R I L A P M A E A G O O
X E E Y L I I J C L L H W R
B L Y A X L N R C J E O T G
D L M Z T C E E B N X K S E
E E O O Y M H S R A A W A L
U B N O M Q U Y P G N U E L
H T T O M V R A R I D K H I
P U C W U E S U M M E R S S
O L D C A N T O N Y R R E T
```

SUMMER FUN

No musical group has defined summer fun more than the Beach Boys. The group was formed in 1961 in Hawthorne, California, by Brian Wilson, and included his brothers Carl and Dennis, their cousin Mike Love, and school friend Al Jardine. Although surfing was a recurring theme in their early hits, Dennis was the only member of the band who actually surfed. Below are 30 terms related to this special time of year.

BARN DANCES

BASEBALL

BEACHES

BIKES

BOATS

CAMP

CROQUET

FAIRS

FIREFLIES

GARDENS

GOLF

HIKES

ICES

LAWNS

LEISURE

LEMONADE

MELONS

PARKS

PICNICS

ROSES

SAILING

SANDALS

SHORTS

STROLLS

SWIMMING

SWINGS

TENNIS

TRIPS

VACATION

WADING

```
E D I F F H I K E S K R A P
L L L M A L P C S A D N I N
S A L G W I E E C I G G B R
T N W A C S R M S L N A I B
R I O N B U N S O I R N K O
O S I L S E G E D N V K E A
H C M I E P S A D G A M S T
S S E C I M W A O R C D E S
P L L A L A N L B G A P E F
I A L R F C B N N T G W L
R D L O E S W I M M I N G R
T N N S R H T E U Q O R C O
L A M E I T O S W I N G S S
K S U S F U S E H C A E B V
```

THE Z'S HAVE IT!

Here's your chance to **DAZZLE** us with your solving skills as you **ZOOM** through this **MAZE** of words containing the letter "Z."

BUZZER

COZY

CRAZY

DAZE

DAZZLE

DIZZY

FAZE

FIZZLE

FRIZZ

FUZZY

GAUZE

GAZE

GUZZLE

HAZEL

JAZZ

LAZY

MAZE

MUZZLE

NOZZLE

OOZE

OZONE

PIZZA

PUZZLE

QUIZ

SIZE

SIZZLE

TIZZY

ZANY

ZEAL

ZERO

ZIGZAG

ZINC

ZINNIA

ZIRCON

ZOOM

```
A Z Z I P N O C R I Z J F Z
N G E I Z O O R O Y Z A R C
U L Z G U Z Z L E E Z Z O A
R T A A H Q D D L Z E Z S T
E Z D U I R A Z A N Y E I A
E N O Z O P Z N E Y Z Z Z D
Z N O E A U Z B L E Z A E B
I O H I M Z L M Z Y U I O U
M F M A E Z E E Z A F L G Z
C A I L Z L W I I A Z O A Z
N O Z Z L E N E S Q O O Z E
I R J A Z N L Z N S N R G R
Z H E I I L L A Z Y Y I I P
E Z N A A R E M F R I Z Z L
```

FELONS IN THE FUNNIES

"Dick Tracy," the detective-action comic strip, made its debut in 1931. The strip became famous for its oddly named and often rather grotesquely ugly villainous characters. FLATTOP, the most "popular" of Tracy's idiosyncratic enemies, had a large head that was as flat as an ironing board. Here's a rogue's gallery of 29 bad guys (and gals) who faced off against Dick Tracy.

BIG BOY

BROW (The)

CHUCK

DAHLIA DELL

DEAFY

DUBBS

ETAH

FIFTH

FLATTOP

FREEZ

GARGLES

HAIRY

INFLUENCE

IRMA

JOE LEAD

KARPSE

KITTY

KROME

LAFFY

LILY

LISPY

MAMMA

MIMI

MOLE (The)

MR INTRO

MURKY

NAH-TAY

OODLES

TOGO

```
O Y E C N I O G O T N I L S
O W T S K F N I O I O H I A
H B A T Y B R F D U B B S F
D A H L I A D E L L Y N P B
D Y I G U K T D E A F Y Y B
J L B B H H P H S Z T E E G
Z O N M U Y F F A L C T W J
Y R I A H C K S S N R U O K
I T E M E U H G E N F E R P
O N L M I T Y U L L S B Y
I I O A F M L F C E G P K Y
P R M I B F B L A K E R W H
K M F S N J P D G P U A A M
F A Z I F F R B U M C K U G
```

SOLUTIONS

Wordsearch 1

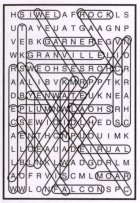

Wordsearch 2

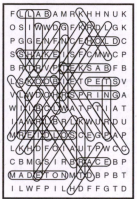

Wordsearch 3

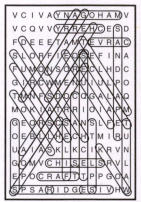

Wordsearch 4

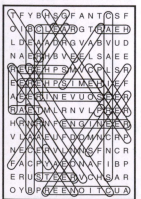

Wordsearch 5

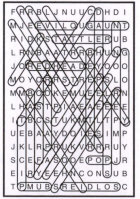

Wordsearch 6

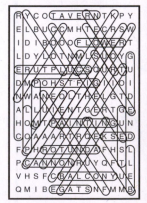

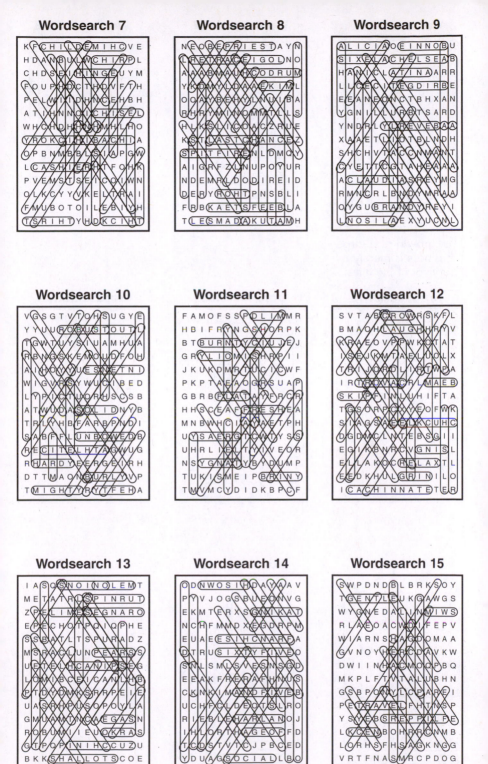

Wordsearch 7

Wordsearch 8

Wordsearch 9

Wordsearch 10

Wordsearch 11

Wordsearch 12

Wordsearch 13

Wordsearch 14

Wordsearch 15

Wordsearch 16

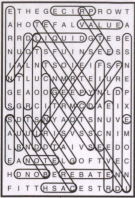

The growth of a large business is merely a survival of the fittest.

Wordsearch 17

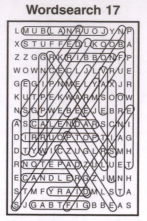

Wordsearch 18

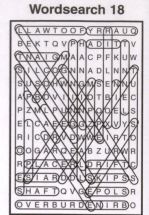

Wordsearch 19

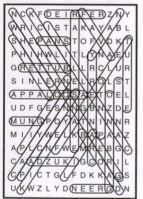

Wordsearch 20

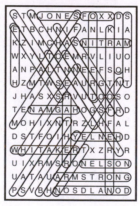

Wordsearch 21

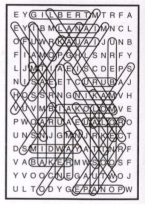

Wordsearch 22

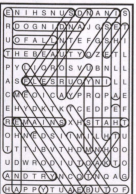

Wordsearch 23

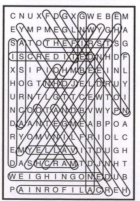

Wordsearch 24

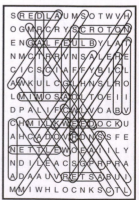

WORD SEEK 25

WORD SEEK 26

WORD SEEK 27

... a little less than they
want to know.

WORD SEEK 28

WORD SEEK 29

WORD SEEK 30

WORD SEEK 31

WORD SEEK 32

WORD SEEK 33

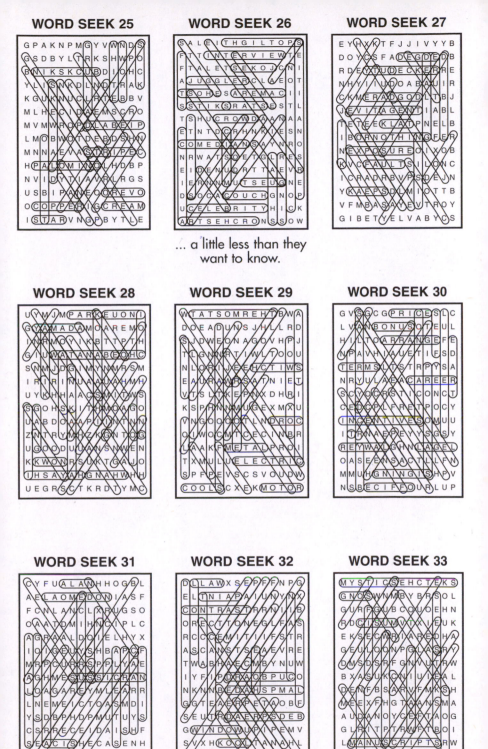

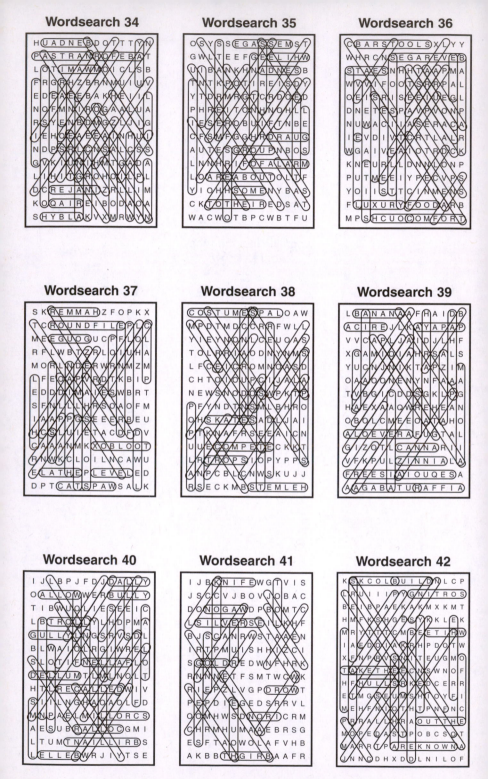

350

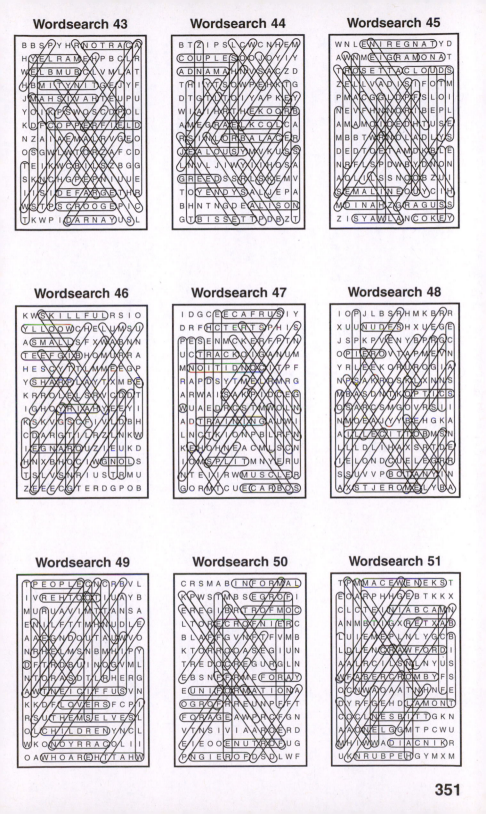

Wordsearch 52

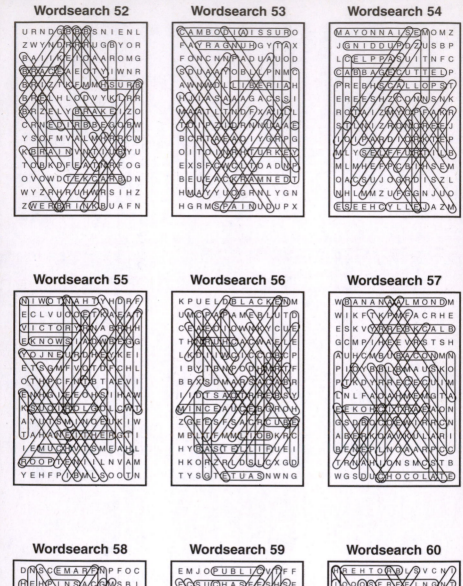

Wordsearch 53

Wordsearch 54

Wordsearch 55

Wordsearch 56

Wordsearch 57

Wordsearch 58

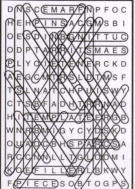

Wordsearch 59

Wordsearch 60

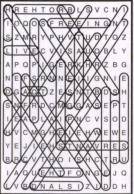

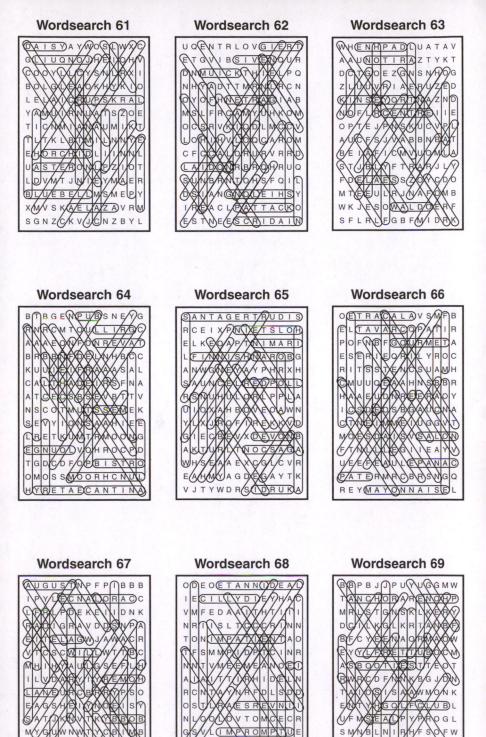

Wordsearch 61

Wordsearch 62

Wordsearch 63

Wordsearch 64

Wordsearch 65

Wordsearch 66

Wordsearch 67

Wordsearch 68

Wordsearch 69

353

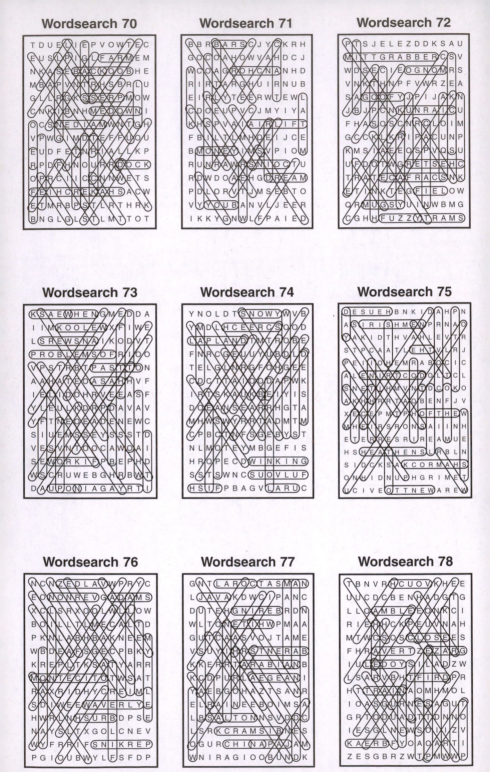

Wordsearch 70

Wordsearch 71

Wordsearch 72

Wordsearch 73

Wordsearch 74

Wordsearch 75

Wordsearch 76

Wordsearch 77

Wordsearch 78

Wordsearch 79

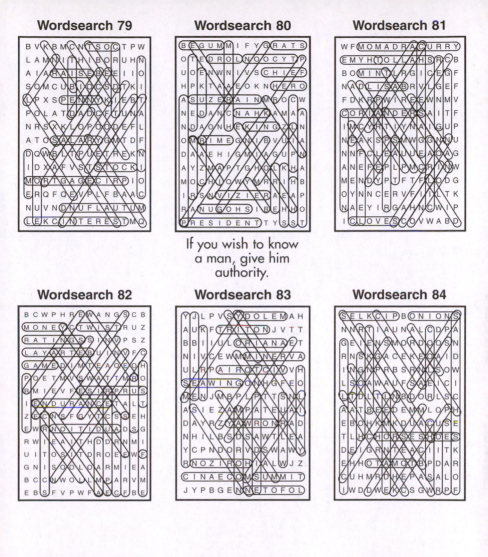

Wordsearch 80

Wordsearch 81

If you wish to know
a man, give him
authority.

Wordsearch 82

Wordsearch 83

Wordsearch 84

Wordsearch 85

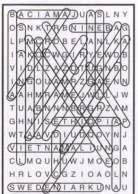

Wordsearch 86

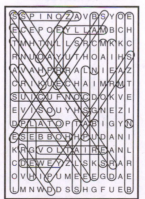

Wordsearch 87

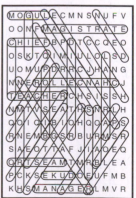

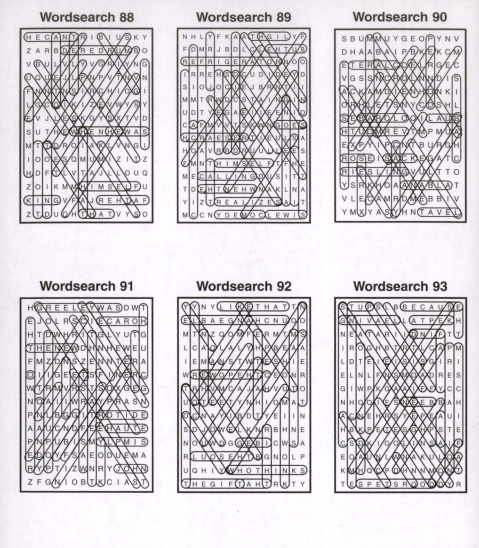

Wordsearch 88

Wordsearch 89

Wordsearch 90

Wordsearch 91

Wordsearch 92

Wordsearch 93

Wordsearch 94

Wordsearch 95

Wordsearch 96

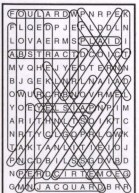
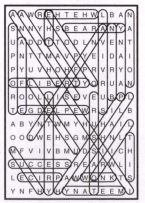
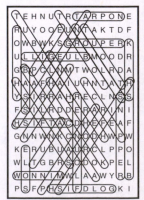

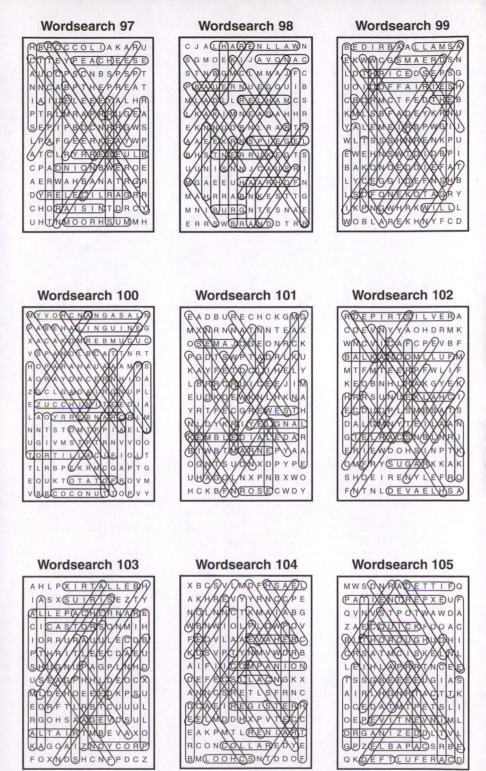

Wordsearch 97

Wordsearch 98

Wordsearch 99

Wordsearch 100

Wordsearch 101

Wordsearch 102

Wordsearch 103

Wordsearch 104

Wordsearch 105

357

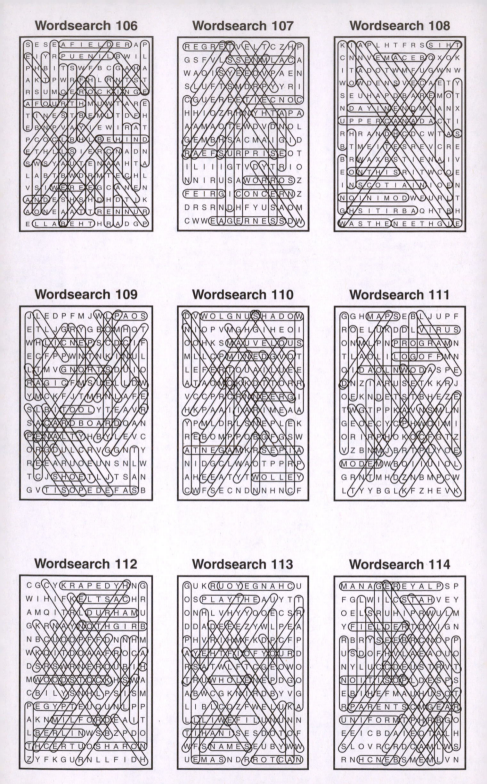

Wordsearch 106

Wordsearch 107

Wordsearch 108

Wordsearch 109

Wordsearch 110

Wordsearch 111

Wordsearch 112

Wordsearch 113

Wordsearch 114

358

Wordsearch 115

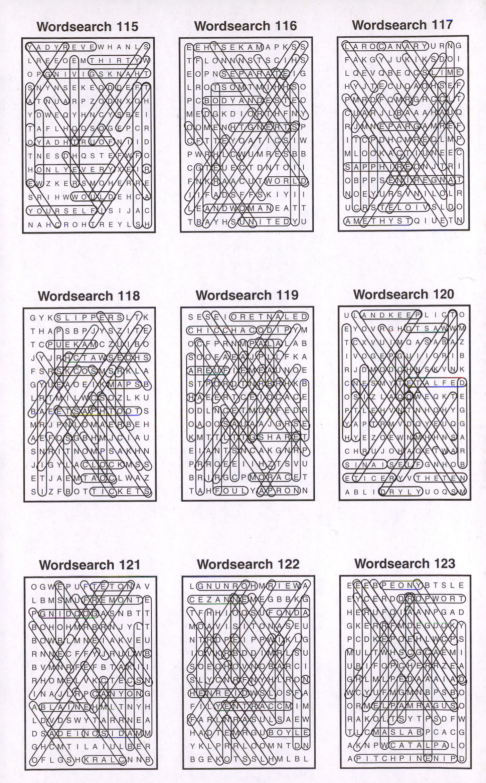

Wordsearch 116

Wordsearch 117

Wordsearch 118

Wordsearch 119

Wordsearch 120

Wordsearch 121

Wordsearch 122

Wordsearch 123

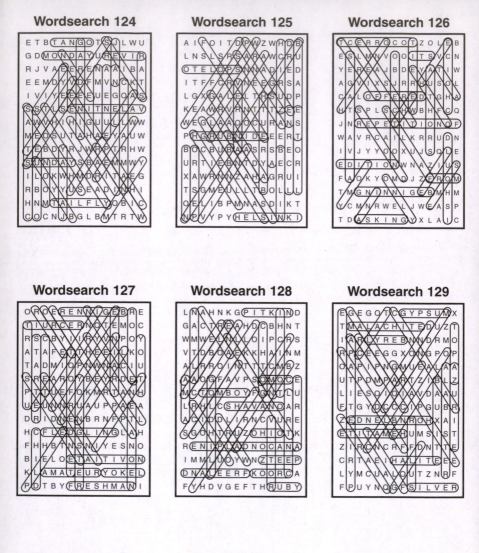

Wordsearch 124

Wordsearch 125

Wordsearch 126

Wordsearch 127

Wordsearch 128

Wordsearch 129

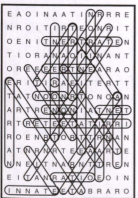

Wordsearch 130

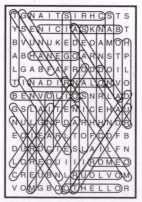

Wordsearch 131

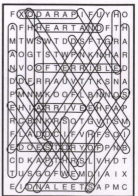

Wordsearch 132

Wordsearch 133

Wordsearch 134

Wordsearch 135

Wordsearch 136

Wordsearch 137

Wordsearch 138

Wordsearch 139

Wordsearch 140

Wordsearch 141

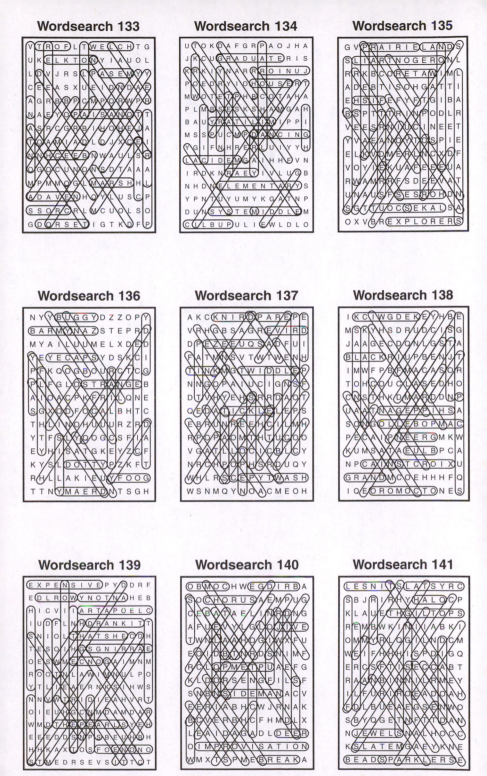

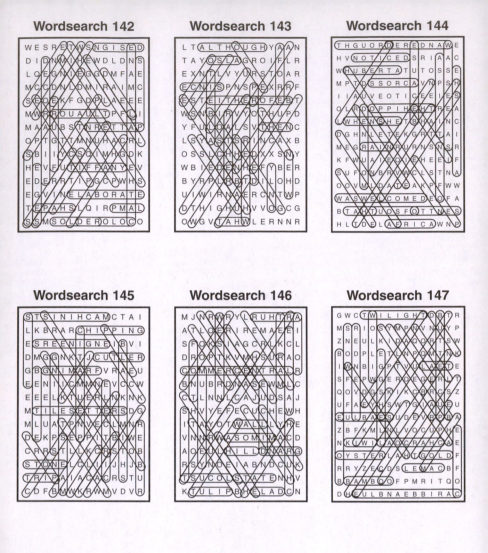

Wordsearch 142

Wordsearch 143

Wordsearch 144

Wordsearch 145

Wordsearch 146

Wordsearch 147

Wordsearch 148

Wordsearch 149

Wordsearch 150

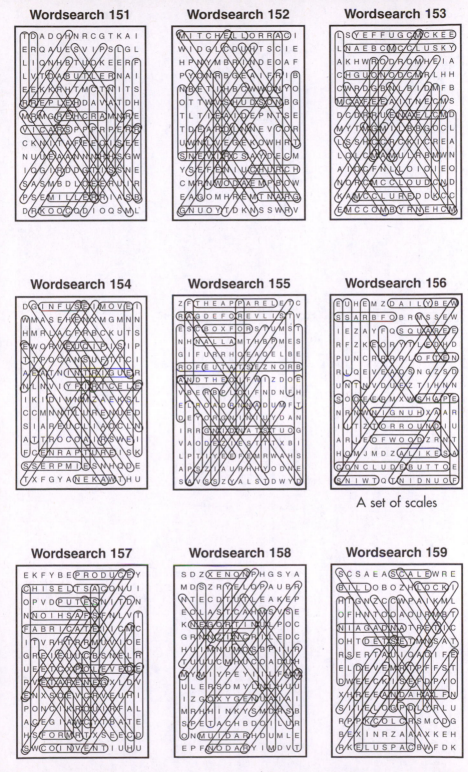

Wordsearch 151

Wordsearch 152

Wordsearch 153

Wordsearch 154

Wordsearch 155

Wordsearch 156

A set of scales

Wordsearch 157

Wordsearch 158

Wordsearch 159

Wordsearch 160

Wordsearch 161

Wordsearch 162

Wordsearch 163

Wordsearch 164

Wordsearch 165

Wordsearch 166

Wordsearch 167

Wordsearch 168

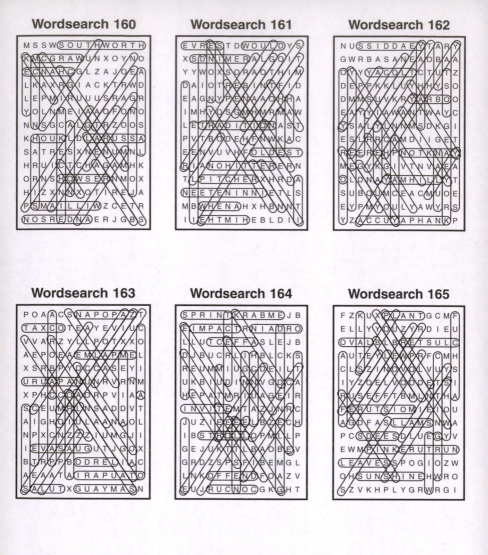

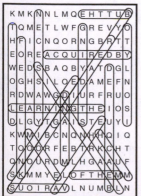

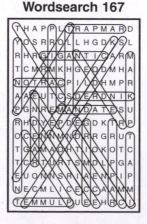

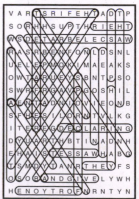

Wordsearch 169

Wordsearch 170

Wordsearch 171

Wordsearch 172

Wordsearch 173

Wordsearch 174

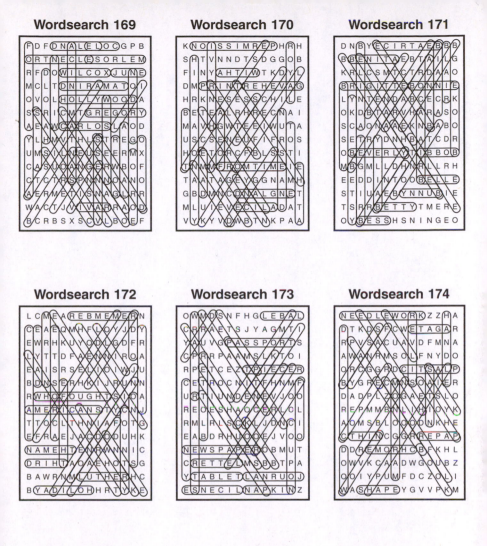

Wordsearch 175

Wordsearch 176

Wordsearch 177

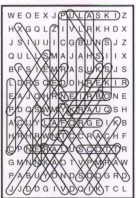
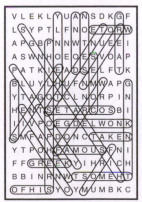
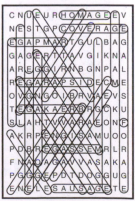

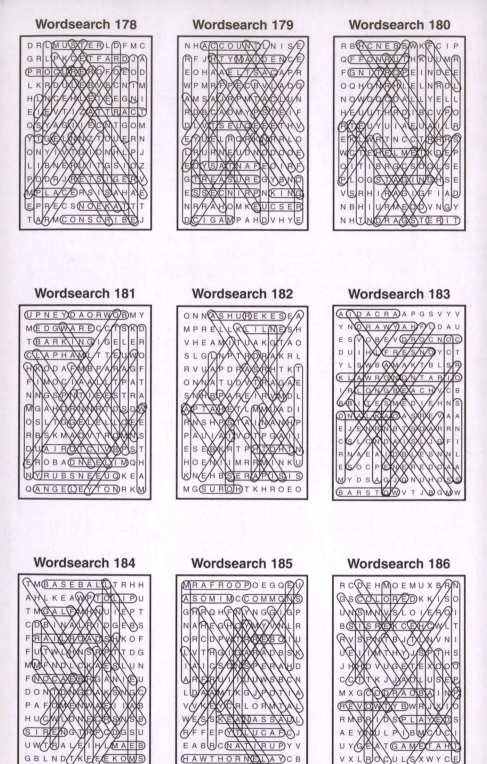

Wordsearch 178

Wordsearch 179

Wordsearch 180

Wordsearch 181

Wordsearch 182

Wordsearch 183

Wordsearch 184

Wordsearch 185

Wordsearch 186

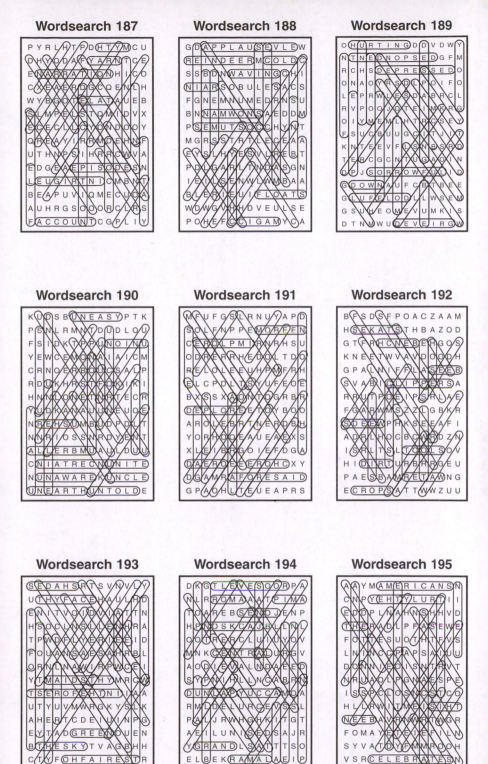

Wordsearch 187

Wordsearch 188

Wordsearch 189

Wordsearch 190

Wordsearch 191

Wordsearch 192

Wordsearch 193

Wordsearch 194

Wordsearch 195

367

Wordsearch 196

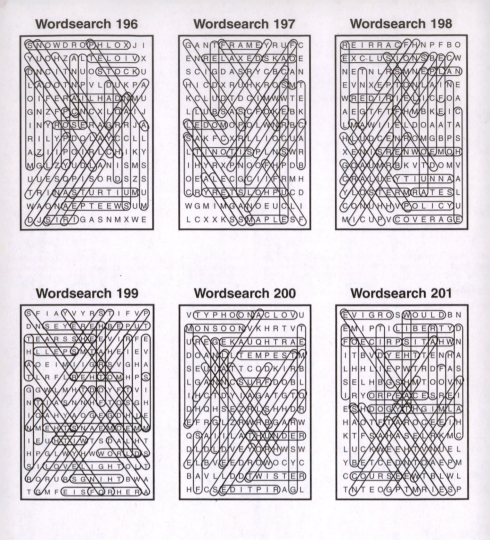

Wordsearch 197

Wordsearch 198

Wordsearch 199

Wordsearch 200

Wordsearch 201

Wordsearch 202

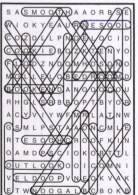

Wordsearch 203

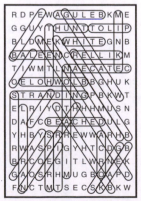

Wordsearch 204

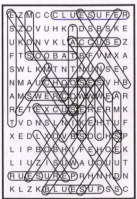

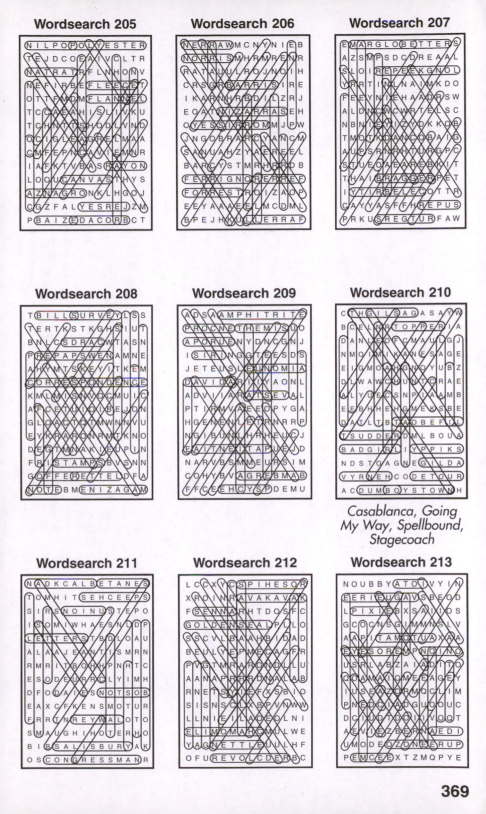

Wordsearch 205

Wordsearch 206

Wordsearch 207

Wordsearch 208

Wordsearch 209

Wordsearch 210

Casablanca, Going
My Way, Spellbound,
Stagecoach

Wordsearch 211

Wordsearch 212

Wordsearch 213

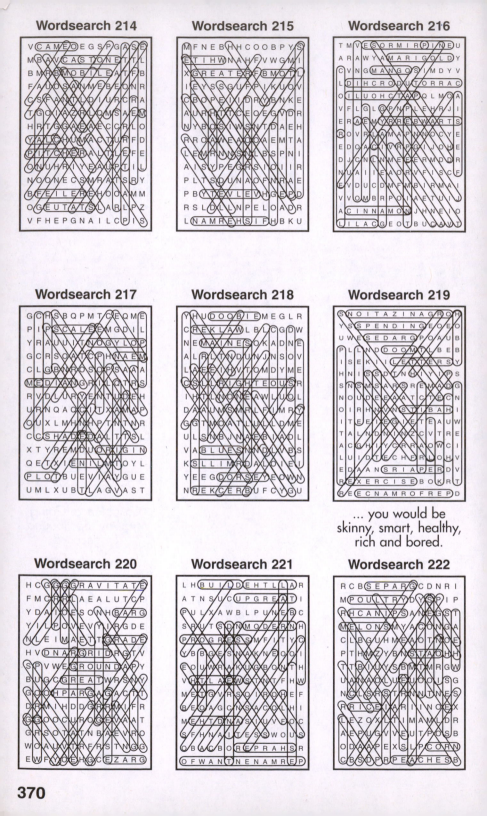

Wordsearch 214

Wordsearch 215

Wordsearch 216

Wordsearch 217

Wordsearch 218

Wordsearch 219

... you would be skinny, smart, healthy, rich and bored.

Wordsearch 220

Wordsearch 221

Wordsearch 222

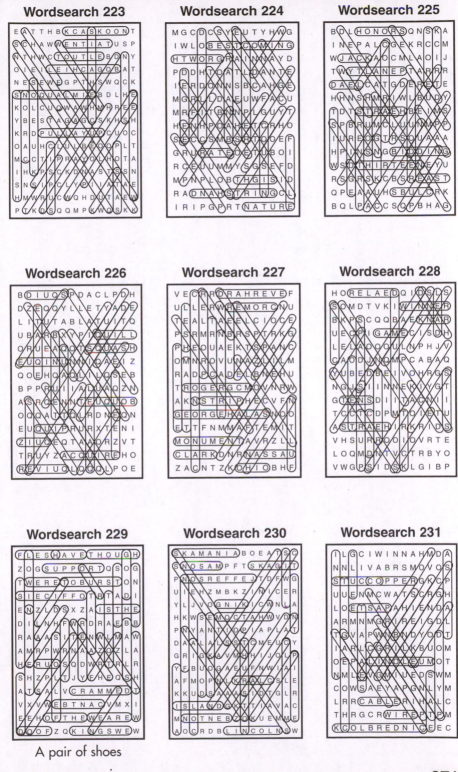

Wordsearch 223

Wordsearch 224

Wordsearch 225

Wordsearch 226

Wordsearch 227

Wordsearch 228

Wordsearch 229

A pair of shoes

Wordsearch 230

Wordsearch 231

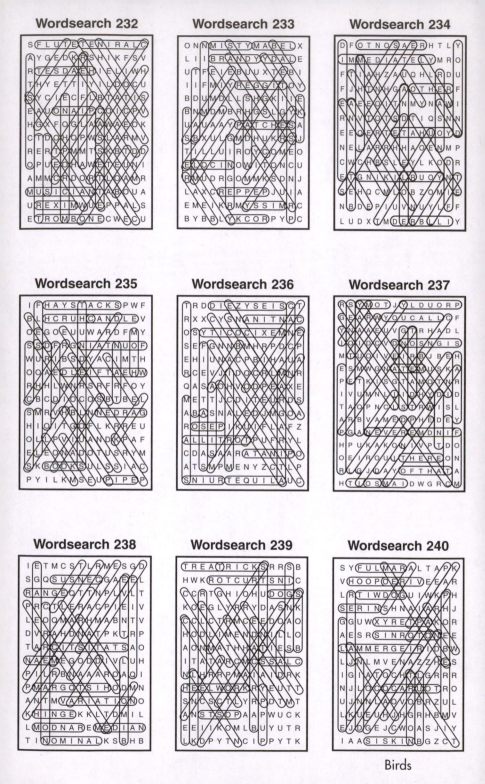

Wordsearch 232

Wordsearch 233

Wordsearch 234

Wordsearch 235

Wordsearch 236

Wordsearch 237

Wordsearch 238

Wordsearch 239

Wordsearch 240

Birds

Wordsearch 241

Wordsearch 242

Wordsearch 243

Wordsearch 244

Wordsearch 245

Wordsearch 246

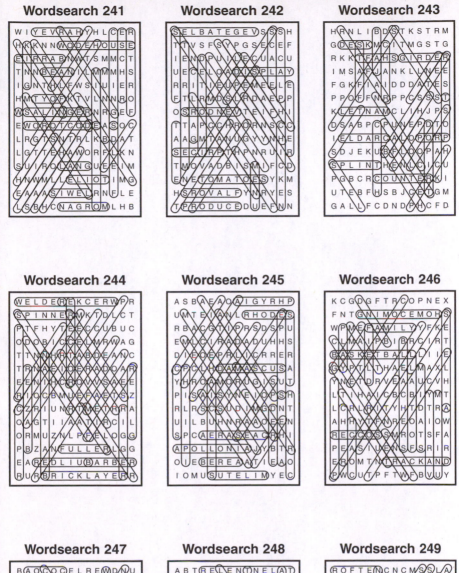

Wordsearch 247

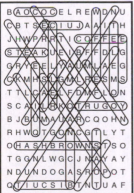

Wordsearch 248

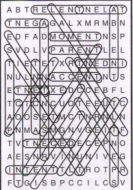

Wordsearch 249

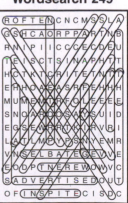

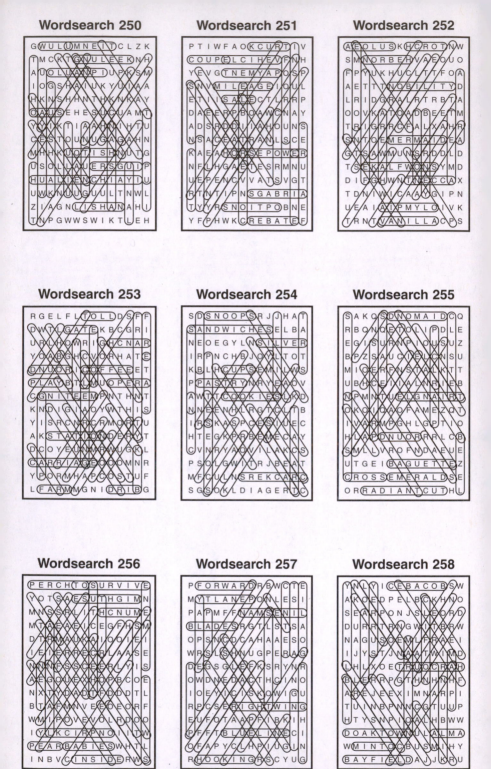

Wordsearch 250

Wordsearch 251

Wordsearch 252

Wordsearch 253

Wordsearch 254

Wordsearch 255

Wordsearch 256

Wordsearch 257

Wordsearch 258

Wordsearch 259

Wordsearch 260

Wordsearch 261

Wordsearch 262

Wordsearch 263

Wordsearch 264

Wordsearch 265

Wordsearch 266

Wordsearch 267

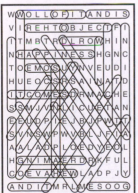

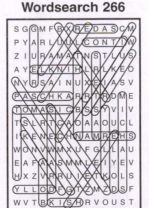

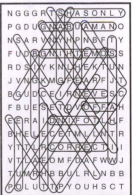

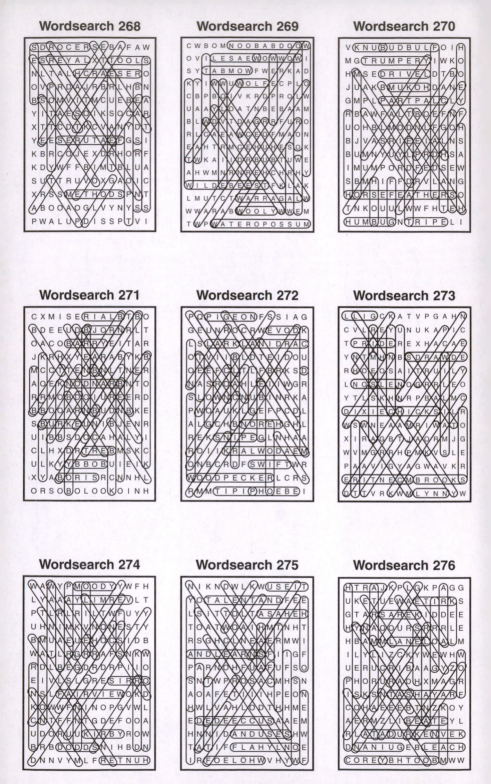

Wordsearch 268

Wordsearch 269

Wordsearch 270

Wordsearch 271

Wordsearch 272

Wordsearch 273

Wordsearch 274

Wordsearch 275

Wordsearch 276

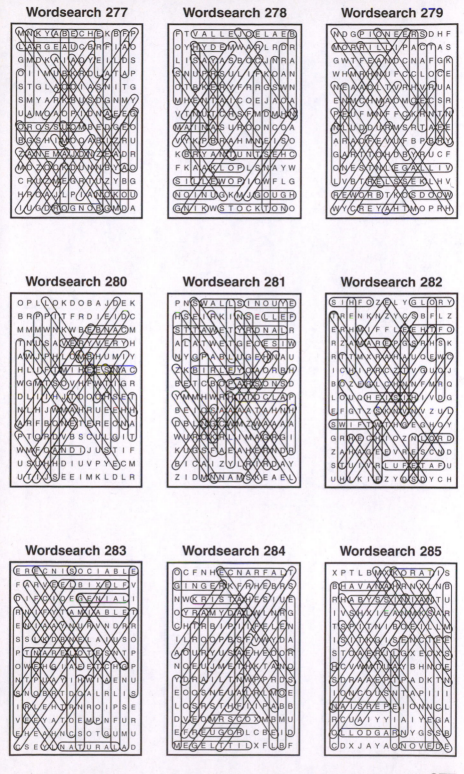

Wordsearch 277

Wordsearch 278

Wordsearch 279

Wordsearch 280

Wordsearch 281

Wordsearch 282

Wordsearch 283

Wordsearch 284

Wordsearch 285

Wordsearch 286

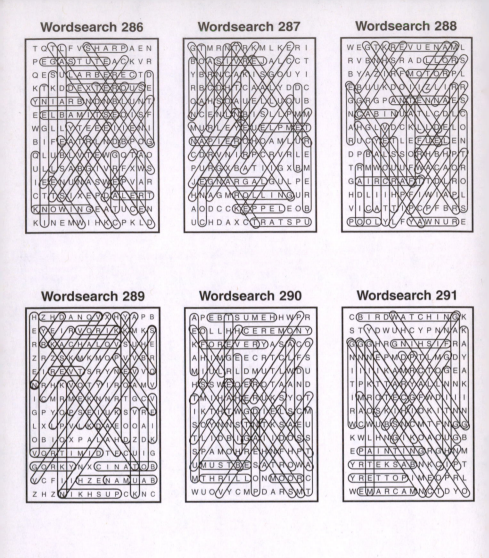

Wordsearch 287

Wordsearch 288

Wordsearch 289

Wordsearch 290

Wordsearch 291

Wordsearch 292

Wordsearch 293

Wordsearch 294

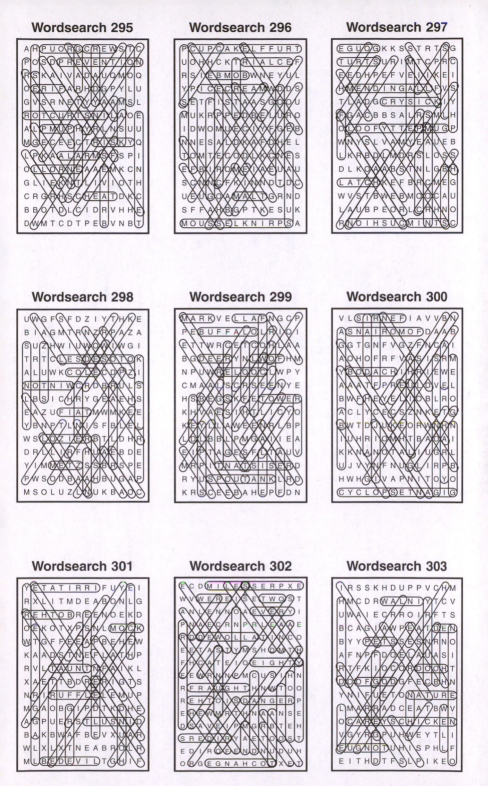

Wordsearch 295

Wordsearch 296

Wordsearch 297

Wordsearch 298

Wordsearch 299

Wordsearch 300

Wordsearch 301

Wordsearch 302

Wordsearch 303

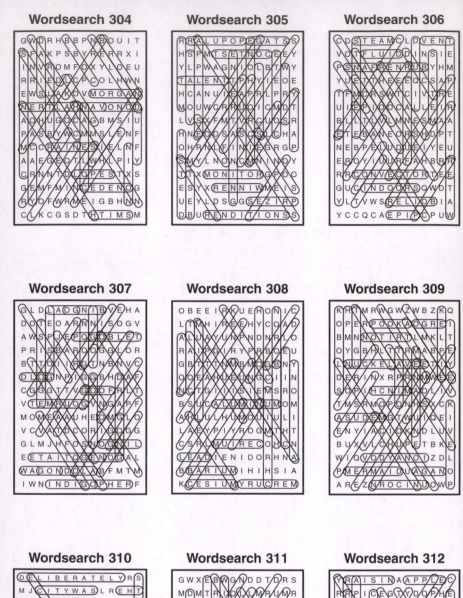

Wordsearch 304

Wordsearch 305

Wordsearch 306

Wordsearch 307

Wordsearch 308

Wordsearch 309

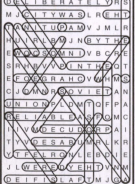

Wordsearch 310

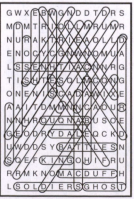

Wordsearch 311

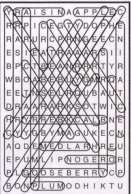

Wordsearch 312

380

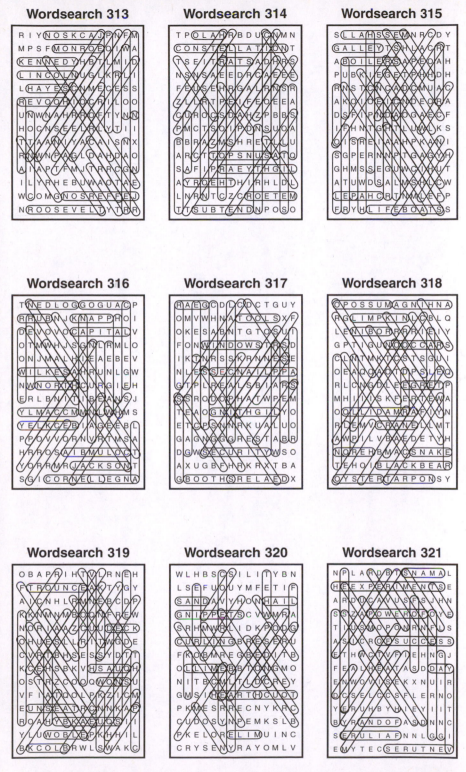

Wordsearch 313

Wordsearch 314

Wordsearch 315

Wordsearch 316

Wordsearch 317

Wordsearch 318

Wordsearch 319

Wordsearch 320

Wordsearch 321

Wordsearch 322

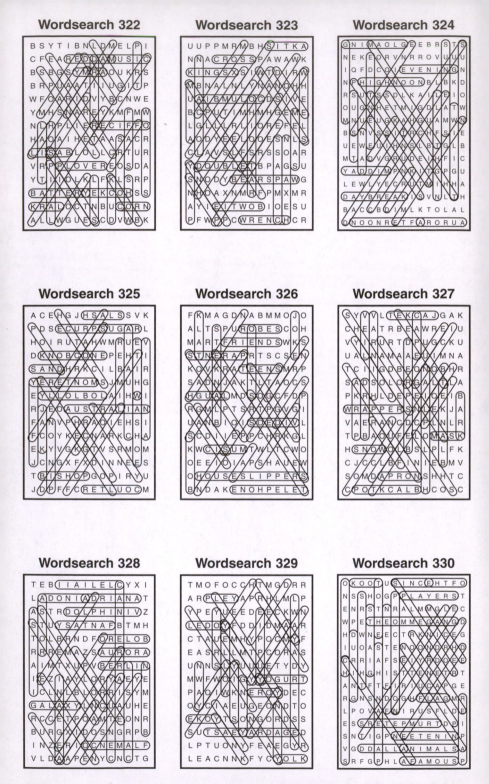

Wordsearch 323

Wordsearch 324

Wordsearch 325

Wordsearch 326

Wordsearch 327

Wordsearch 328

Wordsearch 329

Wordsearch 330

382

Wordsearch 331

Wordsearch 332

Wordsearch 333

Wordsearch 334

Wordsearch 335

Wordsearch 336

Wordsearch 337

Wordsearch 338

Wordsearch 339

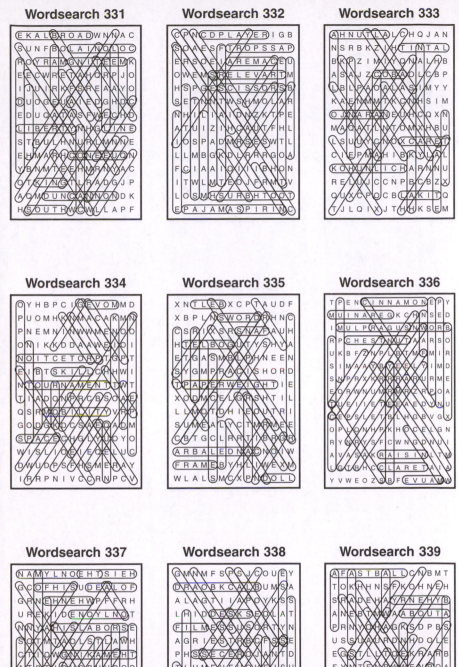

Wordsearch 340

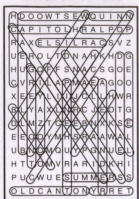

Wordsearch 341

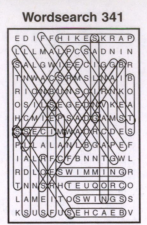

Wordsearch 342

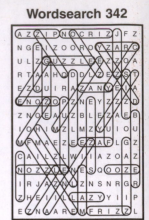

Wordsearch 343

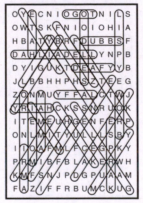